student's manual

LABORATORY
AND
FIELD INVESTIGATIONS

BSCS GREEN VERSION

AMERICAN INSTITUTE OF BIOLOGICAL SCIENCES

BIOLOGICAL SCIENCES CURRICULUM STUDY · *University of Colorado, Boulder*

RAND McNALLY & COMPANY · *Chicago*

High
School
Biology

THE BSCS WRITERS

MARSTON BATES, University of Michigan, Ann Arbor: *Supervisor, 1960–61*
C. HAVEN KOLB, Overlea Senior High School, Baltimore County, Maryland: *Supervisor, 1961–63*
NORMAN B. ABRAHAM, Yuba City Union High School, California
DEAN A. ANDERSON, Los Angeles State College, California
RICHARD P. ANDERSON, West High School, Salt Lake City, Utah
TED ANDREWS, Kansas State Teachers College, Emporia
WALTER AUFFENBERG, Biological Sciences Curriculum Study, Boulder, Colorado
RICHARD P. AULIE, Evanston Township High School, Illinois
JOHN BEHNKE, Ronald Press, New York City
MARJORIE BEHRINGER, Alamo Heights High School, San Antonio, Texas
JOHN BODEL, The Hotchkiss School, Lakeville, Connecticut
RODNEY BOLIN, Wheatridge High School, Colorado
CHARLES R. BOTTICELLI, Harvard University, Cambridge, Massachusetts
JOHN W. BREUKELMAN, Kansas State Teachers College, Emporia
DONALD H. BUCKLIN, University of Wisconsin, Madison
PETER BURI, San Francisco State College, California
C. FRANCIS BYERS, Elmira College, New York
ARCHIE CARR, University of Florida, Gainesville
JOHN CARROLL, Pattengill Junior High School, Lansing, Michigan
EDWIN H. COLBERT, American Museum of Natural History and Columbia University, New York City
JOHN W. CRENSHAW, University of Maryland, College Park
ROBERT A. DASPIT, St. Martinville High School, Louisiana
J. MAXWELL DAVIS, William Henry Harrison High School, Evansville, Indiana
EDUARDO DEL PONTE, University of Buenos Aires, Argentina
INGRITH DEYRUP, Barnard College, New York City
JUDITH DOBKIN, Miami Senior High School, Florida
ROBERT H. DUNK, Berkeley High School, California
HAROLD DURST, Southeast High School, Wichita, Kansas
GERALD EINEM, Melbourne High School, Florida
FRANK C. ERK, State University of New York, Long Island Center, Oyster Bay
CHINAKA ESIABA, Nigeria
DORIS FALK, Fresno State College, California
JOHN G. FARROW, Scarsdale High School, New York
JACK FISHLEDER, West High School, Phoenix, Arizona
ELENA MARTÍNEZ FONTES, Instituto Nacional del Profesorado Secundario, Buenos Aires, Argentina
PHILLIP R. FORDYCE, Oak Park & River Forest High School, Oak Park, Illinois
JACK FRIEDMAN, Syosset High School, New York
O. FROTA-PESSOA, UNESCO, Instituto Brasileiro de Educação, Ciencia e Cultura, São Paulo, Brazil
THOMAS FURMAN, U.S. Office of Education, Washington, D.C.
ROBERTO GALÁN, Universidad de Los Andes, Bogotá, Colombia
EUGENE GENNARO, Wisconsin High School, Madison
RALPH GERARD, University of Michigan, Ann Arbor
BYRON GIBBS, Arizona State University, Tempe
RONALD K. GIBBS, Alexander Ramsey High School, St. Paul, Minnesota
BENTLEY GLASS, Johns Hopkins University, Baltimore, Maryland
DONALD GLITTENBERG, Lakewood High School, Colorado
HUMBERTO GÓMEZ, Universidad del Valle, Cali, Colombia
JOHN GUNDLACH, Neenah High School, Wisconsin
WESLEY HALL, Fairview High School, Boulder, Colorado
ROBERT S. HAMILTON, Boulder High School, Colorado
PHILIP HANDLER, Duke University, Durham, North Carolina

PAUL DeH. HURD, Stanford University, California
ROJANEE JARUPRAKORN, Bangkok, Thailand
JEWEL JORDAN, Commerce High School, Georgia
PANEE KAOCHARERN (CHIOWANICH), Chulalongkorn University, Bangkok, Thailand
WILSON KISPERT, Cass Technical High School, Detroit, Michigan
EVELYN KLINCKMANN, San Francisco College for Women, California
MYRIAM KRASILCHIK, UNESCO, Instituto Brasileiro de Educação, Ciencia e Cultura, C. P. 2921, São Paulo, Brazil
VICTOR LARSEN, JR., Adelphi College, Garden City, New York
M. C. LICHTENWALTER, Wells High School, Chicago, Illinois
MARGARET J. McKIBBEN (LAWLER), Formerly of National Science Teachers Association, Washington, D.C.
WILLIAM V. MAYER, Wayne State University, Detroit, Michigan
DE WOLF MERRIAM, Highland Park High School, New Jersey
LORUS J. MILNE, University of New Hampshire, Durham
MARGERY MILNE, Durham, New Hampshire
WILLIAM MILSTEAD, University of Kansas City, Missouri
JOHN A. MOORE, Columbia University, New York City
HUGH MOZINGO, University of Nevada, Reno
ALFRED NOVAK, Stephens College, Columbia, Missouri
RUSSELL C. OAKES, Huntington High School, New York
ELRA M. PALMER, Baltimore City Public Schools, Maryland
ARTHUR PAPENFUS, Golden High School, Colorado
S. M. PATTEE, Jefferson Senior High School, Cedar Rapids, Iowa
PAUL G. PEARSON, Rutgers University, New Brunswick, New Jersey
GLEN E. PETERSON, University of Houston, Texas
GORDON E. PETERSON, San Marino High School, California
DAVIDA PHILLIPS, Hale High School, Tulsa, Oklahoma
EDWIN A. PHILLIPS, Pomona College, Claremont, California
JAMES F. RAGIN, Jack Yates Senior High School, Houston, Texas
FREDERICK A. RASMUSSEN, Chadsey High School, Detroit, Michigan
CLARENCE W. RICE, Eastern High School, Detroit, Michigan
LEON RINTEL, Forest Hills High School, New York City
L. M. ROHRBAUGH, University of Oklahoma, Norman
IMOGENE RUSSELL, Sandia High School, Albuquerque, New Mexico
JOSEPH J. SCHWAB, University of Chicago, Illinois
GEORGE SCHWARTZ, Forest Hills High School, New York City
DALE SMITH, University of Illinois, Urbana
FRANCIS W. SMITH, JR., Los Altos High School, Mountain View, California
RICHARD S. SMITH, Haverford Senior High School, Havertown, Pennsylvania
G. LEDYARD STEBBINS, University of California, Davis
WILSON STEWART, University of Illinois, Urbana
DENNIS STRAWBRIDGE, Michigan State University, East Lansing
ZACHARIAH SUBARSKY, Bronx High School of Science, New York City
GERALD D. TAGUE, Wichita High School East, Kansas
JOYCE B. THOMPSON, San Jacinto College, Pasadena, Texas
JANET TWENTE, University of Utah, Salt Lake City
JOHN TWENTE, University of Utah, Salt Lake City
R. W. VAN NORMAN, University of Utah, Salt Lake City
PAUL A. VESTAL, Rollins College, Winter Park, Florida
HENRY M. WALLBRUNN, University of Florida, Gainesville
ARTHUR C. WALTON, Knox College, Galesburg, Illinois
EDGAR WARREN, South High School, Denver, Colorado
CLAUDE WELCH, Michigan State University, East Lansing
F. W. WENT, Missouri Botanical Gardens, St. Louis

2393

Jonathan Westfall, University of Georgia, Athens
Betty Wislinsky, West High School, Madison, Wisconsin
Robert L. Wistort, High Point High School, Beltsville, Maryland
Harry K. Wong, Menlo-Atherton High School, Atherton, California
J. D. Woolever, Riverview Senior High School, Sarasota, Florida
Delaphine G. R. Wyckoff, Wellesley College, Massachusetts

THE BSCS ARTISTS

Jane Larson, *Illustration Supervisor*
James E. Bramlett
Eugene J. Diodato, Jr.
Clarence W. Gardephe
Margery A. Gardephe
Robert G. Haynes
Orra Irwin
Robert T. Kusserow
William Lewis
Rita Linn
Robert N. Nesby, Jr.
Ross Norris

Barbara Nygren
Raymond S. Orosz
Kent Pendleton
Harry H. Platt
Gardner J. Ryan
T. W. Sielaff
Lawrence Strand
Roy M. Udo
Sarah B. Whitman
Robert F. Wilson

THE BSCS STAFF

Arnold B. Grobman, *Director*
William V. Mayer, Associate Director
Norman B. Abraham, Consultant
Walter Auffenberg, Associate Director (1960–1963)
Nathan Cohen, Photography Editor
Donald D. Cox, Consultant
J. Maxwell Davis, Consultant
Harold Durst, Consultant
Margaret Grant, Editor (1961)
Hulda Grobman, Consultant

Francis C. Harwood, Consultant
Paul DeH. Hurd, Consultant
Evelyn Klinckmann, Consultant
James Koevenig, Consultant
Lorenzo Lisonbee, Consultant
Alfred Novak, Consultant
Gordon E. Peterson, Consultant
John R. Schaefer, Consultant
Joseph J. Schwab, Editor (1960)
George I. Schwartz, Consultant
Margaret Sterling, Business Manager

THE AIBS

James Ebert, *President*
Hiden T. Cox, Executive Director
Gairdner Moment, Chairman, Education Committee
Bentley Glass, Chairman, BSCS

RAND McNALLY

William B. Miller, *Editor,* 1962———
Roberta McAllister, Copy Editor
Gordon Hartshorne, Designer
Ruth N. Coleman, Production Editor
Janice Johnson, Photography Editor
Marcel Godfriaux, Cartographer

CONTENTS

Introduction

There are two major aims in studying any natural science.

One aim is to become acquainted with scientific facts and with the big, general ideas that are built upon them. These are ideas that have profoundly altered our views of man's place in nature. These are also ideas that have tremendously enlarged human abilities to use the forces and resources of nature. In short, these are the ideas that make our lives today so different from those of our ancestors.

The other aim in studying a natural science is even more important. Upon it depends our ability to participate intelligently in the life of our scientific age. This second aim is to understand what science really is—to recognize its spirit and to appreciate its methods.

If most citizens in a democracy think of science as a kind of magic, our scientific civilization will certainly not endure. For science is not magic. It is a complex process by which we can arrive at reliable knowledge of our surroundings. It is compounded of curiosity, observation, and thought. It engages the emotions, the senses, and the minds of men.

Science has no <u>necessary</u> connection with efforts to improve the circumstances of human life, although it brings about such results more frequently than does any other human enterprise. It is a social undertaking, depending on accurate and free communication. It is a progressive activity, each generation building on the accumulated knowledge of the past. As knowledge accumulates, the general ideas and theories that hold the knowledge together often have to be changed. Because of our accumulating knowledge, our view of the living world today is different from the view we would have had one hundred or two hundred years ago. And the view one hundred years from now will undoubtedly be different again, because we shall have learned a great deal more.

Science, then, is a particularly human activity, without any element of magic about it. If science is to flourish, the whole community must understand to some degree its aims, its methods, and its consequences. Thus all of us—not only those of us who are scientists or who wish to become scientists—must understand what science is.

It might be possible, by using textbooks only, to achieve the first aim of studying science—that is, to become informed. But to pursue the second aim—the more important aim—requires experience in scientific work. Such experience cannot be gained by reading; it cannot be gained by listening—even listening to the most accomplished scientists; it can be gained only by doing the kind of things scientists do in the laboratory.

The laboratory, in its broadest sense, is the place where the work of the scientist is carried on. It may be either outdoors or indoors, but it is always a place where the scientist is asking questions of nature. It is a place where accurate observation is of first importance, where precise measurement aids observation, where controlled conditions make it possible to conduct experiments from which clear conclusions can be drawn by logical thinking. Only by experience in the laboratory is it possible to see what science really is.

No matter how much you learn about the facts of science, you will never quite understand what makes science the force it is in human history, or scientists the kinds of people they are, until you have shared with them such experience. Therefore, our biology course must contain this kind of experience.

This laboratory manual cannot provide the experience itself; that must come from your own efforts. And your success in gaining this experience will depend upon more than mere "laboratory work." The laboratory is the heart of the scientific enterprise, but no scientist locks himself alone in the laboratory. He needs libraries, so that he can view his own work in relation to the whole of science; he needs conversation with fellow scientists, so that he can obtain the stimulation of many viewpoints; he needs skill in writing, so that he can report his work for checking and verification. Locked in the laboratory, you might become skilled in handling laboratory apparatus, but you could never gain the experience of science.

The purpose of the laboratory manual, then, is to provide some direction to your experiences in biological science. The exercises are of various kinds; different ones stress different aspects of science. Some are designed to acquaint you with biological apparatus; some, to acquaint you with biological thinking. Some involve the gathering of data; some make use of data gathered by others. A number of the exercises are real experiments. But—whatever the exercise— if you are to get full value for your time in the laboratory, you must think of each experience in relation to the whole of biology, to the whole of science.

GENERAL LABORATORY PROCEDURES

In general, biologists are perhaps no more orderly or cleanly than other people. But the nature of their work demands that an unusual amount of orderliness and cleanliness be observed in the laboratory. First, observations and experiments must be verifiable. Therefore, the biologist must know what he has done and how he has done it. Good order in the laboratory helps ensure this. Second, the biologist frequently works with dangerous, disease-producing microscopic organisms. The biologist who is not cleanly is not likely to survive very long.

In the classroom laboratory there is additional need for orderliness and cleanliness, because space and apparatus must be shared with other classes. How to achieve these conditions depends upon each classroom situation. The teacher will establish proper procedures for your classroom.

USE OF MATERIALS

Apparatus

It is still possible to do some kinds of biological work with very few and very simple tools. But as biologists have probed deeper, they have often found it necessary to use many kinds of apparatus for handling and observing their materials. There are right ways and wrong ways to use each piece of apparatus—right ways that will aid in obtaining scientific information, and wrong ways that will hinder or even mislead. Therefore, it is necessary to learn the proper use of such equipment—from beakers and flasks to balances and microscopes.

Living Materials

All biologists deal with living things—this is what marks them as biologists. Though some biologists have no need to handle living things directly in their daily work, no general biology laboratory, no biology classroom, can get along without living materials. This poses some special problems in caring for such materials.

Plants. Most plants must be provided with light, soil, and water. Requirements for these differ a great deal among different kinds of plants. Therefore the care of classroom plants should be the responsibility of individual students, who will learn how to deal with the plants in their charge. All students, however, need to realize that plants—being living things—can be injured or killed, so it is necessary to handle plants carefully and gently.

Animals. Most animals require more care and more frequent attention than do plants. General rules are:

1. Provide an escape-proof container suitable for the animal.
2. Keep the container clean. This is necessary for the health of the animal. Cages of small birds and mammals should be cleaned daily.
3. Provide water at all times.
4. Feed regularly. The frequency of feeding depends upon the kind of animal being fed. Small birds and mammals may be provided with a continuous food supply.
5. Treat laboratory animals with humanity and kindness at all times. Cruelty has no place in biology.
6. When animals must be disposed of or released, the teacher will provide a suitable method.

Microorganisms. Very special methods are needed for the handling of most microorganisms. Special instructions will be given in this manual when needed.

RECORD-KEEPING

Science deals with verifiable observations. No one can check an observation that is hazy, indefinite, or half-remembered. All scientists must, therefore, keep clear and accurate records of what they have observed, made at the time of observation.

The Data Book

The best method of keeping the primary record—the record of your own observations made at the time of observation—is to jot them down in a data book. This should be a stiff-cover book (not looseleaf), preferably with unlined pages. It should be kept in diary form, the date being the first item recorded. If observations on two or more exercises are made on the same day, the exercise numbers or abbreviations of the titles can be used as subheadings.

Data to be recorded are usually in one of three forms. First, they may be observations recorded in words. In the laboratory, time will be short, so you should make these notes brief but to the point. It is not necessary to write complete sentences; but single words are seldom satisfactory, either. Phrases are usually most useful.

Second, observations may be recorded in the form of sketches. A drawing often records an observation more easily, completely, and accurately than words. Remember that sketches of this kind are not intended to be works of art.   Their success depends upon your ability to observe, not upon your artistic talent.   They should be simple, usually without shading, and drawn with a hard pencil.

Third, data may frequently be recorded numerically, as measurements.   It is important to give the units in which measurements are made.   Often, numerical data are most easily recorded in the form of a table.   Your lab directions will suggest forms for recording such data; these should be drawn in your data book before the laboratory period begins.

The data book is your record.   Your teacher may wish to look at it occasionally to help you with your work or to check on the source of information you have included in written reports, but it is not to be handed in for grading.

Under no circumstances should data be jotted down on other papers to be copied into the data book later.   This practice might increase neatness, but it will decrease accuracy.   Both may be virtues in a scientist, but neatness is of value only when it increases accuracy.   Your teacher is interested in the accuracy of your data, not in the blots and stains that are a normal hazard of the laboratory.   Remember to:

1. Record accurately.
2. Record completely.
3. Record immediately.

More and more, science is becoming a coöperative enterprise— a team activity.   Much of your own laboratory work will be done as a member of a team.   Therefore your data book will sometimes contain data contributed by other members of your team.   It is important that you know what you have observed yourself and what other members of your team have observed.   You can do this if you encircle (or record in a different color) the observations made by others.   You should be able to say: "This I know because I saw it; that I believe because I have confidence in my teammates."

The data book should not be used to record information from reading, from class discussion, or from observations of other teams or other classes.   Such information may be useful, but it is not a part of your laboratory data.

Reports of Laboratory Work

Communication is a most important part of science.   Discoveries become a part of science only when they are made known to others —when they are published.   In publishing scientific work, the writer must state the results in such a way that another person can repeat the procedures exactly.   The reader must know what material was used (in biology, this includes the kind of organism) and be able to comprehend every detail of the work.   Scientists must be free to communicate, and they must know how to communicate.   Scientific reports

are usually written in a rather standard form, somewhat as follows:
1. Title
2. Introduction: Usually states how the problem arose, and often gives a summary of past work
3. Materials and equipment
4. Procedure (or Method): Complete and exact account of what was done in gathering the data
5. Results: Data obtained from the procedure, usually in the form of tables and graphs
6. Discussion: Relates the data to the purpose of the work
7. Conclusion: Summary of the meaning of the results; often suggests further work that might be done
8. References: Other scientific reports that have been specifically mentioned

If you undertake work on an independent problem, your report should follow this form. But for the exercises in this manual, you will not have to be so elaborate. You will be communicating with your fellow students and your teacher, who already know a great deal about the exercises from reading this manual. Occasionally your teacher may wish you to do a rather complete job of reporting—for the sake of practice. Usually, however, he will want a much shorter report—perhaps merely the answers to the questions in the manual.

Use material from your data book as the basis for your reports. In a report, however, you are not writing for yourself; you are trying to communicate ideas to others. Therefore you need to be especially careful of your style—neatness, spelling, sentence structure, and clearness of expression. Often you will need to construct graphs to make your data easier to understand. In short, the task of writing a report is very different from recording data in the laboratory. But both are a part of the work of the scientist.

THE WORLD OF LIFE:
THE BIOSPHERE

CHAPTER 1

The Web of Life

EXERCISE 1.1

OBSERVING LIVING THINGS

INTRODUCTION

The first requirement in science is accurate observation. (See text, page 5.) Observation takes many forms. It involves more than just the use of the eye; observation can come through the ear or the nose or any other sense organ. Much scientific observation is indirect, coming by way of instruments—for example, through the lenses of a microscope or through the movement of a needle over a dial, as in an automobile speedometer.

But mere observation is not science. Observation needs to be directed toward some end—toward answering some question, solving some problem. When observations are directed toward a problem, they need to be organized and, eventually, examined to see what they can tell us about the problem. If we have enough observations, we may arrive at a conclusion.

PURPOSE

The first requirement in <u>biological</u> science is accurate observation of living things (organisms). Therefore, the basic purpose of this exercise is to give you an opportunity to observe some living things (or their dead remains) accurately—scientifically.

To direct your observations, you may use the problem of separating organisms into two groups, plants and animals (text, page 3). Do not be surprised, however, if you find that your short period of observation fails to clear up this problem.

MATERIALS AND EQUIPMENT

1. Labeled specimens of a number of organisms
2. Hand lenses
3. Microscopes

PROCEDURE

Arranged around the classroom you will find many living (or recently living) organisms. Each is labeled with a number and a name. Take a position at one of the specimens, as assigned by your teacher. You will be allowed a definite length of time to examine the specimen. When a signal is given by your teacher, move to the specimen with the next higher number. Repeat at each signal until you reach the highest number. From the highest number go to number 1, and continue until you are back at your starting point.

In your data book prepare a chart to aid in recording your observations, as follows:

NAME OF ORGANISM	COLOR	SIZE	ROOTS	FLOWERS	SEEDS	EYES	LEGS	SHELL	OTHER CHARACTERISTICS
a	b	c	d	e	f	g	h	i	j

In columns d to i, you need only make a check if the characteristic is present; leave the column blank if the characteristic is absent. In column j, you might record "scaly," "hairy," "lives in water," or any other characteristic you observe. The chart should help you to record your observations quickly.

STUDYING THE DATA

Remember the problem: Can we separate organisms into two groups—plants and animals? And if we can, how do we do it? Your recorded observations constitute the data on which you will base an answer. First you must study these data to see just what they tell about the problem.

Begin by placing the letter A in front of the name of an organism if you think it is an animal, the letter P if you think it is a plant, and U if you are undecided whether to call it a plant or an animal. Now look over the characteristics of all the organisms you have decided to call plants. Do the same with the ones you have called animals.

Decide which characteristics seem to belong to plants rather than to animals. On a sheet of notebook paper, list these under the heading "Plant Characteristics."(1) Decide which characteristics seem to belong to animals rather than to plants. List these under the heading "Animal Characteristics."(2)

You may find a need to change your first classification of some organisms. If necessary, do not hesitate to change the letters in the first column of your chart. But the observations—the data—should not be changed unless you go back and observe the specimens again.

Are there still any organisms that do not seem to fit either the plant or the animal characteristics (those marked U)? If so, can you name any characteristics that they all seem to share?(3) On the basis of your data, do you think it would be safe to answer a definite Yes or No to the statement "All organisms are either plants or animals"? Why or why not?(4)

EXERCISE 1.2

AN EXPERIMENT: THE GERMINATION OF SEEDS

INTRODUCTION

The previous laboratory exercise emphasized careful observation. One of the most frequent results of observations is to raise questions in the mind of the biologist. We do not know how this occurs, nor do we know why certain questions stir the curiosity of some persons and not others. But with curiosity aroused, the biologist applies his imagination to the task of seeking possible answers to his question. Such a possible answer is a hypothesis. It is the starting point for an experiment.

An experiment attempts to test the truth of a hypothesis. For example, you find a very light piece of rock. You hypothesize that it should float in water. You test the hypothesis by putting the rock in water. This simple experiment gives you information about a particular piece of rock. Such information may be valuable, but usually the hypotheses of scientists are concerned with groups of objects or with comparisons between objects rather than with one particular object. Therefore, most experiments require at least two setups. These are alike in all respects except one. The one condition in which the setups differ is called the variable. A setup in which the condition is not varied, or is varied least, is the control setup. All other setups (one or more) are experimentals.

Designing an experiment that will result in data from which a conclusion can be drawn is a difficult task. Among other things, it requires a great deal of experience. If you are interested in a scientific career, this kind of experience is worth getting as soon as possible. During this course, your teacher will point out opportunities to design experiments. Right now, however, we are concerned with the way in which a biological experiment is carried out. Therefore, the designing has already been done; in other words, you have been given the procedure.

PURPOSE

The underlying purpose of this exercise is to allow you to become acquainted with experimental method.

The experiment itself tests two hypotheses:
1. Moisture applied to seeds before planting influences their germination.
2. The length of time required for germination varies with different kinds of seeds.

BACKGROUND INFORMATION

A mature seed consists of a small plant and a store of food surrounded by a protective coat.

When you plant a seed, the young plant that has been inactive within it begins to grow. As a result of this growth, part of the young plant breaks through the seed coat. This is called sprouting. Sprouting is one indication of the more complete process of renewed growth called germination.

MATERIALS AND EQUIPMENT (for each team)

1. Seeds, all of one kind, 50
2. Beaker or jar, large enough to hold all seeds
3. Beakers or jars, each large enough to soak 10 seeds, 5
4. Petri dishes, 5
5. Clear plastic bags, each large enough to contain a petri dish, 5
6. Filter paper or paper toweling, cut to fit the petri dishes, 20 pieces
7. Rubber bands, string, or scotch tape, to seal plastic bags
8. Fungicide, 300 milliliters (abbreviated, ml)
9. Glass-marking crayon
10. Paper towels
11. Ordinary graph paper, several sheets per student

PROCEDURE

Select one kind of seed you would like to study. (Check with your teacher. He may want you to work with a particular kind of seed.) Place 50 seeds in a beaker or jar. Add fungicide solution until there appears to be two or three times as much fungicide solution as seeds. Avoid getting the fungicide on your skin. Allow the seeds to remain in the fungicide for the period of time recommended by your teacher.

While the seeds are being treated with fungicide, mark 5 soaking jars or beakers with a glass-marking crayon, as follows: A—0 hours, B—4 hours, C—24 hours, D—48 hours, E—72 hours (Figure 1.2-1). Add the team symbol to each jar.

Pour off the fungicide solution into a container provided by your teacher. Rinse the seeds with water, and spread them out to dry on paper towels. After the seeds have dried, place 10 in each of the 5 marked jars. It is important that all the seeds, no matter how long they are soaked, should be "planted" at the same time. Set up the schedule for the soaking so that all seeds will have soaked the allotted time when you are ready to plant them. At the times indicated on your schedule, add water to the soaking jars until there appears to be about three times as much water as seeds.

On the day scheduled for "planting," obtain 5 clean petri dishes and 20 pieces of filter paper, each piece cut to fit snugly, without wrinkling, into the bottom half of a petri dish. Remove the top of each dish, and place 4 pieces of the filter paper in the bottom half. Wet the paper thoroughly. Drain off any excess water, and replace the top half of each dish. Mark the 5 petri dishes as you did the soaking jars.

Pour off any water that is in the soaking jars, and place each group of seeds in its petri dish. Be sure that you "plant" the right group of seeds in the right petri dish (A in A, B in B, etc.). Put each

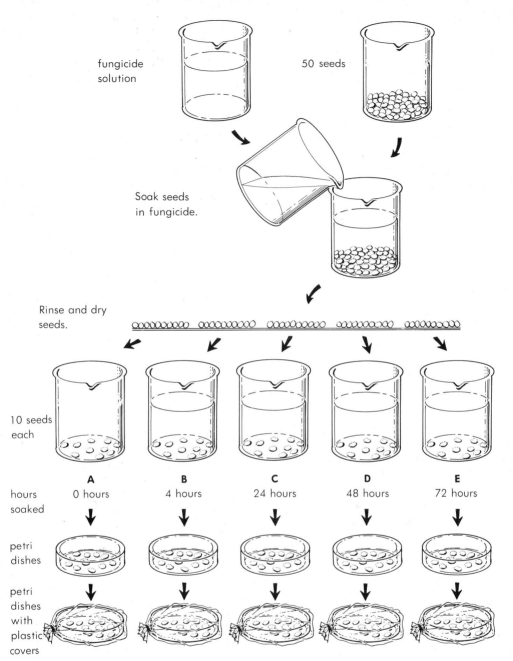

Figure 1.2-1

petri dish into a clear plastic bag. Close the bag and fasten it with a rubber band or scotch tape. Store all petri dishes in a place where temperature and light will vary little.

Observe the seeds each day for ten days, and record the number of seedlings (young plants) that have broken through the seed coats in each of the containers.

To simplify the recording of the data, prepare a form in your data book like the form at the right.

Kind of Seed_____

	HOURS SOAKED				
	0	4	24	48	72
Day 0					
Day 1					
Day 10					

STUDYING THE DATA

Draw 5 bar graphs, one for each dish. Place the number of germinated seeds on the vertical axis and the number of days on the horizontal axis. (See Figure 1.2-2.) On each graph show the total number of seeds that have germinated up to and including the time of each daily count. For all days after Day 1, add the data of all previous days.

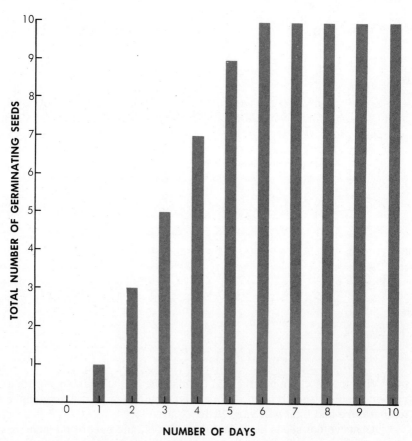

Figure 1.2-2. Germination of zinnia seeds soaked for twenty-four hours before planting

To test the second hypothesis (page 5), it is, of course, necessary to compare the results of teams using different kinds of seeds. This can best be done with numbers rather than with graphs. Using the data from the seeds that were soaked 0 hours (Group A), calculate the percent that germinated by the third, the seventh, and the tenth days. In a table drawn on the chalkboard, enter these figures opposite the name of your kind of seed.

CONCLUSIONS

From the data on the graphs, you may be able to draw a conclusion concerning the first hypothesis. However, no matter how carefully an experiment is designed, there is no guarantee that the data obtained will permit you to come to a clear conclusion. Do your data clearly affirm the first hypothesis, do they clearly negate the first hypothesis, or are they inconclusive (not clear in meaning)? Briefly state the reason for your answer.(1)

Now, using the data obtained from all the teams in your class, draw a conclusion for the second hypothesis in the same way you did for the first. (2)

DISCUSSION

What was the variable for testing the first hypothesis?(3) Which group of seeds serves as the control for the first hypothesis?(4) Can you suggest more suitable soaking times for particular kinds of seeds?(5) What was the variable for the second hypothesis?(6) Can you call any one kind of seed the control for the second hypothesis? Why or why not?(7)

EXERCISE 1.3

INTERRELATIONSHIPS OF PRODUCERS AND CONSUMERS

INTRODUCTION

In nature there are so many varying conditions in the surroundings that it is often difficult to determine which variables affect what we observe and which do not. One way to decrease the number of these varying conditions is to place organisms in containers and then seal them off from the atmosphere.

PURPOSE

The purpose of the exercise is to obtain data that will enlarge our understanding of the relationships between producers and con-sumers—especially their place in the carbon cycle.

BACKGROUND INFORMATION

An indicator is a substance that shows the presence of a chem-ical substance by changing color. Bromthymol blue is an indicator that changes to a green color in the presence of an acid. Carbon di-oxide (CO_2), which we have mentioned in the text (page 12), is a gas that forms an acid when dissolved in water. Therefore, in this exper-iment, bromthymol blue can be used to indicate, indirectly, the pres-ence of CO_2.

MATERIALS AND EQUIPMENT

1. Screw-cap culture tubes, 20 x 150 millimeters (abbreviated, mm) or longer, 4
2. Test-tube rack, 1
3. Small water snails, 2
4. Elodea (Anacharis), 2 pieces
5. Bromthymol blue solution
6. Container of melted paraffin
7. Pond water
8. Glass-marking crayon, 1

PROCEDURE

Number the screw-cap culture tubes from 1 to 4.
Fill each tube with pond or aquarium water until the water sur-face is approximately 20 mm from the top. Add 3 to 5 drops of brom-thymol blue solution to each tube. To Tube 1 add a small snail; to Tube 2 add a small snail and a leafy stem of elodea; to Tube 3 add elodea only; do not add anything to Tube 4 (Figure 1.3-1).

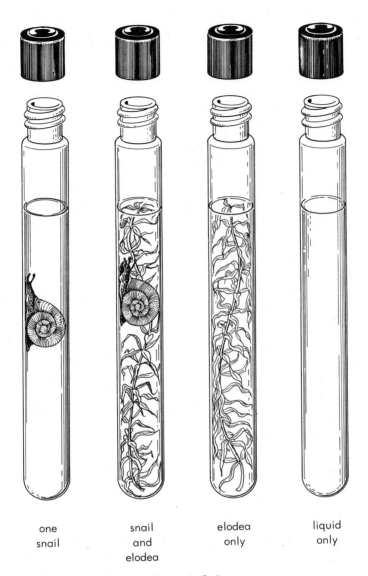

one
snail

snail
and
elodea

elodea
only

liquid
only

Figure 1.3-1

Place a cap on each tube and screw it down tightly. Dip the cap end of each tube in melted paraffin. After allowing the paraffin to cool and harden, test the seal by turning the tubes upside down for about five minutes. There should be no leakage.

If all tubes are watertight, place them in strong, indirect light— not in direct sunlight. Make observations each morning and afternoon. Record any changes in the color of the indicator (bromthymol blue) and in the condition of the plants and snails.

In your data book prepare a form for recording your observations:

DATE	TIME	TUBE 1	TUBE 2	TUBE 3	TUBE 4
	a.m.				
	p.m.				
	a.m.				
	p.m.				

DISCUSSION

In which tube did the organisms die first ?(1) Since these organisms usually survive well in an aquarium or pond, we might suspect that being cut off from air might have had something to do with their death. What substance in air may have been needed ?(2) Another possibility is that death may have resulted from the accumulation of a poisonous material in the water. What does the indicator show ?(3) Now recall what you have read about photosynthesis and the carbon cycle in the text. Using this information and your answers to the previous questions, explain the data you recorded while observing the other tubes that contain organisms.(4) Did the indicator change color in Tube 4? If so, how might you explain this (keeping in mind the source of the water) ?(5) Considering this exercise as an experiment, what would you call Tube 4 ?(6) What results might you have expected if all tubes had been kept in total darkness ?(7)

EXERCISE 1.4

USE OF THE MICROSCOPE: INTRODUCTION

INTRODUCTION

Because of the limitations of our senses, many things we would like to find out about living organisms can be discovered only by making use of instruments. One of the most frequently used instruments is the microscope, which makes it possible to observe objects and movements so small that they are invisible to our unaided eyes.

There are many different kinds of microscopes. A magnifying glass is the simplest kind. But usually when we use the word "microscope," we are referring to an instrument made up of a series of glass lenses held together in a tube—a compound microscope.

The type of compound microscope most commonly used in the biology laboratory is the monocular microscope. In working with this kind of microscope, we use only one eye, so we see an image having length and width but little apparent depth. Most objects examined under the monocular microscope must be so small or thin that light can pass through them. We are able to distinguish form and structure in such objects because some of their parts absorb more light than others. Things seen in this way under the microscope are said to be observed by transmitted light.

PURPOSE

This exercise is to acquaint you with the monocular microscope, its use and care.

MATERIALS AND EQUIPMENT (for each student or pair of students)

1. Glass slides and cover glasses (cover slips)
2. Lens paper
3. Paper toweling
4. Strips of newspaper and photographs from magazines
5. Scissors
6. Transparent or translucent millimeter rule
7. Finger bowl or beaker
8. Medicine dropper
9. Forceps
10. Monocular microscope

PROCEDURE

A. Setting Up the Microscope

Remove the microscope from its case or space in the storage cabinet. Grasp the curved arm of the instrument with one hand, and place the other hand under the base. Always use two hands when carrying the instrument. Set the instrument down gently on the laboratory table, with the arm toward you and the square stage away from you. The base should be a safe distance from the edge of your table.

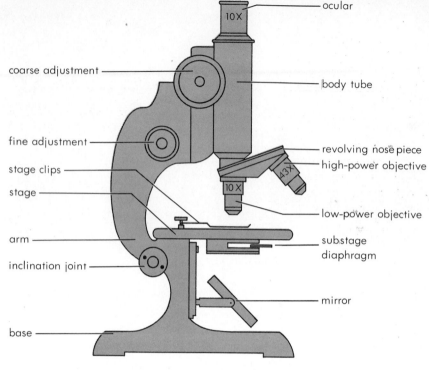

ocular

10X

coarse adjustment

body tube

fine adjustment

revolving nose piece

high-power objective

stage clips

43X

stage

10X

low-power objective

arm

substage
diaphragm

inclination joint

mirror

base

Figure 1.4-1. The monocular microscope

B. Identification of the Parts of the Microscope

Your teacher will help you identify each part of the instrument
(Figure 1.4-1) and explain its use. Make certain that you are familiar with each part before proceeding further with this exercise.

C. Preliminary Adjustments

Using the coarse-adjustment knobs, raise the body tube so that
the objectives do not hit the stage when the revolving nosepiece is rotated. Turn the nosepiece so that the low-power (shorter) objective
is in line with the ocular, at the upper end of the body tube. You will
hear a click when the objective moves into position. Now turn the
substage diaphragm to the largest possible opening. Adjust the mirror so that it reflects light upward through the opening in the stage.
Never let direct sunlight strike the mirror. Why? Look into the ocular, and make final adjustment of the mirror so that the circular
field of view is evenly illuminated. If there is glare, adjust the diaphragm to eliminate it.

If the lenses of the ocular or the objective appear to be cloudy
or dusty, wipe them gently with a piece of lens paper, using a circular motion and light pressure. Never use any other kind of paper or
cloth. If this procedure does not clean the lenses, consult your
teacher. When a piece of lens paper has been used once, discard it.

D. Preparation of Materials for Examination with a Microscope

Materials to be studied are usually placed on a piece of glass of standard size called a microscope slide. In most cases the material is covered with a small, thin piece of glass called a cover slip. Both slide and cover slip should be as clean as possible before use.

To clean glass slides, hold them by the edges, between finger and thumb, and dip in water. Then wipe them clean and dry, using a soft piece of clean cloth or paper towel.

Cover slips are much more fragile than slides. Hold them by the edges, using a finger and thumb of one hand, and dip into water.

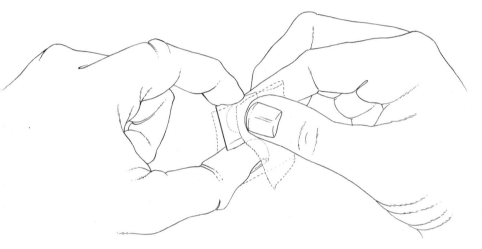

Figure 1.4-2

A piece of thin, soft cloth or lens paper should then be folded and held between the finger and thumb of the other hand. Next, insert the wet cover slip in the fold and apply pressure to both surfaces at the same time by bringing thumb and finger together (Figure 1.4-2). A gentle, circular, wiping motion is most effective. Avoid touching the flat surfaces of slides and cover slips with your fingers. Always handle them by the edges.

We will now prepare a wet mount for microscopic observation. Using scissors, cut a piece of newspaper about 3 x 3 mm square that includes at least one letter e. If possible, find a piece that has printing on only one side of the paper. Place the piece of newspaper in the center of a slide, printed side up. Using a medicine dropper, put a single drop of water on the piece of newspaper. After a few minutes some of the water will soak into the newspaper, but some should still remain surrounding it. If necessary, add another drop of water. The cover slip should then be placed over the newspaper. If this is done properly, the remaining water will spread out in a thin, even layer between cover slip and slide, with the newspaper sandwiched between them. It requires some skill to place the cover slip on the slide in such a way that no air bubbles are included in the mount. The best method is to hold the cover slip at an angle of about 45° to the

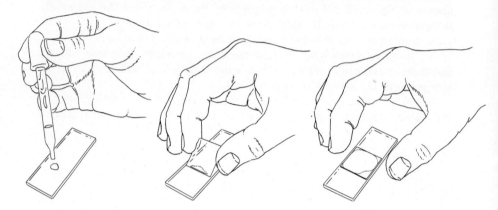

Figure 1.4-3

slide; then bring the cover slip down to the slide until the lower edge touches the drop of water. Continue to lower the slip slowly until it is parallel to the surface of the slide (Figure 1.4-3). Even when this is done carefully, air bubbles will occasionally be trapped in the mount. In some cases these may be removed by gently tapping the cover slip with the point of a pencil. A few bubbles may not interfere with your observation.

E. Focusing the Microscope

Using the coarse-adjustment knobs, raise the body tube until there is a space of approximately 2 centimeters (abbreviated, cm) between the low-power objective and the surface of the stage. Now place the slide—cover-slip side up—on the stage of the microscope. Position the slide so that a letter e on the newspaper is located in the center of the stage opening. Use the stage clips to hold the slide in position. While looking at the microscope from the side, and again using the coarse-adjustment knobs, slowly lower the body tube until the lower end of the objective is approximately 1 mm above the upper surface of the cover slip. Never allow the objective to come into contact with the cover slip. Some, but not all, microscopes are provided with mechanical stops, which prevent this.

Now look through the ocular, and slowly raise the body tube until the print on the newspaper becomes visible. If you still see no image after you have raised the objective more than 1 cm, you have missed the position for correct focus. Refocus—look at the microscope from the side, lower the objective to its original position, and try again.

Never lower the body tube with the coarse adjustment while you are looking into the ocular. When an image of the printed material is seen, the fine-adjustment knobs should be rotated back and forth to obtain the best possible focus. Further adjustment of the diaphragm will, in many cases, improve the clearness of the image.

Compare the position of the image of the letter e in the ocular with the position of the printed e (the object) on the slide. Is it upside down, or is it in the same position as it would be when seen with the unaided eye ?(1) Does it appear to be reversed as it would be if seen in a mirror ?(2) While looking into the ocular, slowly move the slide from right to left. Which way does the image move ?(3) Move the slide away from you. Which way does the image move ?(4)

Now rotate the revolving nosepiece so that the high-power (longer) objective is in line with the ocular. In doing this, make sure that the lower end of the objective does not touch the cover slip. If this does happen, you will have to repeat the entire sequence of operations already described, beginning with the focusing of the low-power objective. When the high-power objective is in correct focus, its lower end will be much closer to the cover slip than was the low-power objective. The distance between the objective and the cover slip is called the working distance. In most cases, less than one full turn (in either direction) will bring the high-power objective into focus.

Is the field of view larger or smaller ?(5) Does the switch from low power to high power change the position of the image ? You will have to move the slide about slightly to see the whole image of the letter.(6) Is the illumination brighter or less bright than it is with low power ?(7) Adjust the diaphragm so that the brightness of the high-power image is about the same as that when low power is used.

Remove your wet mount from the microscope, but save it for use later in the exercise.

F. Magnification

Now let us consider what is actually meant by the terms "low power" and "high power." These refer to the degree of magnification obtained. When using the microscope, it is important to know exactly how much the instrument is magnifying the object. If a microscope magnifies an object 50 diameters (50X), the image you see is 50 times longer and wider than if the object were viewed with the unaided eye at a distance of 25.4 cm. Engraved on each objective or ocular is a number indicating the degree of magnification it provides. The combined magnification produced by both ocular and objective is equal to the product of these numbers. If, for example, the number on the ocular is 5X and that on the low-power objective is 12X, the combined magnification is 5 x 12, or 60 diameters. Using the same ocular and a high-power objective that magnifies 45X, a magnification of 5 x 45, or 225 diameters, will be obtained. Find the magnification numbers on the ocular and objectives of your microscope, and calculate the magnifications obtained when using low power(8) and when using high power(9).

G. Measurement with the Microscope

Because objects observed with the microscope are usually quite small, biologists find it convenient to use units of length smaller than centimeters or millimeters for microscopic measurement. One such unit, commonly used, is the micron (1/1000 mm), for which the Greek letter μ is the symbol. We can estimate the size of a microscopic object by comparing it with the size of the circular field of view. The size of the field may be determined as follows:

Place a plastic millimeter rule on the stage. Following the directions already given for focusing, obtain a well-defined image of the millimeter divisions on the rule with the low-power objective. Carefully move the rule until its marked edge passes through the exact center of the field of view. Now count the number of divisions that can be seen within the field of view, from one side to the other. The marks on the rule will appear quite wide; 1 mm is the distance from the center of one mark to the center of the next. What is the diameter of the low-power field of your microscope in millimeters ?(10) In microns ?(11)

To measure the diameter of the high-power field, use the following procedure. First, divide the magnification number of the high-power objective by the magnification number of the low-power objective. Then divide the diameter of the low-power field of view by this quotient. This is the diameter of the high-power field of view. For example, if the magnification of your low-power objective is 12X and of your high-power objective 48X, the quotient you obtain is 4. If the diameter of the low-power field of view is 1600 μ, the diameter of the high-power field of view is 1600 ÷ 4, or 400 μ. Using this method of calculation, what is the diameter of your high-power field ?(12)

Remove the plastic rule and replace it with the wet mount of the letter e. Using low power, compare the height of the letter with the diameter of the field of view. Estimate, as accurately as possible, the actual height of the letter—in millimeters (13) and in microns (14).

H. Resolving Power

Remove the slide from the stage and carefully lift off the cover slip. Discard the piece of newspaper. Dry the slide and the cover slip. Now prepare another wet mount, using a small piece of paper cut from a photograph in a magazine, following the same procedure for preparing slides outlined in D, pages 15-16. Examine this mount under low power. How does the magnified image of the specimen compare with the photograph as seen with the unaided eye ?(15) You have just seen an example of the <u>resolving power</u> of a microscope, the ability to clearly separate small details present in the object. For most people, any objects that are separated by less than 0.1 mm space cannot be seen as separate objects by the unaided eye. The microscope permits us to separate objects that are much closer together than this —objects that would otherwise appear as one.

You can observe the limited resolving power of your unaided eyes by studying the headlights of a distant automobile as it approaches you at night. At first you see only a single point of light. As the car comes nearer, you begin to see the lights as two separate points; at this distance your eyes have "resolved" the lights.

Thus a microscope actually does two things: it provides magnification, and it permits us to distinguish objects that are separated by spaces too small to otherwise distinguish them.

I. Care of the Microscope

The microscope, like all other instruments in the laboratory, must be given proper care. It should always be carried in an upright position, with one hand firmly grasping the arm and the other hand supporting it under the base. If it is necessary to tilt the instrument, use the <u>inclination joint</u>, and always return the microscope to its untilted position at the conclusion of your work.

At the end of the laboratory period, turn the revolving nosepiece until the low-power objective is in place. Adjust the position of the body tube so that the lower end of the objective is approximately 1 cm above the stage. Turn the stage clips so that they do not extend beyond the side of the stage. Return the microscope to the proper storage space. Clean all slides and cover slips.

FOR FURTHER REFERENCE

CORRINGTON, J. D. <u>Exploring with Your Microscope</u>. New York: McGraw-Hill Book Co., Inc., 1957. (An excellent introduction to the use of the microscope and methods for preparing materials to be examined with it.)

STEHLI, G. J. <u>The Microscope and How to Use It</u>. New York: Sterling Publishing Co., Inc., 1961. (A brief but interesting introductory guide.)

STONG, C. L. <u>Scientific American Book of Projects for the Amateur Scientist</u>. New York: Simon and Schuster, Inc., Publishers, 1960. Pp. 463-476. (This article on amateur microscopy includes directions for making a powerful microscope from very inexpensive and easily obtained materials. Instruction for preparing and mounting diatoms and procedures for making and using a camera to take photographs with a microscope objective are briefly but clearly outlined. The preparation of diatoms should be carried out only under the direct supervision of your teacher.)

EXERCISE 1.5

USE OF THE MICROSCOPE: BIOLOGICAL MATERIAL

PURPOSE

Our purpose in this exercise is to learn how to prepare biological materials for microscopic examination.

MATERIALS AND EQUIPMENT

1. Glass slides and cover slips
2. Lens paper
3. Paper towel
4. Beaker or finger bowl, for cleaning slides and cover slips
5. Medicine dropper
6. Monocular microscope
7. Iodine—potassium-iodide (I_2KI) solution in bottle with dropper
8. Small piece of white potato
9. Yeast culture in dilute molasses
10. Mixed culture of microorganisms

PROCEDURE

In this exercise, follow the general procedures used in the previous exercise for setting up the microscope, cleaning slides and cover slips, and preparing wet mounts. Specific additional instructions will be included below, when necessary.

A. Mounting, Staining, and Observing Starch Grains

Place a clean slide on your laboratory table. Place a small piece of white potato in the center of the slide, and apply pressure with your fingers until a small amount of juice is forced out of the potato onto the surface of the slide. Distribute this juice in a more or less even layer over the center of the slide by rubbing the piece of potato in a circular pattern. Discard the piece of potato. Immediately add a drop of water and a clean cover slip to the slide, avoiding, if possible, the inclusion of air bubbles in the mount.

Examine this preparation under low power, using the focusing procedure you learned in the previous exercise. The starch grains that you will find in the mount can be more readily observed if the size of the opening in the substage diaphragm is decreased. This will increase contrast between the starch grains and the water surrounding them. Move the slide on the stage until you have located a field in which well-separated grains are clearly visible. Center a group of these grains in the field and examine them again under high power.

Describe the shape of an individual starch grain.(1) Can you see any internal structures in these grains? If you can, describe what you observe.(2)

When you have completed your observations, turn again to low power. Now stain the starch grains, using the following procedure: Place a small drop of iodine—potassium-iodide (I_2KI) solution on the slide, at one side of the cover slip. Tear off a small piece of paper towel, and place the torn edge in contact with the water at the opposite edge of the cover slip. Water will be absorbed by the paper towel. As water is removed at one edge of the mount, I_2KI solution will be drawn under the cover slip at the opposite edge. Continue until the I_2KI solution is drawn about halfway across the space under the cover slip. I_2KI solution will then continue to spread slowly throughout the mount. By examining various regions of the mount, you can observe the effects of different concentrations of the I_2KI solution on the starch grains. Examine your mount, first under low power and then under high power. What changes do you observe in the starch grains exposed to relatively high concentrations of I_2KI solution?(3) What differences do you observe between these grains and others exposed to low concentrations of I_2KI?(4) Can you observe internal structure more clearly in the stained grains than in the unstained grains? If so, describe the structures you can see.(5)

When you have completed your observations, remove the slide from the stage, lift off the cover slip, and dip both slide and cover slip into the container of water. Dry them, and carefully wipe off any liquid that may have run off the slide onto the microscope stage, using a piece of soft paper towel.

B. Examining Yeast Cultures

The culture of yeast that you are about to examine was prepared a day or so ago by placing a few grains of dried yeast in a solution of molasses and water. Yeast organisms multiply so rapidly that millions of them will be available for study.

Place a small drop of the culture on a clean slide, add a cover slip, and examine first under low power, then under high power. Describe the shape of the yeast organisms.(6)

Study the arrangement in small groups of these organisms. From your observations, can you come to any conclusions about how new yeast organisms are formed ?(7) What internal structures (if any) can you see in the organisms ? Show in a sketch any such structures that you observe.(8)

Using I_2KI solution, stain the yeast in the same way you stained the starch grains. Compare the effects of the I_2KI solution on the yeast organisms with its effects on starch grains.(9) Can you see any structures that were not visible in the unstained yeast organisms ? If so, describe them.(10)

C. Procedures for Examining a Mixed Culture of Microorganisms

Using a medicine dropper, remove a small amount of liquid from the upper part of the mixed culture of microorganisms. Place one drop at the center of a clean glass slide, and add a cover slip. Focus with low power and adjust the substage diaphragm to obtain good contrast. Move the slide around on the stage so that all areas under the cover slip are examined. A variety of organisms should be visible. Study these, with particular attention to variations in size, shape, movement (twisting, wiggling, crawling, etc.), and internal structure.

As water evaporates from its edge, the cover slip will be drawn closer to the surface of the slide. As this occurs, the movements of larger organisms will be more and more restricted. Locate one or more of the organisms that have been either slowed down or stopped. Turn to high power and attempt to examine them under higher magnification. To follow moving organisms and keep them in the field, it is usually necessary to use both hands—one on the slide and the other on the fine adjustment. As organisms move about, they not only change position in the field but they also move in and out of focus. Why ?(11) If you do not constantly readjust the focus, you will see only a part of the detail to be observed.

. When seen under high power, do the organisms appear to move more rapidly or more slowly than when seen under low power ?(12)

Now stain the mount, repeating the procedures that you used with the starch grains and yeast. Do moving organisms continue to move when exposed to I_2KI solution ?(13) What changes in color do you observe ?(14) Can you observe any changes in internal structure as staining proceeds ? If so, record these in sketches.(15)

At the end of the laboratory period, clean the slides and cover slips. Place the microscope in its proper storage place, following the procedures outlined in Exercise 1.4.

EXERCISE 1.6

USE OF THE STEREOSCOPIC MICROSCOPE

INTRODUCTION

The stereoscopic microscope, or <u>stereomicroscope</u>, has advantages for some types of microscopic work. It consists of two complete microscopes, one for each eye, united to form a single instrument. Each of these microscopes provides separate and somewhat different images, since the object is viewed from slightly different angles. In our minds we are able to combine and interpret these images so that we observe the object in three dimensions—length, width, and depth.

The stereomicroscope, like the monocular microscope, may be used to view objects by transmitted light. Usually, however, we use the stereomicroscope to look at objects by <u>reflected</u> light. This means that the observer looks at an object as he might view a book or his own hand. The object is visible because light is reflected from its surface. The stereomicroscope is particularly useful for studying things that are too small to be observed with the unaided eye but too large to be seen as a whole with the monocular microscope. Instruments of this type usually provide magnifications varying from 5 to 60 diameters.

PURPOSE

Our purpose in this exercise is to learn how to make use of a stereomicroscope.

MATERIALS AND EQUIPMENT

1. Glass slides
2. Half of a glass petri dish—top or bottom
3. Medicine dropper
4. Paper towel
5. Lens paper
6. Pond culture
7. Several small, dead insects
8. Small piece of newspaper
9. Small piece of cotton cloth
10. Stereomicroscope

PROCEDURE

A. Setting Up the Stereomicroscope

Remove the microscope from its case or the storage cabinet. Carry it to your laboratory table, using both hands. The instrument should be a safe distance from the edge of the table, in a position where the stage is well lighted.

There are several ways to change the magnification of stereomicroscopes. Your teacher will give you specific instructions on how this is done with the microscope you are using.

Calculate the magnification obtained when the low-power objectives of your microscope are used. This is done by multiplying the magnification of one of the oculars by that of one of the objectives. Your teacher will show you how to obtain the necessary data. What is the low-power magnification?(1) Now determine the magnification at one of the higher powers you will use in making your observations, and record it.(2)

B. Observing with the Stereomicroscope

Begin by adjusting your microscope so that it gives the lowest possible magnification.

Place a small piece of newspaper in the center of the stage. Using the focusing knobs, move the body of the microscope as close to the stage as possible.

On most stereomicroscopes, one of the ocular tubes can be rotated and the other is fixed. Look into the fixed ocular, using only one eye. (If the left ocular is fixed, use your left eye; if the right ocular is fixed, use your right eye.) Slowly raise the body by rotating the focusing knobs until the newspaper comes into sharp focus. If the lenses of the oculars or objectives need cleaning, wipe them gently with a piece of lens paper. Next, move the ocular tubes toward or away from the midline of the microscope until the distance between their centers matches the distance between the centers of your eyes. When this is done correctly, you should see only a single circular field of view. Finally, without changing the position of the microscope body, rotate the movable ocular tube until the newspaper is in sharp focus again.

While looking into the oculars, move the newspaper to your left. In what direction does the newspaper appear to move?(3) Now move the newspaper away from you. In what direction does it appear to move?(4) How do these observations compare with those you recorded in Exercise 1.4, Items 3 and 4?(5)

Now change the magnification to a higher power, and, if necessary, adjust focus. Has the size of the field of view changed? If so, in what way?(6)

Change back to low power and examine a small piece of lens paper; then examine a small piece of cotton cloth. How does the arrangement of fibers differ in these two materials ?(7)

Now place several small, dead insects in the center of a clean glass slide. A cover slip should not be used. Place the slide on the stage and examine the insects, using low power and all available higher magnifications.

Next, pour enough water from the pond culture into the petri dish to fill it to a depth of 3 mm. Examine under low and then higher powers, looking for different kinds of living organisms. Observe how they differ in size, shape, color, and pattern of movement. Your microscope may be equipped with a mirror that permits observation by transmitted light. If so, adjust the mirror so that light passes <u>through</u> the stage and the culture in the petri dish. Note the difference in appearance when the same organisms are viewed by transmitted rather than by reflected light.

Finally, clean the stage of your microscope with a piece of soft paper towel. Adjust the magnification for low power. Return the microscope to the proper storage space. Carry it, using both hands. Clean all slides. Empty the petri dish into the pond culture and dry it. Dispose of all other materials, as directed by your teacher.

Write a brief paragraph comparing the uses of the stereoscopic microscope with those of the monocular microscope.(8)

CHAPTER 2

Individuals and Populations

EXERCISE 2.1

POPULATION GROWTH: A MODEL

INTRODUCTION

Just as we need tools like the microscope to help us extend our powers of observation, so we need mental "tools" to help us extend our thinking. One such mental tool is called a model. Here the word is used in a sense that is somewhat different from the sense in which it is generally used. The model we are discussing is not an object; it is a mental image. This kind of model simplifies a complex, real situation so that we can more easily understand it. Should the model give results similar to those given in the real situation, we can have confidence that it "works" in the same way the real situation does. Of course, the two will never match exactly, but the degree of matching will determine the extent of our confidence.

Because the model is a simplification, it differs in some respects from the real situation. The simplifications we make are called assumptions. To simplify, we assume certain things that may be only approximately true. We must keep these assumptions in mind whenever we use the model to try to understand a real situation.

PURPOSE

The purpose of this exercise is to observe the way in which a "model" population might grow. In the next exercise (2.2) we will set up an experiment to see how closely a real population fits our model.

MATERIALS

1. Ordinary graph paper, 1 sheet per student
2. Semilogarithmic graph paper, 1 sheet per student

PROCEDURE

A. Setting Up the Model

We can build our model, our mental tool, around a real organism —the house sparrow. We will begin on an island, in the spring of 1961, with a population of 10 house sparrows—5 pairs, that is, 5 males and 5 females.

Assumption 1: Each year each pair of sparrows produces 10 offspring, always 5 males and 5 females.

Assumption 2: Each year all the breeding (parent) birds die before the next spring.

Assumption 3: Each year all offspring live through the next breeding season. (In most real situations, some parents would live and some offspring would die. But taken together, Assumptions 2 and 3 tend to balance each other, thus reducing the difference between our model and a real situation.)

Assumption 4: During the time of our study, no other sparrows arrive on the island, and none leave.

B. Growth of the Model Population

Now we want to see how this model population (we can call it a hypothetical population) will grow. To do this, we must calculate the size of the population at the beginning of each breeding season (each spring). According to Assumption 1, in 1961 we have 5 pairs, each producing 10 offspring, a total of 50 offspring. According to Assumption 2, the 10 breeding birds of 1961 will die before the next spring. According to Assumption 3, all of the 50 offspring live to the spring of 1962. Thus, at the start of the 1962 breeding season, there will be 50 house sparrows on the island. According to Assumption 1, 25 of these will be males and 25 will be females—25 pairs, each of which will produce 10 offspring. Go on with this kind of reasoning to calculate what the island's sparrow population will be at the beginning of the breeding season in 1963, 1964, 1965, 1966, and 1967.

We now have a series of numbers, but they probably do not give us any clear idea of the way the population grows. A graph will show us more. Construct the graph so that the years are shown along the horizontal axis (abscissa) and the number of birds, along the vertical axis (ordinate). You will need to make the vertical scale large enough to show the small 1961 population. Plot as many of the generations as you can.

The difficulty we meet in plotting our data on population growth—the choice of a scale large enough to show small gains but not so large that later generations will go beyond the height of the ordinate—can be overcome with another tool. This tool is semilogarithmic (usually called "semi-log") graph paper. It is not necessary to fully understand the mathematics of logarithms to appreciate our present use of this tool. Your teacher will explain what you need to know to be able to plot the data.

Now construct your semi-log graph with the same data you used before. What advantage(s) does the semi-log graph have over the ordinary graph for plotting data on population growth ?(1)

STUDYING THE DATA

Place the two graphs in front of you. How does the slope of the line connecting the plotted points change as you go from left to right (from year to year) across the ordinary graph ?(2) What does this mean in terms of rate of population growth ?(3) What kind of line shows the same thing on the semi-log graph ?(4)

Finally, we must relate our results to the purpose of the exercise. In one or two sentences, describe the growth of a hypothetical population that is limited by the assumptions stated in this exercise.(5)

FOR FURTHER INVESTIGATION

We can examine the effects that changes in our assumptions will have on population growth. By doing this we can expect to gain a better understanding of the factors involved in population changes. (See text, pages 32-38.)

1. Change Assumption 2 as follows: Each year two-fifths of the breeding birds (equally males and females) live to breed again a second year and then die. All other assumptions remain unchanged. Calculate the population size of each generation. Compare these results with the results of the original assumptions by drawing a graph on the grid used for the original data.

2. Change Assumption 3 as follows: Each year two-fifths of the offspring (equally males and females) die before the next breeding season. All other assumptions remain unchanged. As before, calculate the populations, and draw a comparative graph.

3. Change Assumption 4 as follows: Each year 50 new house sparrows (equally males and females) arrive on the island from elsewhere. None leave. All other assumptions remain unchanged. Calculate the populations and draw a comparative graph.

Devise other problems for yourself by changing the assumptions.

EXERCISE 2.2

STUDY OF A YEAST POPULATION

INTRODUCTION

In the study of a hypothetical population (Exercise 2.1), the data on the numbers of house sparrows were derived from the assumptions built into the model. Now we shall obtain data from a real population. Gathering data on the growth of a real population of house sparrows would require years of observing and counting. Since we do not have time for such census-taking, we must turn to an organism that reproduces rapidly. Yeast organisms, which we observed in Exercise 1.5, are suitable for this study.

PURPOSE

The purpose of this experiment is to study the pattern of growth in a real population under controlled laboratory conditions. We can set up the following statement as our hypothesis: In a real population the pattern of growth is the same as that of the model studied in Exercise 2.1.

BACKGROUND INFORMATION

Yeast organisms are used not only because they reproduce at a rate that will allow us to complete our investigation in about ten days

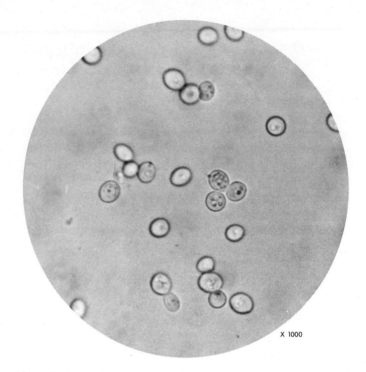

X 1000

Figure 2.2-1. Yeast organisms in a microscopic field. The magnification in this photograph is greater than that obtained with the usual high-power objective. How does an increase in magnification affect the size of the field?

but also because they are conveniently small—several million can be kept in a test tube. Dry yeast grains are composed of many inactive plants. These tiny plants become active and reproduce in a suitable medium, a mixture of materials that will support their growth. A population of organisms in a medium is called a culture. Figure 2.2-1 shows yeast organisms in the medium, as they would appear under a microscope.

MATERIALS AND EQUIPMENT

A. For Preparation of Medium

1. 2000 ml Erlenmeyer flask or a glass pyrex saucepan of similar capacity
2. Graduated cylinder
3. Large stirring rod or tablespoon
4. Source of heat (preferably gas)
5. Autoclave or pressure cooker
6. Test tubes of about 20 ml capacity, 1 per student plus 1 per team of 10 students

7. Square of aluminum foil, large enough to form a cap over a test tube, 1 per student
8. Balance
9. Spatula
10. Clean, soft cloth
11. Yeast extract, 2.5 grams (abbreviated, g)
12. Monobasic potassium phosphate, 2 g
13. Glucose, 40 g
14. Peptone, 5 g
15. Distilled water, 1000 ml

B. For Preparation of Cultures

1. Test tubes (same as in Item A-6, page 30) containing 10 ml of medium, 1 per student
2. Glass-marking crayons, 1 per team of 10 students
3. Dry active yeast, 1 package
4. Fine-pointed forceps
5. Square of aluminum foil to make yeast packet, 1 per team

C. For Counting Day

1. Test tubes (same as in Item B-1 above) containing yeast cultures, 10 per team
2. Microscopes, 1 per pair of students
3. Microscope slides, 2 per student
4. Cover slips (all same size), 2 per student
5. Medicine droppers or 1-ml pipettes, 1 per student
6. Test tubes containing 10 ml of medium, for determining the number of cells at "zero" hours of growth, 1 per team
7. Test tubes containing 9 ml of water, about 15 per team

D. For Examining the Results

1. Ordinary graph paper, 1 sheet per student

PROCEDURE

A. Preparation of Medium
(to be done for the whole class by a small team of students)

You need 10 ml of medium for each student, plus 10 ml additional for each team. (The quantities listed above will make a little more than 1000 ml of medium.) Compute the needed amount of each material. Weigh out the amounts of dry materials, and add them to the required volume of water. Dissolve the materials by stirring continually over a low heat source.

When properly prepared, the medium is sparkling clear and slightly yellow in color. If it is cloudy, you have done something wrong. Check your calculations.

Pour 10 ml of the medium into each tube (1 per student plus 1 per team). Shape a square of aluminum foil as a cap over the mouth of each test tube. Sterilize in an autoclave or pressure cooker, at 15 lbs pressure, for fifteen minutes. Store the sterile test tubes of yeast medium as directed by your teacher.

B. Growing the Population

Each team of 10 students should have a set of 10 test tubes of yeast medium. Using a glass-marking crayon, mark each tube with a team symbol. Number the tubes from 1 to 10, and assign a number to each team member.

From a package of dry, active yeast, choose 15 to 20 grains of yeast—all the same size. Put a grain of yeast in Tube 10. Be sure the grain is in the medium. Mix by holding the tube firmly between the fingers and thumb of one hand and striking the bottom of the tube forcefully with the fingers of the other hand. Place the tube in a warm, dark place as directed by your teacher; in other words, incubate it. Put the remaining grains of yeast in an aluminum-foil packet, and label with the team symbol. Store as directed by your teacher.

On each succeeding day, take out the tube of medium with the next lower number (Tube 9, 8, 7, etc.). Add a yeast grain from the storage packet, mix, and incubate as before. Make daily observations of any change in the yeast cultures. Record these observations in your data book.

C. Counting the Population

When the last culture in the series (Tube 1) has been incubated for twenty-four hours, a count of yeast organisms in all 10 tubes must be made. All counts must be taken at the same time. The members of each team will work in pairs—students 1 and 2 together, 3 and 4 together, etc. Each student will make a count from his own tube and a count from the tube of his partner. Thus there will be two counts on each of the 10 tubes. You will need to prepare two forms, each one like the form at the top of page 33.

Use one form for recording the counts made from your culture by you (A) and by your partner (B). Use the other form for recording the counts made from your partner's culture by you (A) and by your partner (B).

Team _____   Culture No. _____   Dilution Factor _____

MEMBER OF PAIR	FIELDS					TOTAL	AVERAGE	AVERAGE X DILUTION FACTOR
	1	2	3	4	5			
A								
B								
						Pair Average _____		

First, shake your own test tube until the yeast organisms are evenly distributed. Using a pipette, immediately place 0.1 ml of the culture on a clean slide (or, using a medicine dropper, place 2 drops on the slide). Place a clean cover slip over the culture on the slide. Do not press down on the cover slip. Position the slide on your microscope stage, and focus under low power; then switch to high power. Do not tilt the stage!

Count the number of individual organisms in 5 different high-power fields, all on your slide, as indicated in Figure 2.2-2. Caution: Yeast organisms are difficult to see if the light is too bright. Yeast organisms often stick together. Each individual organism in any clump is to be counted separately. Buds also count as individuals. Record the 5 counts in your data book (first form, line A).

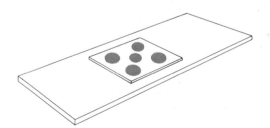

Figure 2.2-2

If the fields are too crowded for easy counting, you must make a dilution of the culture. To do this, obtain a test tube containing 9 ml of water and label this dilution D1. Then shake the yeast culture until the organisms are evenly distributed. Using a clean pipette, transfer 1 ml (or, if you use a medicine dropper, 20 drops) of the culture into the dilution tube. Rinse the pipette (or the medicine dropper) several times by running clean water in and out of it. Mix the contents of the dilution tube thoroughly. Now transfer 0.1 ml (with a pipette) or 2 drops (with a medicine dropper) from the dilution tube to a slide, and proceed to count the cells as directed above. If the microscopic field is still too crowded for easy counting, transfer 1 ml of the contents of

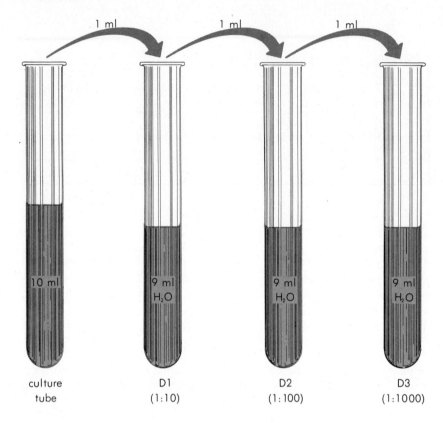

Figure 2.2-3

Tube <u>D1</u> to another test tube containing 9 ml of water. Mark this dilution <u>D2</u>. It may even be necessary to use a third dilution. See Figure 2.2-3 (series of dilution tubes). In Tube <u>D1</u> the culture will be diluted 10 times; in Tube <u>D2</u>, 100 times; in Tube <u>D3</u>, 1000 times. If you make dilutions during counting, record the proper number (10 or 100 or 1000) after "Dilution Factor" on the data form. If you make no dilutions, the dilution factor is 1. Now make a slide from your partner's culture. Make 5 counts as before, and record them in your data book (second form, line A). Copy your partner's data (<u>his</u> lines A) onto <u>your</u> lines B.

As soon as you have finished recording the data, total the 5 counts in each line of the two data forms. Then divide by 5 to get the average for the line. If, in any one tube, your average and your partner's average differ by more than 10 organisms, prepare new slides and repeat the counts.

One more job remains for each team: to make a count from a tube that has been incubated 0 days. This should be done by the pair that finishes first (or as assigned by the teacher). Put a grain of dry yeast into a test tube containing 10 ml of medium. Allow the tube to stand for 5 minutes, shaking occasionally. Proceed to count as directed above. The students who make this count will need to prepare an extra form in their data books.

STUDYING THE DATA

You have already computed the figures for the "Total" and "Average" columns in the data forms. Now you need to compute the last column, "Average X Dilution Factor," and "Pair Average." The data for the last column is obtained by multiplying the average by the dilution factor. For example, if you made your count from Tube D2, the dilution factor is 100. If your average count was 15, then the number to be recorded in the last column is 1500. The pair average is obtained by averaging the two numbers in the last column of each form. The pair average for each tube will be recorded on a master form on the chalkboard. Here all the counts from all the teams will be brought together.

We have not counted the whole population in any of the tubes. We have obtained an estimate of the populations by a method called sampling. To increase the accuracy of our estimate, we have taken certain precautions. First, we shook the tubes in an attempt to distribute the organisms evenly through them. Second, we counted the organisms in 5 different fields of view. By averaging these, we tended to "smooth out" chance differences in the fields we counted. Third, two people made counts from the same tube, and we averaged their counts. Fourth, we averaged the differences between the figures obtained by all the teams, which further tended to smooth out chance differences between the tubes. What we finally have for the population of each period of incubation is a density expressed as average number of organisms per high-power field of view.

Using ordinary graph paper, list the age of the cultures, in days, on the horizontal axis; list the density of the populations on the vertical axis. Plot the data from each team separately, using a different color for each team. Then use black to plot the averaged data of all teams. On the basis of the discussion in the preceding paragraph, explain the similarities and differences among the graph lines.(1)

CONCLUSIONS

Compare the line drawn from the class average (black) with the line drawn on ordinary graph paper in Exercise 2.1. In what ways are the lines similar?(2) In what ways are the lines different?(3) Keeping in mind the assumptions made in Exercise 2.1 and the conditions under which your yeast populations lived, explain these similarities and differences.(4) Is the hypothesis confirmed?(5)

Optional: Plot the class average on semi-log paper, and compare the resulting line with the graph you drew on semi-log paper in Exercise 2.1. Explain the similarities and differences.

EXERCISE 2.3

FACTORS LIMITING POPULATIONS

INTRODUCTION

In Exercise 2.1 no environmental factors limited the growth of the house-sparrow population. In Exercise 2.2, however, at least two environmental factors limited the growth of the yeast population: the amount of food supplied in the medium and the waste materials that accumulated in the medium. For natural populations food supply is not unlimited, but neither is it a fixed quantity that cannot be renewed. To continue our study, we now need to examine the growth of a natural population.

PURPOSE

The purpose of this exercise is to compare the growth of a natural population, first, with the growth of a laboratory population and, second, with the growth of a hypothetical population.

MATERIALS

1. Ordinary graph paper, 1 sheet per student

PROCEDURE

Gathering data on natural populations is always difficult. For our purposes here, it is not necessary that we gather the data ourselves. Instead we shall use data (gathered by Charles Elton, of Oxford University) on a natural population of English field mice. As is often the case in studying natural populations, the actual number present in the area studied is not known. The density is given as the average number of mice caught per 100 traps per night for one month. Thus, even in this real situation we have to make an assumption: that the actual density of the mice was always in proportion to the number caught. The data are presented in Figure 2.3-1.

MONTHS	AVERAGE NUMBER OF MICE CAUGHT PER 100 TRAPS PER NIGHT
May 1927	1
June	1.3
July	2.3
Aug.	3
Sept.	6.5
Oct.	3.2
Nov.	2.5
Dec.	2.3
Jan. 1928	6
Feb.	5.5
Mar.	5
April	5.7

Figure 2.3-1. Data on a population of English field mice in a woods near Oxford, England

Plot the data on ordinary graph paper, using a vertical scale that will place the highest point for the population near the top of the graph.

STUDYING THE DATA

Compare the graph of the English field-mouse population with the ordinary graphs made in Exercises 2.1 and 2.2. What part of this graph is similar to the other graphs ?(1) How does it differ from the graph of the hypothetical house-sparrow population ?(2) How can you explain the difference ?(3) How does this graph of a natural population of field mice differ from your graph of the laboratory population of yeast ?(4) How can you explain the difference ?(5) Which of the three populations was an open population, that is, one in which immigration and emigration could occur ?(6)

CONCLUSION

We can now try to draw some general conclusions from our three exercises on population. Does the growth of a population tend to follow a basic pattern? If so, what are the characteristics of this pattern ?(7) What is the chief difference between the graph of the hypothetical population (Exercise 2.1) and the graphs of the two real populations ?(8) How do you account for the difference ?(9)

FOR FURTHER INVESTIGATION

1. Ring-neck pheasants (originally a European species) were introduced on Protection Island, off the coast of Washington State, in 1937. Counts of the population were made each spring and fall for the next five years. Figure 2.3-2 presents the data (derived from that published by A. S. Einarsen). Plot the data on ordinary graph paper. How can you explain the regular fluctuations shown on your graph? Now, using a pencil of a different color, connect all the points representing spring counts, skipping the fall counts. What does this line tell you about the population? Remembering that this is a natural population, what do you think the counts after 1942 might have shown if they had been made?

Figure 2.3-2.
Data on the population of pheasants on Protection Island

YEAR	POPULATION SIZE IN SPRING	POPULATION SIZE IN FALL
1937	8	40
1938	30	100
1939	90	425
1940	300	825
1941	600	1520
1942	1325	1900

2. The heath hen was once a common bird along the Atlantic coast from New England to Virginia. By 1880 it had disappeared from all locations except Martha's Vineyard, an island off Cape Cod. Figure 2.3-3 shows the result of a careful study of this population by A. O. Gross. In what way is the part of this graph that shows the population before 1916 different from the "growth" part of the other graphs we have studied? Now we raise the question "What happened in 1907?" After you have thought about this question, refer to Chapman, F. M., Handbook of Birds of Eastern North America (New York: D. Appleton-Century Co., 1932), pages 241-242, for a possible explanation. What environmental factors does Chapman use to explain the history of the population after 1916? What term do we apply to a population that has reached the point attained by the heath hen population in 1932?

3. Figure 2.3-4 presents data collected by F. S. Bodenheimer on a population of Italian bees. Plot the data on ordinary graph paper. Does this graph resemble the graph for the house-sparrow, the yeast, or the field-mouse population most closely? On the bee graph, what is beginning to happen toward the end of the graph line? If you know something about bees, you should be able to tell what probably happened soon after the collection of data was discontinued. Which of the population determiners mentioned in the text is involved in the prediction you make?

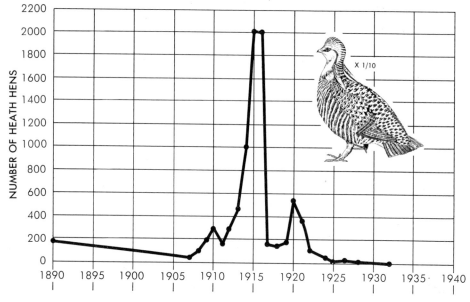

Figure 2.3-3.   Heath hen population on Martha's Vineyard, Massachusetts

Figure 2.3-4.   Data on the population in a colony of Italian bees

DAYS	POPULATION OF COLONY (In thousands)
0	1
7	1.5
14	2.5
21	4
28	8
35	16
42	22
49	32
56	40.5
63	50.3
70	55
77	62.5
84	72
91	72.5
98	71
105	82
112	78
119	81

EXERCISE 2.4

EFFECT OF AN ABIOTIC ENVIRONMENTAL FACTOR
ON A POPULATION

INTRODUCTION

In the preceding exercises, we have been studying the general characteristics of population changes. We have looked only incidentally at the environmental factors involved.

Our text has emphasized the way in which environmental factors are closely interrelated under natural conditions. Laboratory study enables us to untangle and examine these factors one at a time. This improves our understanding of the separate environmental factors, but it does not necessarily improve our understanding of the environmental factors as they affect natural populations of organisms. This last is an idea that must be kept in mind throughout our study of biology.

In Exercise 2.2 we used a microscopic plant as an experimental organism. Now we shall turn to a small animal, the hydra, to aid us in our study.

PURPOSE

Our purpose is to study the effect of different temperatures on the growth of populations of hydra. We might state our hypothesis this way: At three different temperatures, populations of hydra will grow at different rates.

BACKGROUND INFORMATION

Hydras are animals that live in freshwater ponds. There are a number of species. One collected from a local pond would probably be best for this experiment, and water from the same pond would then be the best medium for culturing it. If the hydras are bought, then the species called Pelmatohydra oligactis is desirable, because its large size makes it easy to see without a stereomicroscope. Water from a fresh, clear, and unpolluted pond makes a good medium for culturing purchased hydra, too. If this natural medium is unobtainable, an artificial medium that has proved successful in many laboratories can be made. Your teacher can give directions for making this medium.

Hydras reproduce by two methods. The one we are concerned with in this experiment is called <u>budding</u>. Figure 2.4-1 shows two hydras; the parts we need to refer to are labeled. In budding, a lump appears on the side of the animal, grows outward, and develops a mouth surrounded by tentacles. Eventually this will drop off and become a separate individual. In counting hydras for population purposes, each tentacle-bearing part (<u>hydranth</u>), whether separate or not, is counted as an individual. Buds that have not yet developed tentacles are not counted.

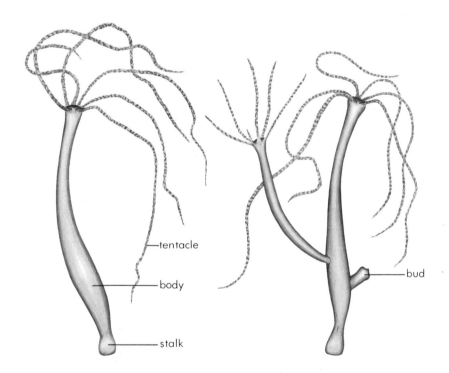

Figure 2.4-1. Hydras

In this exercise we will count the whole population each day. This is unusual in population studies. A sampling procedure, such as we used in Exercise 2.2, is much more usual.

In nature hydras feed on many small aquatic organisms, which they paralyze with stingers in their tentacles. In the laboratory some small, live organism must be supplied. The most convenient species is the brine shrimp, a tiny relative of the shrimp familiar in food markets. Brine-shrimp eggs keep in a dried condition for a year or more. When they are sprinkled on the surface of a salt solution, they hatch in 48 to 60 hours. The eggs are usually available in aquarium and pet stores.

Maintaining the hydra cultures at three different, constant temperatures may be a problem. Most refrigerators can be set for a temperature of about 10 degrees centigrade (abbreviated, 10°C). Room temperature is usually around 20°C; the air in a cupboard against an inside wall of the building will remain closer to this temperature overnight than will the air in the classroom. To obtain a temperature near 30°C, try heating the inside of a closed box by experimenting with incandescent light bulbs of different wattages. However, the best device for maintaining all three temperatures is a Temperature Gradient Box, which your teacher may be able to supply.

MATERIALS AND EQUIPMENT (for each team)

1. Culture dishes for brine shrimp, about 10 cm in diameter, 4
2. Sodium chloride (preferably not iodized), about 50 g
3. Beaker, 600 or 1000 ml capacity, 1
4. Glass stirring rod, 1
5. Brine-shrimp eggs, 2 vials
6. Cardboard box, slightly larger than brine-shrimp culture dish, with hole about 2 cm in diameter cut in top (see Figure 2.4-2), 1
7. Light source (adjustable microscope lamp or gooseneck lamp), 1
8. Culture dishes for hydra, about 10 cm in diameter, 6
9. Budding hydras, 15
10. Hydra culture medium, natural or artificial, 1000 to 1500 ml
11. Medicine droppers, 3
12. Net, 125 mesh, or piece of bed sheet about 25 cm square, 1
13. Beakers, 400 ml, 3
14. Bulb syringe, 1
15. Thermometers, 3
16. Refrigerator, 1
17. Box with mounted incandescent bulb or Temperature Gradient Box, 1
18. Hand lenses or stereomicroscopes, 3

PROCEDURE

A. The Brine-Shrimp Culture

Two or three days before starting the hydra populations, set up a culture of brine shrimp as follows: Add about 5 g of sodium chloride to 500 ml of tap water and stir to dissolve. Pour enough of this solution into two brine-shrimp culture dishes to bring the level of the solution within about 3 cm of the rim. Any remaining solution can be set aside for the next day. Place the culture dishes where they will be at

room temperature. Sprinkle dried brine-shrimp eggs on the surface
of the solution. They should not be so thickly strewn that they touch
each other. Do not move the dishes after the eggs are in them. Two
new dishes of the brine-shrimp culture should be set up each day until
two days before the end of the experiment. Each day, after the shrimp
have been removed, the same dishes can be used to set up the new
cultures.

B. The Hydra Culture

On the day the experimenting with the hydra begins, put the box
with the hole in the top over an active culture of brine shrimp. Place
a bright light about 12 cm above the box, and allow the light to shine
into the hole for about ten minutes (see Figure 2.4-2).

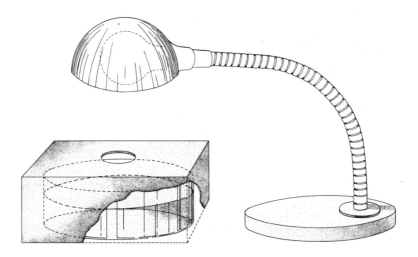

Figure 2.4-2

Next, pour 30 ml of hydra culture medium into each of three culture dishes. Label the dishes A, B, and C. Using a medicine dropper,
transfer 5 budding hydras from the stock culture to each culture dish.
Record in the data book the number of hydranths in each culture. A
convenient form follows:

DISHES	TEMPERATURE	COUNTS				
		Day 1	Day 2	Day 3	Day 4	Day 5
A						
B						
C						

By this time the brine shrimp should have collected in the bright spot of light in the culture dish. With the bulb syringe, pick up some shrimp and transfer them to a net of cloth cupped in the top of a beaker (see Figure 2.4-3). Drip tap water into the net for about two minutes, to wash the salt from the shrimp and the net. Invert the net over a hydra culture dish. Repeat for each of the three dishes. One culture of shrimp will probably be sufficient to feed all three hydra cultures. Allow twenty to thirty minutes for the hydras to feed. Then gently pour the culture medium and the shrimp off the hydras into three empty culture dishes. Put 30 ml of fresh hydra culture medium into each hydra culture dish. Examine the discarded medium carefully for hydras that may have been accidentally poured off. With the medicine dropper, recover any that are found, and return them to the population.

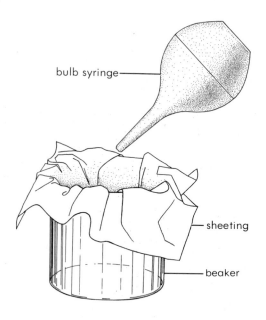

bulb syringe

sheeting

beaker

Figure 2.4-3

Place each hydra culture in a location with a different temperature. The temperature should be as constant as possible. Temperatures of 10°C, 20°C, and 30°C are good intervals. Keep a thermometer at each location so that temperatures may be checked frequently.

The above procedure is repeated each day for five days. Hydranths should be counted before feeding and, if time permits, after feeding, to check for any that might be in the discarded medium.

STUDYING THE DATA

Combine the data from all teams, and obtain a daily average number of hydranths for each temperature. On ordinary graph paper, plot the daily counts for all three temperatures. Connect the points, using a different color for each temperature.

Do the lines coincide (fall precisely on top of each other)?(1) If your answer is Yes, skip the following questions and go on to the conclusion; if No, continue with the questions. Which of the three temperatures resulted in the greatest number of hydranths?(2) Which of the three temperatures resulted in the smallest number of hydranths?(3) What environmental temperature seems most favorable for producing a steady increase in the hydra population?(4)

CONCLUSION

In the light of the results you have obtained, write a brief paragraph discussing the hypothesis with which we began the experiment. Then briefly discuss the following question, suggested in our introduction: Under natural instead of laboratory conditions, what factors might change the effects of temperature on hydra populations?

FOR FURTHER INVESTIGATION

1. Design and carry out an experiment to test the hypothesis that the effect of the temperature on the growth of a hydra population is density-dependent.

2. Would you expect temperature variations to have the same effect on populations of all species of organisms? Since you have had experience with culturing yeasts and estimating their populations by sampling, you can approach this question by growing yeast cultures under the same temperature conditions used for growing hydra.

3. The temperature differences suggested in Exercise 2.4 are rather large. A Temperature Gradient Box makes possible the control of temperatures within narrow limits. If one is available, you might use $5^\circ C$ intervals instead of $10^\circ C$ intervals.

CHAPTER 3

Communities and Ecosystems

EXERCISE 3.1

THE STUDY OF A BIOTIC COMMUNITY

INTRODUCTION

All of us have lived in biotic communities during our whole lives. But we are much more conscious of the relationships within the human population than we are of the interrelationships between species in the biotic community, even when one of the species in the latter is man. Students who come from family farms often do not see that their fathers' business is an attempt to control biotic communities by encouraging some species and discouraging others. We cannot expect that city students will easily see the biotic community around them.

Reading about community interrelationships is not enough. We must look at living organisms, look at where and how they live, try to figure out how they affect each other, even perhaps measure their relative population sizes. And still we may be disappointed in the understanding we gain. More than a century ago, Henry David Thoreau, who had had much practice in such matters, wrote, "We must look a long time before we can see."

PURPOSE

In this exercise we shall examine a natural biotic community to identify as many kinds of interrelationships between species as possible. We may also, as time and opportunity permit, make rough measurements of the populations of some species in the community; or we may make such population measurements in two or more communities, for comparison.

MATERIALS AND EQUIPMENT

The materials and equipment that are needed will depend largely upon which biotic communities are available and which procedures the class chooses to follow. You will find necessary items listed, with some of the specific procedures described. Such items are needed only if the class chooses to follow the suggested procedures. Where a variety of methods may be used to carry out the work, no lists of materials or of equipment are given.

GENERAL PROCEDURES

Different schools will have different kinds of communities available for study. Different kinds of communities require different study procedures. Therefore, the procedures to be used in each school will have to be worked out by the teacher and the class to fit the biotic community most convenient to the school.

On pages 47-49 we shall consider some general matters that will apply to all or nearly all situations. We shall then give some procedures that may be helpful in a fairly large number of situations. We shall suggest some of the kinds of outcomes that should appear at the end of the study. Finally, we shall list some books in which methods of ecological study are described more fully.

A. Selecting a Study Area

You may not have much choice, but let us examine some alternatives. On land, a forest provides the most complex community study. It permits different class members to become specialists in certain aspects of the community structure. It is the easiest community from which to obtain a wealth of data. But it is the most difficult to picture as a whole. And it requires the most time.

A natural prairie is almost as complex as a forest, but a study of it requires fewer procedures. Cultivated areas, such as a cornfield or a potato patch, are of special interest because so much of the land area of our country now supports such communities. A pasture, particularly if not too heavily grazed, is also suitable for study.

Most of the places mentioned so far may not be available to city schools. But many schools have some area of campus with lawns, planted trees, and shrubs. Here there may be fewer kinds of organisms than in other communities we have mentioned. But what is lost in complexity is usually gained in the thoroughness with which a community close at hand can be studied. Further, by mapping the campus and leaving permanent records, a class can provide good materials for a comparative study by classes in future years.

But suppose there is not even a campus or a piece of lawn? Then we must turn to vacant lots and waste spaces between buildings. Instead of studying an area of 100 m^2, instead of listing species of birds that feed in the trees, we may have to concentrate our efforts on a search among the weed stalks for insects. It is even possible to study the communities that spring up in cracks in sidewalks, in curbs, or even in street pavement.

All these are land communities. Water communities could also be studied, but the methods of studying them are not considered here. However, if you happen to have a good pond available, look ahead to Exercise 9.1.

In all major communities microorganisms are important, and no complete understanding of a community can be obtained without taking them into consideration. But the procedures for studying microorganisms, especially for discovering their niches in the community organization, are complex and difficult. Therefore we recommend that classes do not try to study microorganisms at this time.

B. Organizing the Work

The first job is to survey the area. Then the class must decide just what kinds of data to collect. It must decide whether to limit the study to one place or to make it a comparative study. Finally, the different parts of the data-gathering will have to be assigned to teams.

Teamwork has been done before, but now there is need for a much tighter organization. Each team should have a leader, who will be responsible for directing the work of the team. The more complex the community, the more important it will be to have each team do its job well so that all the data will fit together in the end.

C. Collecting the Data

Data books may be taken into the field, but they are likely to be cumbersome. It is easier to handle sheets of paper attached to a clipboard. These sheets should be pasted into the data books when you return from the field. This plan is especially good if the class prepares special forms for recording the data.

A community consists of interrelationships between different kinds of organisms. However, it is not always necessary to be able to identify every species of organism found during the study. No ecologist can identify every organism he encounters. There are two ways to deal with this problem. One is to identify organisms only by general group terms. For example, we might call them trees, spiders, grass, beetles, or turtles. These are rather vague identifications, but we can still develop ideas about community interrelationships—which is the main purpose of our exercise. Another way is to collect a speci-men—a sample individual of the species or a characteristic part of an individual. We give the specimen a letter (A, B, C, etc.), and whenever we need to refer to the kind of organism represented by this specimen, we refer to its letter. Later we may submit our specimen to some expert; or we may be able to look up its name ourselves, after we have returned to the laboratory. If we find the name for the specimen, we can replace the letter with the name. Most working ecologists follow such a plan.

In Section Two of the course we will be dealing with diversity among organisms. Your class may decide to delay completion of this exercise until everyone is better acquainted with the kinds of organisms. But you will never know all of them.

We are not primarily concerned with collecting organisms in this exercise. Therefore, no specific directions are given for this kind of work. When you need to collect specimens for identification, consult one of the references given at the end of this exercise.

Perhaps your class will decide to make a comparison between two or more communities. Perhaps it will decide to test the following hypothesis: Two different places that appear to be in the same community may not actually be so. In either case quantitative data will have to be gathered; that is, populations will have to be measured.

Even if these aims are not a part of your plan of study, some measurements will be useful. For example, if there are many large trees close together in a forest, they may have an effect on the population of the smaller plants that grow beneath them. Sometimes, too, the relative numbers of organisms may be a clue to their position in the food web: the kinds of insects that are first-order consumers are usually more numerous than the spiders that are second- or higher-order consumers. In any case, it is always wise to measure the size of the area being studied. This sets boundaries and makes the work of the teams comparable.

SOME SPECIFIC PROCEDURES

The procedure which you use depends upon the kind of community you choose for study and upon the decisions you make about how you are going to study it. None of the following procedures is complete. All can be greatly expanded, depending upon the desires of the class. In many cases, further procedures can be found in other sources. The references at the end of the exercise will be useful for this purpose.

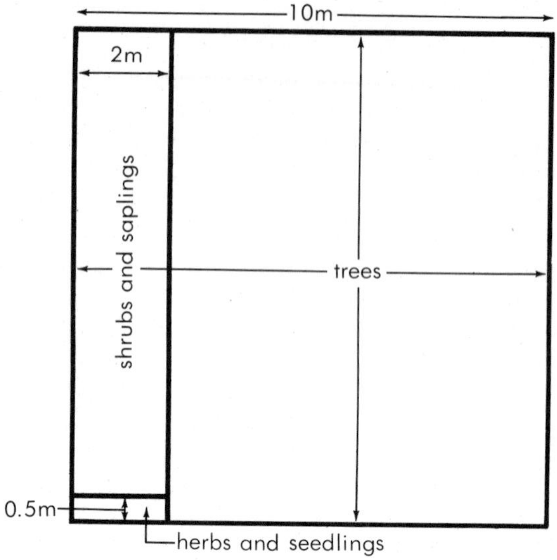

Figure 3.1-1. A plan for quadrats in the study of a forest community

A. Measuring the Area

In a forest community different organisms have to be studied on sample areas of different sizes. These can be set up as in Figure 3.1-1. Square or rectangular study areas are called quadrats. Each team should have its own study area. Materials needed by each team:

1. Plastic clothes line or rope, 12 m long, marked off at 0.5 m intervals (use a felt-tip marker with permanent ink), 1
2. Wooden right triangle 6 X 8 X 10 decimeters (abbreviated dm), 1
3. Wooden stakes, 8
4. Hammer or mallet, 1

Drive a stake in the ground. Tie or hold the line to the stake and measure off 10 m. Drive another stake at this second point. Place the wooden triangle on the ground, with the right angle at the second stake; extend the line at a right angle to the direction of the first measurement. At 10 m drive a third stake, and continue around the square. Then use the line to mark off the two smaller quadrats shown in Figure 3.1-1, driving a stake at each corner. If the forest is thick, the main quadrat may not be precisely square, because tree trunks and bushes stand in the way of the line. Be as accurate as the situation permits.

In unforested study areas the quadrats need not be so large. For example, in cultivated fields, quadrats 5 m on a side may be used, with a quadrat 1 m² in one corner. The same measuring procedure may be followed as in the forest. In vacant city lots and other "wastelands," it may be better to have smaller teams (and more of them), each working on a 1 m² quadrat. In this case no line is needed, only a meterstick and four stakes. Or a stiff wire may be bent into a circle that has a circumference of 354 cm. Laid on the ground, this circle encloses a study area 1 m² in size.

B. Studying the Plants

In studying the plants of a forest community, it is convenient to divide them into three groups: trees, shrubs, and herbs.

Trees are woody plants with a single stem (trunk). Those that are over 4 cm in diameter (approximately 13 cm in circumference) are studied in the main quadrat (Figure 3.1-1). One pair of students should make this study. The data to be gathered will depend upon the plan of the study. Some attempt should be made to identify the kinds of trees; the end of a twig with a few leaves is a sufficient specimen in most cases. The kind of trees that reach the canopy (the top of the forest, which receives direct sunlight) should be noted separately from those that do not reach the canopy.

If comparisons are to be made between areas studied by different teams or different classes, a count of the trees (either by species or just as "trees") should be made. The count divided by the area of the quadrat will give the population density. A further refinement may be made by measuring the trees. This can be done with calipers, to get the diameter, or with a tape, to get the circumference. One student in the pair studying the trees should measure, and the other student should record. From either the diameter or the circumference, the area covered by the trunk can be calculated and divided by the area of the quadrat. This gives us a measure of density that is frequently used by foresters because it is related to the amount of lumber that can be cut.

Shrubs are woody plants that branch at or near the ground level and, therefore, lack trunks. Saplings are simply young trees with trunks less than 4 cm and more than 2.5 cm in diameter. Both shrubs and saplings should be studied in a smaller area (Figure 3.1-1). Another pair of students should be assigned to this study. Notes should be taken on the relationships of these plants to the larger trees above and the smaller plants below. If the trees have been identified by species, then at least the saplings should be, too. Counts of the saplings may be made and related to the counts of the trees of the same species. Counts of the shrubs may be rough because of the difficulty of distinguishing individuals (text, page 23).

Herbs (in the ecological sense) are nonwoody plants that die back, at least to ground level, in winter. (In the tropics they are more difficult to describe.) Tree seedlings are very young trees with stems less than 2.5 cm in diameter. Another pair of students should study these plants on the smallest quadrat. Relationships between these plants and the plants in the layers overhead should be noted. Relationships between the species of herbs may also be noted. A spade may be used to dig a small trench along one side of the "herb quadrat," and the relationships between the underground parts of the plants may be noted. Note, also, the presence of toadstools, mushrooms, and other fungi. Again, if your class is making a comparative study, counts of the different kinds of herbs and saplings should be made. Finally, the proportion of this quadrat that is covered by moss may be noted.

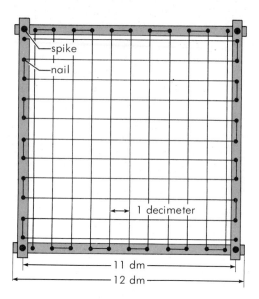

Figure 3.1-2.
Frame for study of a quadrat
in a nonforested community

In nonforested areas the directions given above can be adapted to the nature of the community. When no woody plants are present, the study of plants is confined to herbs. Many special problems may arise, however. In a lawn, for example, there is no need to count blades of grass; but a count of the "weeds" might be of some value, especially if comparisons are made between a well-trodden area and a protected one. A frame (Figure 3.1-2) may be helpful in this case.

C. Searching

In a forest study this activity should cover the large quadrat. It should be carried on after the studies of plants have been completed, preferably on a later day and by a pair of students—one to search, the other to record. Turn over stones, dead logs, and other cover. Make notes on the kinds of organisms discovered and on what they are doing. Various kinds of organisms may be found on the plants, too. Look in flowers, especially.

Specimens may need to be collected for identification, but all sheltering stones, logs, etc., should be replaced. Rough counts of the organisms may be made. These searching activities can be carried on just as well in nonforested communities.

D. Studying the Litter and Soil

To study the smaller organisms that live close to and in the soil, you should gather samples of the litter (loose organic material on the surface of the soil) and of the upper part of the soil. These are to be taken back to the laboratory, where they can be more conveniently examined. The students responsible for this will need:

1. Plastic bags, 4 or more
2. Rubber bands
3. Glass-marking crayon
4. Wire circle, 78.7 cm in circumference (encloses 0.1 m^2).
   This can be made from a wire clothes hanger.
5. Trowel
6. Centimeter rule

Before the field work, plastic bags should be labeled with the team number and the date of the field collection. The wire circle is used to mark out the area from which the loose litter is scraped. Since the area of the circle is known, the density of the organisms in the sample can be computed. Each sample of litter should be placed in a separate plastic bag and the mouth of the bag tightly fastened by a rubber band twisted several times. After the litter has been removed, use the rule to mark out a square 10 cm on a side, and, with a trowel, dig up the sample of soil in the square to a depth of 1 dm. Place the soil sample in a separate plastic bag, and fasten with a rubber band. At least two such pairs of samples (litter and soil) should be taken from different places in the large forest quadrats. On the smaller quadrats in other kinds of communities, only one pair should be taken per quadrat, and the samples should not be taken until after the plants have been studied. In some kinds of communities, litter may be so scarce that only one sample need be taken. If you are working in cracks in a paved area, there may even be no possibility of a measured soil sample.

The students doing this work will need the following materials and equipment in the laboratory:

1. Ether or chloroform
2. White-enameled pan or large sheet of white paper
3. Light source
4. Forceps, 1 per student
5. Bottles or jars, with caps, several per student
6. Alcohol or formalin, 50 ml per bottle
7. Berlese apparatus (Figure 3.1-3)
8. Glass-marking crayon

Place a few drops of ether or chloroform in the bags containing the litter. Wait five minutes. Then empty the contents into a large, white-enameled pan or onto a table covered with white paper. A strong light should shine on the litter, but not into the observer's eyes. Pick through the litter carefully with forceps, and place all organisms found in a small jar of alcohol or formalin.

The soil samples should be loosened up and, if very dry, moistened—but we do not want mud! Then the samples should be placed in the berlese apparatus, illustrated in Figure 3.1-3. The heat and light from the bulb cause many small organisms to crawl downward and fall into the preservative. The bottles should be labeled with the team number and the date of collection. The berlese funnel should be left in operation about five days.

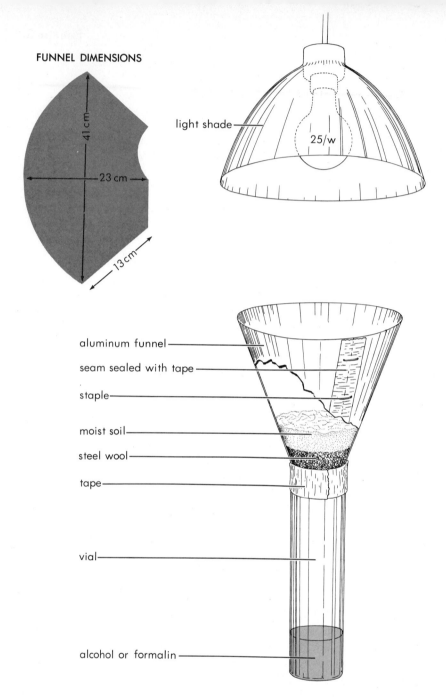

FUNNEL DIMENSIONS

41 cm

23 cm

13 cm

light shade

25/w

aluminum funnel

seam sealed with tape

staple

moist soil

steel wool

tape

vial

alcohol or formalin

Figure 3.1-3. Berlese apparatus

E. Netting Insects

In thick forest it is somewhat difficult to use nets to catch flying insects. But the vegetation can be beaten with a stout net. This will recover many insects and spiders that would be overlooked in hand-picking. In open fields nets swept through the vegetation are more effective. After a series of sweeps, the net can be placed for a few minutes in a large plastic bag containing several drops of chloroform. Then the organisms can be sorted out, placed in jars of alcohol or formalin, and labeled with the team number and the date. The drawback to this method of study lies in the fact that it is difficult to tell what the organisms are doing or even just where they live.

F. Studying the Larger Animals

To study amphibians, reptiles, birds, and mammals, it is usually necessary to cover much larger areas than the ones we have been considering and to observe for longer periods of time. The searching method described above may uncover amphibians and reptiles. Unless there is some good reason to keep the animals, they should be noted but not collected. These organisms may occur far inside cities, in larger vacant lots or old cemeteries.

It is probable that no major land community exists without birds, but they may not be present or active at the time the class is collecting the data. A few students may want to take on the special job of noting birds at different times over a period of several days.

Most mammals cannot be observed as easily as birds can. The most convenient way to begin a study of smaller mammals is to trap them alive and unharmed. There are several good ways to livetrap small mammals; but unless the community you study is fairly large, or unless some members of the class are especially interested in this study, it will not be worthwhile to construct the necessary traps. However, even if trapping is not attempted, do not overlook animal tracks. In cities keep in mind the possible presence of rats, mice, stray dogs, and alley cats as members of the community. And don't forget man!

STUDYING THE DATA

Since this exercise calls for the collection of data by teams, the data gathered by each team will have to be exchanged with other teams. This can best be done by placing all data gathered by one team on stencils, from which copies can be made for all members of the class. Team leaders should make up a form that will permit easy comparison of the reports of all teams. The form, of course, will depend upon the original plan of the study.

It is important to keep in mind the purpose of the work. We are trying to discover the structure of the community and how it operates. Here is a sample of the kind of questions we need to consider:

1. What producers are in the community? This can be answered by naming species or, more simply, by using such terms as trees, shrubs, and herbs.

2. Are the producers abundant, or are they rare? This may be answered in general terms, or you may have density figures. Does the community produce all of its own food?

3. If there are different groups of producers, which group seems to contribute most to food production?

4. Are there layers of producers? If so, what relationships can we find between the producers in different layers?

5. What consumers are in the community? This, too, may be answered with such general terms as insects, spiders, birds, etc., or with names of identified species.

6. Which consumer orders (first, second, etc.) are represented among the different kinds of animals?

7. If some quantitative data have been obtained, what relations can we find between the numbers of a particular organism and the numbers of another organism that eats it?

8. What evidence do we have for predator-prey or parasite-host relationships, or for scavenging, mutualism, commensalism, or any other interspecies relationship?

9. How many niches can we describe? Remember that <u>where</u> an organism lives is not its niche, but its home may be a good clue to its niche.

A survey of a community should always raise more questions than it answers. In studying the data, part of the job is to look for questions that need answering.

CONCLUSIONS

Each student should write his own report on the work as a whole. It should include the purpose of his investigation, a brief account of the methods used, a summarization of the data, and (most important of all) his own detailed interpretation of those data in the form of a description of the community structure and relationships.

FOR FURTHER REFERENCE

BENTON, A. H., and W. E. WERNER. Workbook for Field Biology
    and Ecology. Minneapolis: Burgess Publishing Co., 1957.
OOSTING, H. J. The Study of Plant Communities. San Francisco:
    W. H. Freeman & Co., Publishers, 1956.
PHILLIPS, E. A. The Ecology of Land Plants and Animals. Boulder,
    Colorado: Biological Sciences Curriculum Study, 1961.

EXERCISE 3.2

COMPETITION BETWEEN TWO SPECIES OF PLANTS

INTRODUCTION

Competition is of two kinds, intraspecific and interspecific. Interspecific competition is a somewhat easier kind of community relationship to subject to experiment than are most others. Many problems of human ecology involve such artificial biotic communities as gardens and cultivated fields. In this exercise we shall look at two species of plants that would never occur together naturally but are frequently found together in gardens.

PURPOSE

The purpose of this experiment is to test the extent of competition, if any, between two species of plants grown under laboratory conditions.

MATERIALS (for each team)

1. Soil (a good loam), enough to fill 3 flats
2. Trowel
3. Wood block
4. Wooden flats (boxes), approximately 55 X 35 X 10 cm, 3
5. Sharp pencil
6. Tomato seeds, about 450
7. Radish seeds, about 450
8. Sheet glass, enough to cover 3 flats
9. Scissors
10. Paper toweling
11. Triple-beam balance, sensitivity to 0.1 g

PROCEDURE

Prepare the soil by removing stones and breaking all lumps. Place the soil in flats and smooth out to a level surface. Use a block of wood to press the soil down firmly, but do not pack it tight. Use enough soil to make a firmed layer at least 7 cm deep. Water thoroughly and allow to stand twenty-four hours.

With a sharp stick or pencil, draw furrows on the surface of the soil, parallel to the long sides of the flat, about 2 mm deep and 5 cm apart. In one flat place tomato seeds about 1 cm apart along each row. In a second flat place radish seeds about 1 cm apart along each row. These flats are "pure cultures." In the third flat place tomato and radish seeds alternately 1 cm apart along each row. This is a "mixed culture." Use the wooden block to firm the soil again along the lines of planting. This will barely cover the seeds with soil.

To reduce evaporation from the soil until after the seeds germinate, cover the flats with sheets of glass and place in a shaded location. When germination begins, a flat should be moved into the light. Later the glass should be removed. By this time the plants will be large enough to be sprinkled gently without being disturbed. Keep all flats equally moist. If the flats are kept on the classroom windowsill, turn them daily so that the plants on each side of the flats receive about the same amount of light each day.

The experiment may be brought to a conclusion in 35 to 50 days— when the plants are fairly large but before they begin to topple over. At that time all the tomato plants in the mixed culture should be clipped off (with scissors) close to the soil and weighed together. Then clip off and weigh all the tomato plants in the pure culture. Pull up all the radishes in the mixed culture, carefully wash the soil from the fleshy roots, blot dry on paper toweling, and weigh together. Follow the same procedure with the radishes in the pure culture. Since there were only half as many radish seeds and tomato seeds in the mixed culture as there were in the pure cultures, it is necessary to divide the weights of the plants from the pure cultures by 2.

Represent the data in the form of a bar graph, with weight on the vertical axis and type of culture on the horizontal axis. Arrange the bars along the horizontal axis, from left to right, in the order in which the cultures were weighed.

CONCLUSIONS

Is there a difference between the total weight of the tomato plants grown in pure culture and those grown in mixed culture? If so, how do you account for the difference?(1) Is there any difference between the weight of the radish crop grown in pure culture and that grown in mixed culture? If so, how do you account for the difference?(2) Does the growing of tomatoes and radishes together have more effect on the tomatoes or on the radishes? Or is the effect equal? Or is there no effect?(3) Attempt to explain how the effects you noted may have occurred.(4)

We are judging the effects of competition by the weight of the crops developed. In the text (pages 63-64) we discussed the basis on which ecologists prefer to judge the effects of community relationships. Explain why the weights of the crops may be considered <u>indirect</u> evidence of competition. (5)

FOR FURTHER INVESTIGATION

Carry out this same experiment, using other kinds of plants. Spacing between plants and the depth of planting may have to be varied to suit the kinds of plants used.

EXERCISE 3.3

A COMPARATIVE STUDY OF HABITATS

INTRODUCTION

We might look at the whole world and its inhabitants as one ecosystem. Obviously, however, there are many differences in the world ecosystem at different places on the earth's surface—both with respect to the kinds of organisms that are present and with respect to the abiotic factors of their environments. The ecosystem at a depth of 10 m in the middle of the Atlantic is different from the ecosystem at ground level in the middle of Iowa. Part of the difference in these ecosystems lies in the kinds of organisms that live in these two places. But most of the difference lies in the abiotic factors of the two environments. The organisms in each system live in different <u>habitats</u>.

The organisms in one habitat are surrounded by salt water, those in the other by the atmosphere above and soil beneath. There are, of course, many other possible habitat differences. There may be differences in temperature, differences in seasonal changes, differences in the amounts of solar energy received. Whatever the differences in abiotic environment, they may be summed up as differences in habitat.

We do not have to search over large areas to discover habitat differences. We can often find them separated by very short distances. In this exercise we shall consider two abiotic factors—temperature and relative humidity. Temperature is self-explanatory as a measurement and as an abiotic factor affecting organisms. <u>Relative</u> <u>humidity</u> is a measure of the moistness (or the dryness) of a habitat. It is defined as the water vapor in the air at a given temperature compared with the maximum amount of water vapor that the air <u>could</u> hold at that temperature. It is a ratio, and it is expressed as a percentage. In general, organisms will lose water faster in an atmosphere with low relative humidity than in an atmosphere with high relative humidity. Therefore, relative humidity is a habitat factor of special importance to an organism that does not have a thick cover or skin to slow the rate of evaporation.

PURPOSE

In this exercise differences in temperature and relative humidity will be measured to show differences among abiotic environmental factors in different ecosystems.

MATERIALS AND EQUIPMENT (per team of 6 students)

1. Watches, 3
2. Metersticks, 3
3. Thermometers (centigrade, 0°-100° range), 3
4. Thermometers (of same type, with cotton sleeves over the bulbs), 3
5. Bottles with screw tops containing distilled water (30-50 ml), 3
6. Stiff pieces of cardboard, for fanning, 3
7. Umbrellas or other devices for shading, 3
8. Table of relative humidities, 1

PROCEDURE

A team consists of six students working in three pairs. One member of each pair reads the instruments; the other member fans the thermometers and records the data. Before starting, the three recorders synchronize their watches and agree on the time at which each measurement is to be made. These times should be recorded in the data books. At the top of page 61 is a convenient form for keeping this record.

One pair will make measurements in a habitat that has a dense cover of vegetation in several layers—a woods (preferably), a thicket, or a mass of shrubbery in a park. The second pair will make measurements in a habitat with a single layer of herbaceous vegetation (vegetation composed of herbs)—a meadow or a lawn (preferably, not cut close to the ground). The third pair will make measurements in a habitat that has no vegetation—bare ground, a tennis court, or (least

Location_____

HEIGHT	TIME	DRY-BULB TEMPERATURE	WET-BULB TEMPERATURE
0 cm			
30 cm			
90 cm			
150 cm			

preferable) a paved area. The three habitats should be as close to-gether as possible. In each habitat four sets of measurements will be made: the first at ground level, the second at 30 cm above the ground, the third at 90 cm above the ground, and the last at 150 cm above the ground. The greatest differences will be obtained if the work is done in the early afternoon of a sunny day.

The wet-bulb temperature is obtained by soaking the sleeve of a thermometer in water and fanning it vigorously for at least two minutes before making the reading. Readings on both types of thermometers should be taken at the same time. Thermometers should be in their proper positions (see preceding paragraph) for at least five minutes before readings are taken. Thus, if the first reading is to be taken at 1:30 P.M., both thermometers should be in the first position at 1:25 P.M., and the wet-bulb thermometer should be fanned from 1:28 to 1:30. At least eight minutes should be scheduled between readings so that there is time to move both thermometers to their next positions. Use the umbrellas to shield the thermometers from the direct rays of the sun throughout the procedure.

The reading from the dry-bulb thermometer is the air tempera-ture. The relative humidity must be obtained from a table that will be supplied by the teacher. To find the relative humidity on the table, we need both dry-bulb and wet-bulb thermometer readings. When these two measurements are known, it is possible to determine the amount of water vapor actually in the air compared with the amount that the air could hold—the relative humidity. The necessary calculations were made at the time the table was put together. If you are unfamiliar with the calculation of relative humidity, ask your teacher to explain the method used.

Record the data on temperature and humidity at the four eleva-tions above the ground in three parallel columns, one for each habitat.

STUDYING THE DATA

Which of the three habitats is coolest and most humid at ground level ?(1) Which is warmest and least humid at ground level ?(2) How do these two habitats compare in temperature and humidity at higher levels above the ground?(3) At which level above the ground are the three habitats most alike in temperature and humidity?(4) How does the greatest temperature difference in the <u>same</u> habitat compare with the greatest temperature difference <u>between</u> habitats?(5)

DISCUSSION

What differences between the three habitats may account for the differences in temperature and relative humidity?(6) Explain how this is an example of the interaction of biotic and abiotic factors in an ecosystem.(7) Frequently, in weather forecasts temperatures predicted for the center of a city will differ from those predicted for the suburban areas. Relate this fact to the situations you have been observing.(8)

You have been examining the differences among three habitats. Now turn to differences <u>within</u> a habitat. How does the temperature in each habitat vary with respect to elevation? Is the variation the same for each habitat?(9) How does the humidity vary with elevation in each habitat?(10) What differences in temperature and humidity would be experienced by a beetle crawling on the ground in a meadow and a gnat hovering at 1.5 m above the meadow?(11) In a general sense, we may say that the beetle and the gnat are in the same habitat; but the small differences we have observed within a habitat are often important to the existence of some organisms. We can therefore distinguish <u>micro-habitats</u> (small habitats within larger habitats) on the basis of measurements such as those we have made in this exercise. Would it be useful to measure factors in microhabitats if we were studying the ecological relationships among cows in a meadow?(12) Judging from the measurements of temperature and humidity, are the microhabitats as distinct in the forest as in the meadow or in the habitats on bare ground?(13) What other abiotic environmental factors might vary in the microhabitats just discussed?(14)

DIVERSITY AMONG LIVING THINGS

CHAPTER 4

Animals

EXERCISE 4.1

STRUCTURAL CHARACTERISTICS IN THE CLASSIFICATION OF ANIMALS

INTRODUCTION

In Exercise 1.1 we examined a number of different organisms. At that time we were chiefly concerned with the process of observation. But we also discussed the possibility of classifying organisms into a few large groups.

In this exercise we shall follow a similar procedure of observation; but with our increased experience, we should be able to observe more accurately than before. To aid observation, we shall use charts showing structural characteristics that are helpful in classification. Moreover, one step in classification has already been made—all of the organisms we shall examine are animals.

PURPOSES

The purposes of this exercise are (1) to obtain direct experience with the diversity of structure in the animal kingdom, and (2) to introduce some of the methods used in identifying animals.

MATERIALS AND EQUIPMENT

    1 Labeled specimens of animals, living and preserved

    2. Hand lenses or stereomicroscopes

PROCEDURES

A. Observing Animal Specimens

Before the laboratory period begins, draw two charts in your data book similar to the ones on pages 66-67. The teacher will tell you how many columns to draw on the right side of each chart.

You will find several numbered stations arranged around the classroom. At each station will be one or more specimens of an animal species and a label giving its common name. Both living and preserved specimens may be found at some stations. Some of the preserved specimens may be partially dissected so that you can make certain necessary observations. The teacher will announce the total number of stations and assign a starting station to each student. At each station you will be allowed a definite length of time to make observations and record the data required. When a signal is given by your teacher, move to the station with the next higher number. When you have completed your work at the station having the highest number, go to Station 1 and continue until you are back at the station from which you started.

Begin work at each station by deciding whether the kind of animal you are studying has a backbone and is therefore a <u>vertebrate</u> or does not have a backbone and is therefore an <u>invertebrate</u>. If it is a vertebrate, record its common name on Chart 1, in one of the spaces under the heading "Name of Animal." If it is an invertebrate, follow the same procedure, but use Chart 2.

At the left side of each chart is a list of the characteristics to be observed. Each of the sections includes two or more characteristics. After studying the specimens, indicate the presence of the characteristics you observed by placing a check ($\checkmark$) in the appropriate box. Let us suppose that the first specimen you study is a cat. Because a cat has a backbone, you write "Cat" in the space at the top of the first vertical column in Chart 1. Now look at the four choices indicated in the section entitled "Skin Structures." Only one of the choices applies to the cat: "Hair present." Therefore, you put a check in the box that is under "Cat" and to the right of "Hair present." Next look at the choices in the section entitled "Appendages." Again there is only one choice that applies to the cat, so you check the box under "Cat" and to the right of "Legs present." Proceed down the column in this manner. Terms that may be unfamiliar are numbered. A brief explanation of each is given below the chart; further explanation is to be found in Chapter 4 of the text.

Chart 1. Vertebrates

		NAME OF ANIMAL							
SKIN STRUCTURES	Hair present								→
	Feathers present								→
	Scales present								
	None of above present								
APPENDAGES	Wings present								→
	Legs present								
	Fins present								
	None of above present								→
SKELETON	Bony [1]								
	Cartilaginous [2]								
TEETH	Present								→
	Absent								
		Class	Class	Class	Class	Class	Class	Class	→

[1]Bony skeleton: a skeleton in which most of the parts are hard and relatively rigid, because of the hard mineral matter they contain

[2]Cartilaginous skeleton: a skeleton in which all the parts are tough but flexible, because they are composed of cartilage – a substance that does not contain hard minerals

Chart 2. Invertebrates

		NAME OF ANIMAL						
EXOSKELETON[1]	Present							
	Absent							
BODY SYMMETRY	Radial[2]							
	Bilateral[3]							
	Part bilateral, part spiral							
JOINTED WALKING LEGS	3 pairs present							
	4 pairs present							
	More than 4 pairs present							
	Absent							
BODY SEGMENTATION[4]	Present							
	Absent							
TENTACLES[5]	More than 4 present							
	4 or fewer present							
	Absent							
ANTENNAE[6]	2 or more pairs present							
	1 pair present							
	Absent							
		Phylum	Phylum	Phylum	Phylum	Phylum	Phylum	Phylum

[1]Exoskeleton: a skeleton on the outer surface of an animal, enclosing the animal

[2]Radial symmetry: a plan in which the parts are arranged in a circular manner around a central point or region — as in a bicycle wheel

[3]Bilateral symmetry: a plan in which the parts occur in pairs along the right and left sides of a line running from one end of the object to the other — as the body of a bus

[4]Body segmentation: a structural pattern in which the body is divided into a series of more or less similar sections, the boundaries of which are usually indicated by grooves encircling the body

[5]Tentacles: slender, flexible structures that can be lengthened or shortened, usually attached near the mouth

[6]Antennae: slender structures that can be waved about but cannot be changed in length, usually attached to the head

B. Using a Key

The process of identifying organisms is difficult because there are so many of them. One of the tools used in biological identification is called a key. There are a number of different kinds of keys. The kind we will use here is called a dichotomous key. The word dichoto-mous means "separating into two parts," and it describes the kind of choices we must make in using such a key.

The information you have recorded in Chart 1 is used in Key 1 (below) and enables us to determine the class to which each of the vertebrate animals we have studied belongs.

Key 1
Dichotomous Key to Classes of the Subphylum Vertebrata

1a. Hair present. . . . . Class Mammalia
1b. Hair absent. . . . . go to 2

2a. Feathers present . . . . Class Aves
2b. Feathers absent. . . . . go to 3

3a. Jaws present. . . . . go to 4
3b. Jaws absent. . . . . Class Agnatha

4a. Paired fins present . . . . go to 5
4b. Paired fins absent . . . . go to 6

5a. Skeleton bony. . . . . Class Osteichthyes
5b. Skeleton cartilaginous . . . . Class Chondrichthyes

6a. Skin scales present . . . . Class Reptilia
6b. Skin scales absent. . . . . Class Amphibia

Key 2
Dichotomous Key to Selected Invertebrate Phyla

1a. Body symmetry radial. . . . . go to 2
1b. Body symmetry not radial . . . . go to 3

2a. Tentacles present, body soft . . . . . . Phylum Coelenterata
2b. Tentacles absent, body hard and rough. . Phylum Echinodermata

3a. Exoskeleton present. . . . . go to 4
3b. Exoskeleton absent . . . . go to 5

4a. Jointed legs present . . . . .Phylum Arthropoda
4b. Jointed legs absent . . . . Phylum Mollusca

5a. Body segmented. . . . . .Phylum Annelida
5b. Body not segmented . . . . .Phylum Platyhelminthes

---

Key 3
Dichotomous Key to Selected Classes of the Phylum Arthropoda

1a. Walking legs, more than 5 pairs . . . . go to 2
1b. Walking legs, 5 or fewer pairs . . . . . go to 3

2a. Legs, 1 pair for each body segment . . .Class Chilopoda
2b. Legs, 2 pairs for each body segment . . Class Diplopoda

3a. Antennae present . . . . go to 4
3b. Antennae absent. . . . . .Class Arachnida

4a. Antennae, 1 pair. . . . . .Class Insecta
4b. Antennae, more than 1 pair. . . . . . .Class Crustacea

Begin with the first pair of choices at the top of the key, 1a and 1b. If the animal you are considering has hair, follow the first line over to the right side of the key and you will find that it belongs to the class Mammalia. This information is to be entered in the proper column at the bottom of Chart 1. If the animal does not have hair (choice 1b), follow the second line over to the right and you will find that you are to go to choices 2a and 2b, in the next section of the key. There two more contrasting choices are indicated. By again making the correct choice and following on from numbered pairs, you will sooner or later arrive at the name of the correct class for each of the animals listed in Chart 1.

After you have determined the class to which each of the vertebrates in Chart 1 belongs, use Key 2 to determine the phylum to which each of the invertebrates in Chart 2 belongs. Record the phyla in the columns at the bottom of the chart.

Finally, use Key 3 to determine the class to which each of the animals included in the phylum Arthropoda belongs, and record this information in a separate section of your data book.

A key is obviously a convenience in making identifications. Keys can be made to carry identifications all the way down to the species level. But we must not assume that the simplified keys in this exercise will indicate the correct classification for any animal we may be studying. A key is an artificial device that will give us a correct identification only if it is used with the group of organisms for which it was constructed. If, for example, we attempt to classify a squid or a slug by using Key 2, the key will indicate that these animals belong to the phylum Platyhelminthes; but both are actually mollusks. Unless we use a key to unlock only the series of doors for which it was designed, we will almost certainly end up in the wrong house!

Therefore, we must check the correctness of our identifications. We can do this by referring to the "Catalogue of Living Things" (following Chapter 20) in the textbook. If the characteristics of each animal match the catalogue description of the group to which the key indicates it belongs, we can feel reasonably confident that our identification is correct. For even greater confidence, we can check our identification with one of the references at the end of Chapter 4 in the text.

STUDYING THE DATA

Having classified all the animals of your laboratory study—the vertebrates into classes, the invertebrates into phyla, and the arthropods into classes—refer again to Charts 1 and 2.

Any vertebrate with hair belongs to the class Mammalia. Is there any other single characteristic that will enable us to place a vertebrate in its class? If so, state what the characteristic is and to which class an animal having this characteristic belongs.(1)

Is there any single characteristic that will enable us to place any invertebrate we have studied in its phylum? If so, what is the characteristic, and what phylum does it indicate?(2)

Is there any single characteristic that will enable us to place an arthropod in its class? If so, what is the characteristic, and what class does it indicate?(3)

FOR FURTHER INVESTIGATION

Select ten students, including yourself; construct a dichotomous key, using characteristics that will enable another person to identify each of the students in the group.

EXERCISE 4.2

THE LEVELS OF CLASSIFICATION

INTRODUCTION

In this exercise we make no direct observations of animals. Instead we rely upon the observations of others, recorded in the form of drawings. From these secondhand observations we will build up some ideas about the use of the levels of classification in the animal kingdom. How reliable—that is, how trustworthy—can these ideas be? Clearly, they cannot be any <u>more</u> trustworthy than the drawings upon which they are based. How much <u>less</u> trustworthy they will be depends upon your own thinking.

PURPOSE

We shall try to discover some of the structural characteristics that zoologists use in separating groups at the different levels of classification.

MATERIALS

    1. Appendix: "A Catalogue of Living Things"
       (follows Chapter 20 in the text)

PROCEDURE

In your data book prepare four forms like the one on page 72.
In the first form, fill in the space at the top so that the heading reads "Table 1." In the numbered spaces under the heading "Animals," list "Man," "Chimpanzee," and "Orangutan." In the column at the left side of the table, under the heading "Characteristics," copy the underlined words in each of the following questions (these words should be sufficient to remind you of the full questions when you review the table):
    a. How does the <u>length of the arms</u> of the animal compare with the length of its legs?
    b. Is there an <u>opposable first toe on the foot</u>? (An opposable toe is one that can be pressed against all the others, as your thumb can press against your other fingers.)

Table _____

CHARACTERISTICS	ANIMALS		
	1.	2.	3.
a.			
b.			
c.			
d.			
e.			
Classification Level _____			

c. Is the brain case of the skull relatively large or is it small as compared with the brain cases of the other organisms shown on the chart?

d. Are the canine teeth relatively large or are they small as compared with the other teeth of the same organism?

e. How many incisor teeth are present in the upper jaw? (Incisor teeth are located in front, between the canine teeth.)

Study Figure 4.2-1. Then for each animal fill in the spaces in Table 1 with the answers to each of the questions. Write the word "Family" in the blank space following "Classification Level." In the Appendix of the text, find the family to which each of these animals belongs. Write the information you have found in the spaces at the bottom of the table.

Now fill in the second form in your data book. Write the number "2" in the space at the top of the table. In the numbered spaces under "Animals," list "Man," "Dog," "Cat." Under the heading "Characteristics," copy the underlined words in each of the following questions:

a. How many appendages (arms and legs) does the animal have?

b. Are nails or claws present on the toes of the foot?

c. To what extent is the clavicle (collarbone) developed?

d. How many canine teeth are present in the lower jaw?

e. How many incisor teeth are present in the lower jaw?

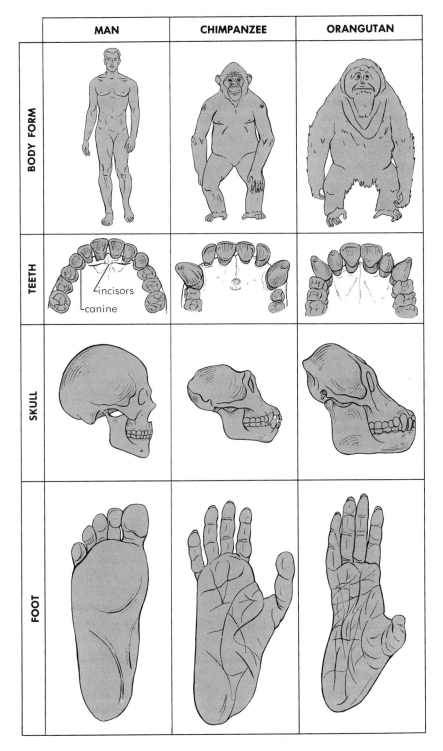

Figure 4.2-1

Study Figure 4.2-2. Then for each animal fill in the spaces in Table 2 with the answers to each of the questions. Write the word "Order" in the blank space following "Classification Level." In the Appendix of the text, find the order to which each of these animals belongs. Write this information in the spaces at the bottom of the table.

Use the same procedure to fill in the other two forms (Tables 3 and 4) in your data book.

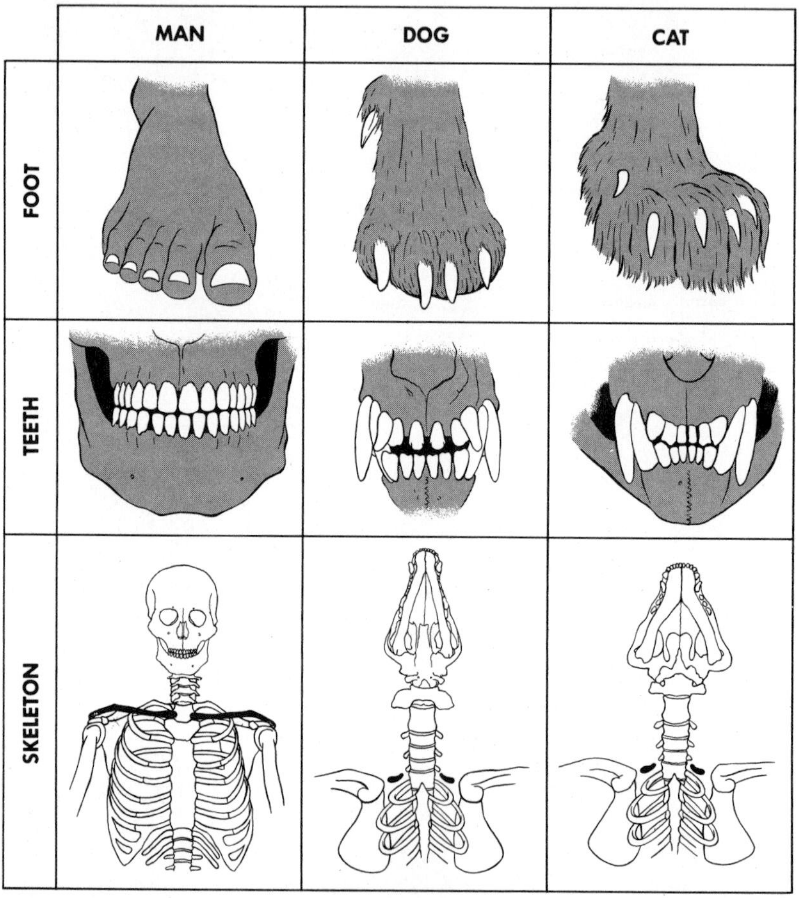

Figure 4.2-2

For Table 3 use the information in Figure 4.2-3 and the following questions:

    a. What kind of <u>body covering</u> (hair, feathers, scales, none) does the animal have?

    b. How many <u>appendages</u> (arms and legs) does the animal have?

    c. How many <u>chambers</u> are present <u>in the heart</u>?

    d. What kind of <u>symmetry</u> is shown by the body plan?

    e. How stable is the <u>body temperature</u>? Is it similar to the temperature of the environment, or is it quite different?

Write the word "Class" in the blank space following "Classification Level," and add the name of the class to which each of the animals in Figure 4.2-3 belongs.

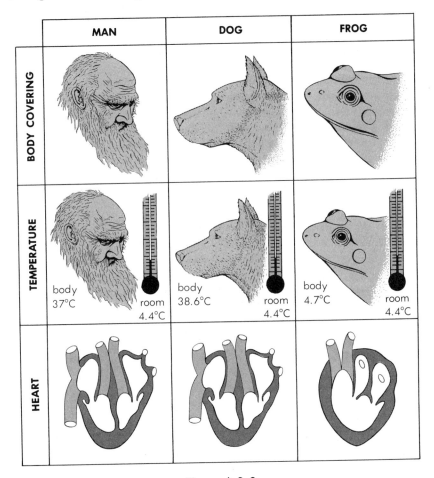

Figure 4.2-3

For Table 4 use the information in Figure 4.2-4 and the following questions:

  a. What kind of skeleton (endoskeleton or exoskeleton) does the animal have?
  b. What kind of symmetry is shown by the body plan?
  c. Is the position of the nerve cord dorsal or ventral?
  d. Are paired appendages present or absent?
  e. Are pharyngeal slits present in the embryo or absent?

Write the word "Phylum" in the blank space following "Classification Level," and add the name of the phylum to which each of the animals in Figure 4.2-4 belongs.

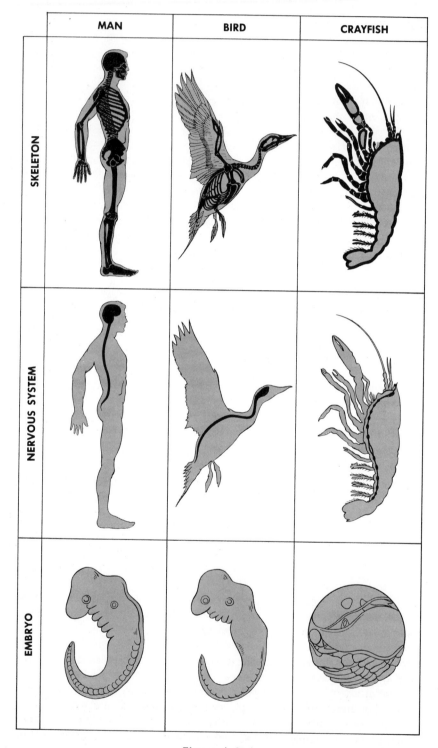

Figure 4.2-4

CONCLUSIONS

How does the system of classification express the fact that there are more structural similarities between chimpanzee and orangutan than between chimpanzee and man?(1) How does the system of classification express the fact that there are more structural similarities between man and dog than between man and frog?(2) How does the system of classification express the fact that there are more structural similarities between man and bird than between man and crayfish?(3) How does the system of classification express the fact that there are more structural similarities between man and chimpanzee than between man and dog?(4)

What general statement can you make about similarities between species A, B, C, and D if you are told that species A and B belong to the same kingdom but different phyla and that species C and D belong to the same phylum but different classes?(5)

EXERCISE 4.3

A DICHOTOMOUS KEY FOR IDENTIFICATION OF INSECTS

INTRODUCTION

In Exercise 4.1 a very simple kind of dichotomous key was used. The key in this exercise (pages 78-82) will enable us to identify most of the adult insects down to the level of order. Because there are many orders of insects and because the key is intended to "work" with most insects—not a select group—it is much more complex than the keys in Exercise 4.1. For example, in some cases the same order may appear in more than one place in the key. To work with this key successfully, you must know more of the terms used to describe organisms. You must also observe the specimens more carefully. But when you have had some experience in the use of this key, you will have gained a skill that can start you on the road to independence in identifying many of the organisms in your environment.

PURPOSE

The basic purpose of this exercise is to develop skill in the use of a key. Secondarily, the exercise serves to develop acquaintance with the largest class of animals.

MATERIALS AND EQUIPMENT (for each pair of students)

1. Specimens of 10 kinds of insects (numbered)
2. Dissecting needles, 2
3. Forceps, 2
4. Hand lens
5. Stereomicroscope

PROCEDURE

First, review the general directions for using a key (Exercise 4.1, pages 68-70). Work with one specimen at a time. As you come to each choice in the key on pages 78-82, examine the specimen and decide which alternative fits it. For example, the first choice in the key is between "Wingless" and "Winged" (1a and 1b). Examine your specimen. If it has wings, go to 16. Here the choice is between "Wings, 1 pair" and "Wings, 2 pairs." Again examine your specimen to make the choice. And so you proceed. There are two ways you can go wrong: You may not understand the choice; this is a matter of reading and vocabulary. Or you may not observe carefully. But, with practice, your skill in interpreting and observing will improve.

In your data book record the number of the specimen and, after it, the numbers of the choices you made in working through the key, ending with the name of the order to which the key led you. Repeat this with each of the ten specimens.

DICHOTOMOUS KEY TO THE ORDERS OF
SOME COMMON ADULT INSECTS

(Common names are in parentheses.)

1a. Wingless . . . . .go to 2
1b. Winged. . . . . .go to 16

2a. "Spring" present on fourth segment
    of abdomen, held by a catch on the
    ventral side; antennae shorter than
    body and usually bent like an elbow
    near the middle—(springtails). . . . . . .Order Collembola
2b. "Spring" absent. . . . . .go to 3

3a. Antennae absent. . . . . .Order Protura
3b. Antennae present (may be difficult
    to see). . . . . go to 4

4a. Antennae shorter than, or about as
    long as, head. . . . . go to 5
4b. Antennae clearly longer than head. . . . .go to 7

5a. Body compressed (flattened from side
    to side); antennae about as long as
    head—(fleas). . . . . Order Siphonaptera
5b. Body not compressed; antennae much
    shorter than head . . . . .go to 6

6a. Sucking mouth parts—(sucking lice). . . . Order Anoplura
6b. Biting mouth parts—(biting lice). . . . . .Order Mallophaga

7a. Abdomen with tubular, pincher-like,
    or threadlike extension behind. . . . . . .go to 8
7b. Abdomen without extensions behind . . . . go to 11

8a. Abdomen with a pair of short tubes;
    mouth parts in form of a tube, for
    sucking—(plant lice). . . . . Order Homoptera
8b. Abdomen without tubes; mouth parts
    for biting or chewing (may be hidden) . . . go to 9

9a. Abdomen with 3 filamentous (thread-
    like) appendages as long as the body;
    body covered with scales—(silverfishes
    and firebrats). . . . . .Order Thysanura
9b. Abdomen with pincher-like structures
    or no more than 2 filamentous append-
    ages; body not covered with scales. . . . .go to 10

10a. Eyes absent. . . . . .Order Entotrophi
10b. Eyes present and conspicuous—(earwigs). .Order Dermaptera

11a. Mouth parts tubular, for sucking . . . . .go to 12
11b. Mouth parts not tubular, for biting
     and chewing. . . . . .go to 14

12a. Body covered with scales; mouth in
form of a coiled tube—(some female
moths) . . . . .Order Lepidoptera
12b..Body not covered with scales; mouth
in form of a straight tube. . . . . .go to 13

13a. Sucking tube long, straight, and beak-
like; body flattened from top to bottom; tips of feet with claws—(water
striders, bat bugs, bedbugs) . . . . Order Hemiptera
13b. Sucking tube short and conical; body
not flattened from top to bottom; tips
of feet with pads—(thrips) . . . . Order Thysanoptera

14a. Antennae and legs long and slender;
body twiglike—(stick insects). . . . . . . Order Orthoptera
14b. Antennae not unusually long and
slender; body not twiglike . . . . go to 15

15a. Abdomen broadly joined to thorax—
(termites) . . . . Order Isoptera
15b. Abdomen constricted and with a
beadlike enlargement at connection
to thorax—(ants) . . . . Order Hymenoptera

16a. Wings, 1 pair—(flies) . . . . .Order Diptera
16b. Wings, 2 pairs . . . . go to 17

17a. Front wings and hind wings similar
in texture . . . . go to 18
17b. Front wings and hind wings not alike
in texture . . . . go to 27

18a. Wings long and narrow, with a fringe
of fine hair; tips of feet with pads—
(thrips) . . . . Order Thysanoptera
18b. Wings without fringe of fine hair;
tips of feet with claws. . . . . go to 19

19a. Wings and body covered with scales;
mouth parts in form of a coiled suck-
ing tube—(butterflies and moths) . . . . . Order Lepidoptera
19b. Wings and body not covered with
scales; mouth parts not in form of
a coiled tube . . . . go to 20

20a. Front wings distinctly narrower
     than hind wings; abdomen may have
     2 short, prominent filaments—(stone
     flies). . . . . .Order Plecoptera
20b. Front wings larger than, the same
     size as, or only slightly narrower
     than hind wings; filaments usually
     absent—(if present, front wings
     much larger than hind wings). . . . . . .go to 21

21a. Front wings and hind wings similar
     size and shape, or front wings much
     larger . . . . go to 22
21b. Front wings longer and wider than
     hind wings . . . . go to 25

22a. Wings with a few longitudinal veins
     but no crossveins; body usually only
     2 to 4 mm in length—(termites). . . . . .Order Isoptera
22b. Wings with crossveins; body usually
     more than 4 mm in length . . . . go to 23

23a. Wings with many crossveins and lon-
     gitudinal veins, forming a network;
     front wings may be slightly narrower
     than hind wings; eyes very large (at
     least half of head area)—(dragon-
     flies and damsel flies). . . . . .Order Odonata
23b. Wings with veins not forming a net-
     work; front wings about same size as
     hind wings; eyes small (less than
     half of head area). . . . . .go to 24

24a. Wings much longer than body, smooth,
     with numerous crossveins, and held at
     an angle (rooflike) over body when at
     rest—(dobson flies, lacewings, snake
     flies). . . . . .Order Neuroptera
24b. Wings not much longer than body,
     smooth, with hairs or patches of scales,
     many longitudinal veins but few cross-
     veins, and held flat on back when at
     rest—(caddis flies) . . . . Order Trichoptera

25a. Abdomen with 2 or 3 filaments longer
     than body; hind wings about one-third
     the size of front wings—(mayflies) . . . .Order Ephemeroptera
25b. Abdomen without filaments; hind wings
     at least half as large as front wings. . . .go to 26

26a. Wings held at an angle (rooflike) over
body when at rest; mouth parts absent
or form a jointed sucking tube—
(cicadas, leaf hoppers, aphids, etc.) . . . Order Homoptera
26b. Wings held flat on back when at rest;
mouth parts for biting, chewing, lap-
ping, or sucking; abdomen often has
a stinger—(ants, bees, wasps) . . . . . . Order Hymenoptera

27a. Front wings leathery at base, membra-
nous at tip; mouth parts in the form of
a long sucking tube—("true" bugs). . . . . Order Hemiptera
27b. Front wings leathery or parchment-
like throughout; mouth parts for biting
or chewing . . . . go to 28

28a. Abdomen with 2 pincher-like or
forceps-like extensions behind; wings
short, not covering all of abdomen—
(earwigs). . . . . Order Dermaptera
28b. Abdomen without pincher-like
extensions behind; wings usually
cover all of abdomen . . . . go to 29

29a. Front wings with veins, long, narrow,
and parchment-like. Hind wings
broad, often fan-shaped—(grasshoppers,
katydids, crickets, cockroaches,
mantises, etc.). . . . . Order Orthoptera
29b. Front wings veinless, usually not
parchment-like—(if long and narrow,
hind wings also long and narrow) . . . . . go to 30

30a. Front wings and hind wings broad;
front wings meet in center of back,
forming hard, veinless cover for hind
wings—(beetles). . . . . Order Coleoptera
30b. Front wings and hind wings long and
narrow; front wings do not form hard
cover for hind wings; tip of abdomen
may be curved forward over back—
(scorpion flies). . . . . Order Mecoptera

EXERCISE 4.4

DIVERSITY IN THE ANIMAL KINGDOM: A COMPARATIVE STUDY

INTRODUCTION

In Exercise 4.1 we examined a number of animals rather briefly, concentrating our attention on the structural characteristics that are useful in classification. In this exercise we examine a smaller number of organisms, but we will study them more carefully, concentrating our attention on living specimens.

PURPOSE

The purpose of this exercise is to compare structure and function in animals representing five different phyla.

MATERIALS AND EQUIPMENT

Station 1
1. Living hydras, 6 to 12
2. Stereomicroscopes or hand lenses, 3
3. Watch glasses, Syracuse form, 3
4. Culture of small crustaceans such as brine shrimp or Daphnia
5. Medicine droppers, 3
6. Camel-hair brushes, 3
7. Monocular microscopes, 3
8. Prepared slides of hydras (longitudinal sections), 3

Station 2
1. Living Planaria, 6 to 12
2. Stereomicroscopes or hand lenses, 6
3. Watch glasses, Syracuse form, 3
4. Camel-hair brushes, 3
5. Monocular microscopes, 3
6. Prepared slides of Planaria (cross sections), 3
7. Raw, fresh liver, small pieces (about 5 by 10 mm), 6 to 12

Station 3
1. Large, living earthworms, 6 to 12
2. Hand lenses, 3
3. Monocular microscopes, 3
4. Prepared slides of earthworms (cross sections), 3
5. Boxes containing damp soil, 3

Station 4
    1. Living crayfish, 3
    2. Finger bowls (20-cm diameter) or other glass dishes, 3
    3. Raw, fresh liver, small pieces, 6 to 10
    4. Preserved crayfish, 2
    5. Dissecting needles, 3
Station 5
    1. Prepared frog skeleton
    2. Live frogs, 3
    3. Freshly dissected frog
    4. Aquarium
    5. Medicine droppers, 2
    6. Dissecting needles, 3

PROCEDURE

A. General Directions

In your data book make an enlarged copy of the chart shown below:

Diversity in the Animal Kingdom: Comparison Chart

CHARACTERISTICS	HYDRA	PLANARIA	EARTHWORM	CRAYFISH	FROG
1.					
2.					
3.					
13.					

This chart, to be prepared before you come to the laboratory, should extend across two facing pages, and each of the thirteen spaces in each column should allow for several lines of writing. Copy the following questions—each in a separate space—in the column headed "Characteristics" (if more than one question follows a number, copy only the first; the thirteenth space is for any additional observations that you may make):

1. What is the habitat of the animal? Does it live in water, on land, or both in water and on land?
2. Is the symmetry of the body radial or bilateral?
3. What kind of skeleton does the animal have? Is it an endoskeleton or an exoskeleton, or is a skeleton lacking?
4. Is the animal segmented or unsegmented?
5. Does the animal have a digestive tube, or does it have a digestive sac? (If it has a tube, there will be two openings, a mouth and an anus.)
6. Does the animal have paired appendages?
7. How does the animal obtain oxygen? (Through lungs, gills, skin, or a combination of these?)
8. Are there any visible sense organs? If so, what kinds, and where are they located?
9. How does the animal move from one place to another?
10. What kinds of movement does the animal make while it remains more or less in one spot?
11. How does the animal capture and take in food?
12. How does the animal react when it is touched lightly with a dissecting needle or camel-hair brush?

All the specimens of one species of animal and the materials and equipment needed for observing them are arranged at one station. There are five species—therefore five stations. The class will be divided into teams, and each team will have a turn at each station.

Following are special directions for the observation of each species. Some are intended to help you make the observations needed to answer the questions; some direct attention to additional observations that should be recorded in the thirteenth space of the chart. You may find some observations impossible to make with the material available. Therefore, there may be some blank spaces on your chart. Do the best you can. Remember that you are recording your observations, not what you have read or heard about elsewhere.

B. Observing the Hydra

1. Food-capture and feeding in hydras should be observed under a stereomicroscope or hand lens. Place a single starved hydra in a small watch glass that contains some of the same water in which the hydra has been living. Wait until the animal attaches itself to the dish and has expanded its tentacles. Then slowly add a few drops of a concentrated culture that contains small crustaceans.

2. Determine the presence or absence of a skeleton, mouth, and anus in this animal by examining prepared, stained slides of longitudinal sections, using a monocular microscope.

3. Through a hand lens or stereomicroscope, observe the hydra's reactions when gently touched with the tip of a dissecting needle or camel-hair brush.

C. Observing Planaria

1. Feeding in <u>Planaria</u> should be observed under a stereomicroscope or hand lens. Place one or two starved planarian worms in a small watch glass that contains pond or aquarium water. Add a small piece of freshly cut liver.

2. Presence or absence of a skeleton, mouth, and anus should be determined by examining prepared slides of cross sections with the monocular microscopes and whole mounts with the stereomicroscopes.

D. Observing the Earthworm

1. Pick up a live earthworm and hold it gently between your thumb and forefinger. Observe its movements as it attempts to escape. Are there any regions on the body surface that feel rough? If so, examine them with a hand lens, and record your observations.

2. Watch the worm crawl about on the slightly moistened tabletop until you have determined which is the anterior end. Examine both ends of the animal with a hand lens. How does the anterior end differ in structure from the posterior end?

3. Place an earthworm on the surface of some loose soil, and observe its movements as it burrows.

4. Using both low power and high power of a monocular microscope, examine a prepared, stained slide containing cross sections of the body. Determine whether or not a skeleton is present.

E. Observing the Crayfish

1. Observe the movements of the appendages and the pattern of locomotion of a live crayfish in an aquarium. Observe the movements of the antennae. Touch them gently with the tip of a camel-hair brush, and note the animal's reaction.

2. Put a small piece of liver in a dish, and observe the way in which the crayfish secures and eats its food.

3. Examine a preserved crayfish in which part of the exoskeleton has been removed in such a way that the gills are visible.

4. Locate the position of the mouth and anus in a preserved crayfish that has been dissected to expose these openings.

F. Observing the Frog

1. Examine a prepared skeleton of a frog, and compare it with a dissected, preserved specimen to determine the position of muscles and other soft tissues in relation to the bones.

2. Study the breathing movements of a live frog that is not moving about. To do this, you should observe from the side, with your eyes at the level of the animal.

3. If hungry frogs are available, your teacher may be able to show you how the tongue is used to capture food.

4. The lungs of a frog are relatively inconspicuous. In a freshly killed, dissected specimen, it is possible to inflate them with air. Your teacher will show you how this can be done.

5. Observe the movements of a frog swimming in an aquarium. How do these movements compare with those observed when the frog hops and moves about on a laboratory table? Your teacher will show you how to catch and hold a frog so that it will not be injured.

When you have completed your observations and recorded the necessary data, review what you have learned about each of the items in the chart. By reading across the chart, you should be able to compare and contrast the characteristics you have studied in the five different animals.

Optional: Using yourself as the animal being observed, answer each of the questions in your chart.

SUMMARY

One of the most important ideas in biology is the principle that the way in which an organism is constructed is related to the way it functions. Organisms living in a particular environment often show special structural adaptations that permit them to carry on these functions. For each of the animals you have studied, select five functions that the animal performs as a part of its way of life, and indicate how, in each case, its <u>structure</u> makes it possible for it to perform these <u>functions</u>.

CHAPTER 5

Plants

EXERCISE 5.1

DIVERSITY IN THE PLANT KINGDOM

INTRODUCTION

In Exercise 4.1 you examined a number of animal specimens and related their structure to their classification. In this exercise we examine a number of plant specimens, taking note of their diversity, but applying a new idea to our study.

Biologists sometimes use the terms "primitive" and "advanced" when discussing diversity among organisms. These terms are linked with the idea developed near the end of Chapter 4: the species existing today are related to each other through their ancestors. From this we can develop the further idea that some of the species living today retain more of their ancestors' characteristics than do other species. An organism that has retained many of the older characteristics—in other words, one that has changed little from its ancestors—is said to be "primitive." An organism that has few of the characteristics of its ancestors is said to be "advanced." Of course, there can be many degrees of advancement, so "primitive" and "advanced" are not absolute terms; they are useful in making comparisons.

Through many kinds of evidence, but chiefly from the study of fossils, botanists have reached fairly general agreement about which characteristics are very ancient in the history of plants and which characteristics have appeared more recently. By studying these characteristics, we can get some idea of how primitive or advanced a particular species of plant may be.

PURPOSE

The main purpose of this exercise is to examine some of the kinds of structural diversity in the plant kingdom. The secondary purpose is to show the degree to which various plants existing today are similar to plants of the past.

MATERIALS AND EQUIPMENT

1. Native plants representing a majority of the phyla of the plant kingdom, 10 specimens
2. Monocular microscopes
3. Hand lenses
4. Stereomicroscopes

PROCEDURE

You will be provided with labeled specimens of 10 different plants. Determine the "Advancement Score" for each of these as follows: Start at the left side of the chart on pages 90-91 (Figure 5.1-1). Arrows from the starting point lead to two descriptions. Choose the one that fits the plant you are scoring. Proceed across the chart by following the arrows and choosing the descriptions that best fit the plant being scored. Continue as far as the arrows go. The "Advancement Score" for the plant is the sum of all the numbers appearing after the descriptions you used in working through the chart.

In your laboratory data book, copy the table shown below:

NAME OF PLANT	NUMERICAL VALUES OF CHOICES MADE	TOTAL "ADVANCEMENT SCORE"	RANK
1.			
2.			
3.			
10.			

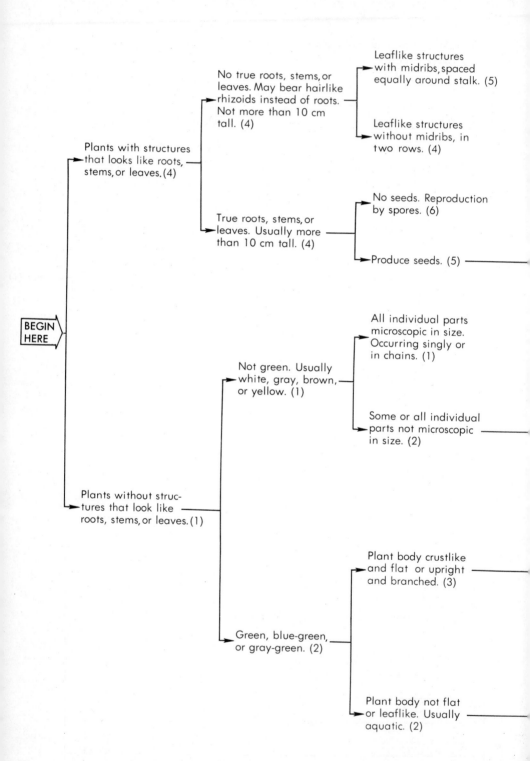

Figure 5.1-1. Chart for Determining "Advancement Score" of Plants

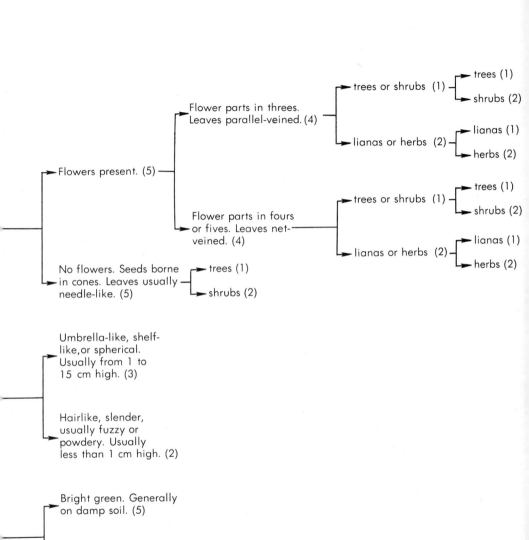

Record the scores and other data required in the table. When you have a total score for each of the plants studied, give the plant having the highest score a rank of "10" and that having the lowest score a rank of "1." Then assign ranks to all the others according to their individual scores. Record the ranks in the column at the right side of the table.

The more alike two plants are, the more alike their scores will be. The greater the degree of difference between two plants, the greater the difference in their scores. Advanced plants will have high scores (maximum, 26), while primitive plants will have comparatively low scores (minimum, 3).

DISCUSSION

Assuming that existing plants have developed from simpler, fewer, and older species, would you expect to find less diversity or greater diversity in the plant kingdom as time goes on?(1) Explain.(2)

Basing your conclusions upon the way the plant score chart was designed, what do you consider to be some of the most important differences among plants?(3) What are some of the less important differences?(4) On what basis do you distinguish between the important differences and those that are less important?(5)

Using the information included in the chart, list the characteristics you would expect to find in a primitive plant.(6) Do the same for a plant you would consider to be highly advanced.(7)

EXERCISE 5.2

DIVERSITY AMONG ANGIOSPERMS

INTRODUCTION

Ever since the time of Linnaeus, flower structure has been important in classifying the angiosperms. Without flowers, angiosperms are very difficult to identify, particularly at the species level. But it is not enough to examine flower structure only when identifying the members of this largest and most conspicuous group of plants.

In this exercise we again make use of a key. The key has a form that is somewhat different from the ones we have used before, but the principle of its use is the same.

PURPOSE

This exercise is designed to emphasize diversity of flower structure and to show how structural characteristics may be used in grouping angiosperms at the family level.

MATERIALS AND EQUIPMENT

1. Specimens (stems with flowers and leaves) of angiosperm plants
2. Dissecting needles, 2 per student
3. Hand lenses, 1 per student

PROCEDURE

You will be provided with specimens (stems with leaves and flowers) of several kinds of angiosperms. Select any one, and begin by determining whether it is a monocot or a dicot. To do this, refer to the keys on pages 94-95, beginning at the large arrow. Moving from this point, you will find two alternative paths, requiring a choice between "ovary superior" and "ovary inferior." Select the correct one on the basis of the specimen you are studying. Follow the path from your choice to the next fork in the path, and again choose the route indicated by the characteristics of the specimen. Continue this process until you reach the end of the route, where you will find the name of a family. In the Appendix of the text, check your identification with the description of the family. Record in your data book the number of the specimen and the name of its family. Repeat this process for each specimen.

Some of the terms used in the keys may be unfamiliar, since not all of them have appeared in the text. For such terms, consult the illustrated glossary on pages 96-97.

FOR FURTHER INVESTIGATION

The ancestor of cabbage, cauliflower, broccoli, Brussels sprouts, and kohlrabi is the wild cabbage plant, Brassica oleracea. These different kinds of food plants are varieties of this single species. Although they obviously differ from one another in size, leaf shape, and a number of other characteristics, their flowers are all very similar.

A number of plants native to the Old World, belonging to the spurge family, have spines and thick green stems and live in desert

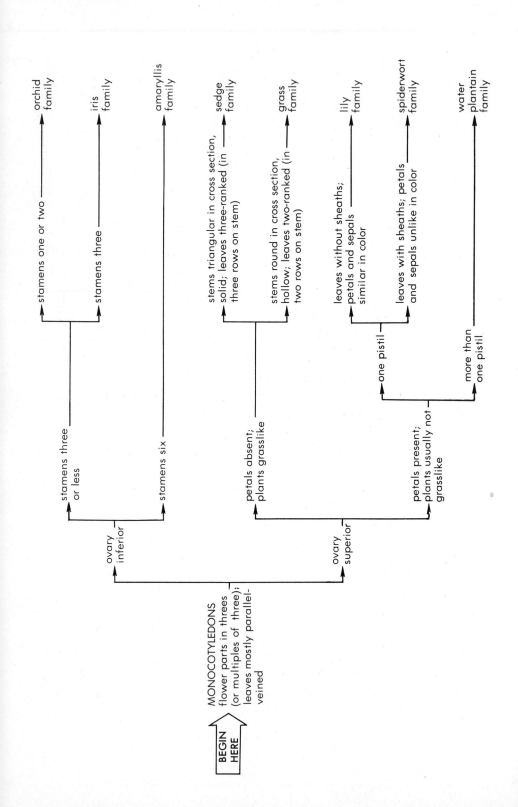

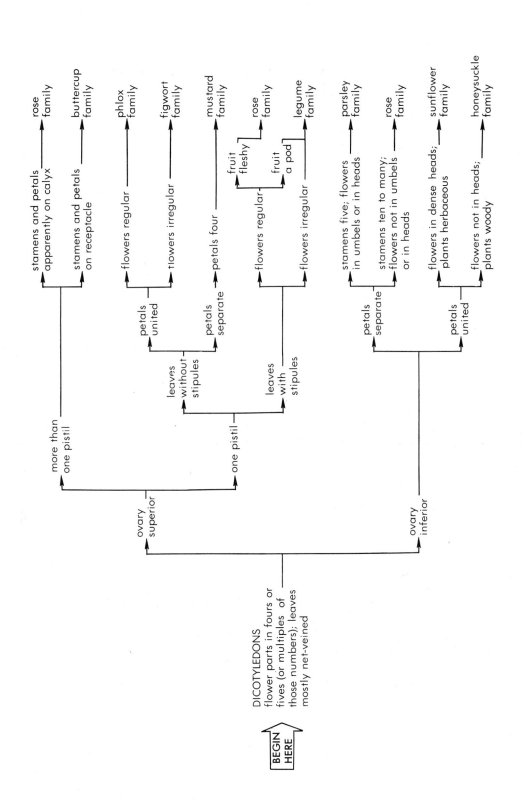

ILLUSTRATED GLOSSARY OF TERMS

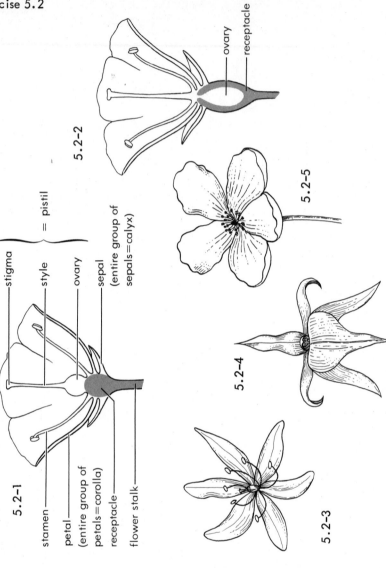

5.2-2

ovary
receptacle

5.2-1

stigma
style
ovary
} = pistil

stamen
petal
(entire group of
petals=corolla)
receptacle
flower stalk

sepal
(entire group of
sepals=calyx)

5.2-5

5.2-4

5.2-3

Figure 5.2-1: Flower with superior ovary. The ovary is an enlargement at the base of the pistil. It is attached to the receptacle at a level above the bases of the petals and sepals.

Figure 5.2-2: Flower with inferior ovary. The ovary is below the bases of the petals and sepals.

Figure 5.2-3: Regular flower. All the parts in each group of floral structures (sepals, petals, stamens, etc.) are alike in shape and size. Such flowers are radially symmetrical.

Figure 5.2-4: Irregular flower. Each group of floral structures includes one or more parts that are unlike others in the group. Such flowers are bilaterally symmetrical or unsymmetrical.

Figure 5.2-5: Petals separate. The petals of the corolla are attached to the receptacle but not to each other.

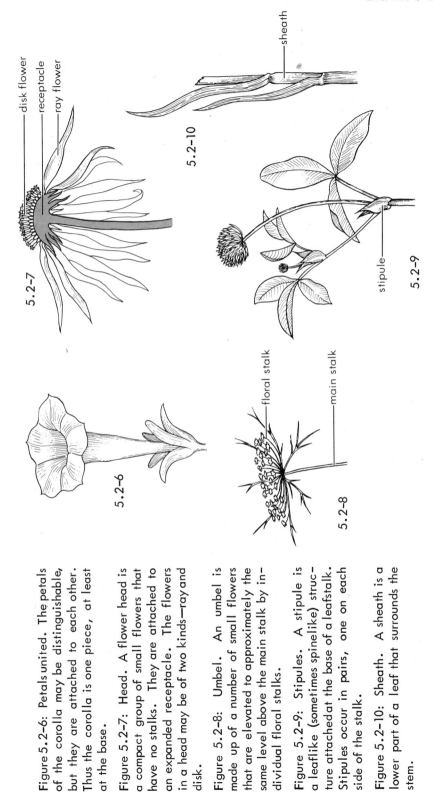

Figure 5.2-6: Petals united. The petals of the corolla may be distinguishable, but they are attached to each other. Thus the corolla is one piece, at least at the base.

Figure 5.2-7: Head. A flower head is a compact group of small flowers that have no stalks. They are attached to an expanded receptacle. The flowers in a head may be of two kinds—ray and disk.

Figure 5.2-8: Umbel. An umbel is made up of a number of small flowers that are elevated to approximately the same level above the main stalk by individual floral stalks.

Figure 5.2-9: Stipules. A stipule is a leaflike (sometimes spinelike) structure attached at the base of a leafstalk. Stipules occur in pairs, one on each side of the stalk.

Figure 5.2-10: Sheath. A sheath is a lower part of a leaf that surrounds the stem.

regions. They rather closely resemble the desert plants native to the New World, which belong to the cactus family. The flowers of the spurge plants are, however, basically very different from those of the cactus plants.

What do these two statements indicate about the importance of floral characteristics in the classification of angiosperms?

FOR FURTHER REFERENCE

CLEMENTS, E. S. Flowers of Mountain and Plain. 3rd ed. New York: The H. W. Wilson Company, 1926.

CUTHBERT, M. J. How to Know the Fall Flowers. Dubuque, Iowa: William C. Brown Company, 1948.

_____. How to Know the Spring Flowers. Dubuque, Iowa: William C. Brown Company, 1943.

DODGE, N. N., and J. R. JANISH. Flowers of the Southwest Deserts. 5th ed. Globe, Ariz.: Southwestern Monuments Association, 1961.

HILL, C. C. Spring Flowers of the Lower Columbia Valley. Illustrated by MARY C. MILES. Seattle: University of Washington Press, 1958.

CHAPTER 6

Protists

EXERCISE 6.1

A GARDEN OF "MICROORGANISMS"

INTRODUCTION

It would be convenient if taxonomists could place all microscopic organisms in the protist kingdom. But many microscopic organisms are clearly plants (many algae, for example), and others are clearly animals (rotifers, for example). Therefore, not all microscopic organisms are protists—and not all protists are microscopic (slime molds, for example).

There is a further complication in studying protists. In biology the word "microorganism" does not always mean a microscopic organism. The methods developed by Koch and his colleagues for working with bacteria were later found suitable for working with many other organisms. Gradually biologists began to extend the meaning of the term "microorganism" to include any organism that could be cultivated and handled by the methods originally developed for bacteria, whether such organisms were microscopic or not. Thus, today we can find in books on "microbiology" much about organisms that are <u>not</u> microscopic (molds, for example) and little or nothing about many organisms that <u>are</u> microscopic (ciliates, for example).

Nevertheless, when we set out to cultivate "microorganisms," we will certainly find many that are protists.

PURPOSES

The purposes of this exercise are: (1) to observe the growth of some common "microorganisms," (2) to distinguish some of the common patterns of microbial growth, (3) to learn to recognize some groups of "microorganisms" <u>macroscopically</u> (with the naked eye), and (4) to observe some microbes under the microscope.

MATERIALS AND EQUIPMENT (for each team)

1. Glass-marking crayon
2. Fruit (a plum, an orange, a lemon, an apple, or similar kinds), very ripe
3. Ripe grapes, 5 to 10
4. Water from pond, lake, or river, containing some of the materials from the bottom and some of the surface scum
5. Hay or dried grass
6. Dried beans
7. Cottage cheese or cream cheese
8. Lettuce
9. Bread
10. Garden soil
11. Cornstarch
12. Filter paper
13. Peppercorns
14. Glass finger bowls (about 250 ml) or any clear plastic containers, 10
15. Glass covers for finger bowls, 3 or 4

The following are in quantities per pair of students:
16. Medicine dropper
17. Forceps
18. Dissecting needles, 2
19. Microscope slide
20. Cover slip
21. Monocular microscope
22. Stereomicroscope

PROCEDURE

A. Setting Up the Cultures

Number the finger bowls from "1" through "10," and add the following to the bowls:

Bowl 1—Fruit, cut to fit into bowl if necessary

Bowl 2—Slightly crushed grapes, with sufficient water to cover

Bowl 3—Water from lake, pond, or river, containing surface and bottom materials

Bowl 4—Enough hay to cover the bottom of the bowl and 200 ml of water

Bowl 5—A few dried beans and 200 ml of water

Bowl 6—Cottage cheese or cream cheese, spread over bottom of bowl

Bowl 7—Half or quarter of lettuce head in a little water

Bowl 8—Two pieces of stale bread and enough water to moisten the material. (Caution: The bread should not be soaked.) Expose to air twenty-four hours before covering.

Bowl 9—Place a piece of filter paper on the bottom of the finger bowl. This will make it easier to clean the bowl after the experiment is completed. Mix 5 g of cornstarch with 95 g of rich soil. While mixing the soil and starch, add enough water to give the mixture a doughlike consistency. Place the mixture in the bowl, on top of the filter paper. Keep the soil mixture moist throughout the exercise.

Bowl 10—1 g of peppercorn and 200 ml of tap water

Place the bowls, except Bowl 1, in stacks of three or four, and cover the top bowls with a piece of glass or an empty bowl. Do not place in direct sunlight. If the bowls fit tightly together, place the flat end of a toothpick between each two of them. Place Bowl 1 a few meters away from the rest of the bowls, and cover it with a piece of glass. The organisms that will develop in it will form spores and may contaminate the other bowls.

B. Observation

Examine the bowls each day. Evidences of microbial growth will appear slowly at first, then more rapidly. In your data book, record your observations on charts similar to the one below. Make a separate chart for each bowl. Your teacher may assign students to observe particular bowls.

Bowl No._____ Material in Bowl_____ Date_____

MACROSCOPIC APPEARANCE	MICROSCOPIC APPEARANCE	NAME OF ORGANISM

In describing the growths, consider the color first. Second, consider the size. In recording the appearance of the growths, you may find some of the following terms useful: fuzzy, cottony, powdery, smooth, rough, shiny, glistening, dull, compact, spreading, irregular (see Figure 6.1-1). You are not, of course, limited to these terms. The identifications will be the last thing to be entered on the charts. They may be merely the names of large groups.

X 1/2

Figure 6.1-1. Growth of molds on two different kinds of food. The culture at the left (Bowl 1) contains cut pieces of fruit; the one at the right (Bowl 8) contains pieces of moist, stale bread.

After good growth has been obtained, a period will be devoted to the microscopic study of some of the living material. Using forceps or dissecting needles, take bits of the visible growths from the solid media, mount in water, and observe with the monocular microscope. (You may wish to review microscope technique—Exercises 1.4 and 1.5.) Next, with a medicine dropper take a drop or two of the liquid media and observe under the monocular microscope. Record your observations in the charts or by making sketches in your data book.

DISCUSSION

Of the groups of microorganisms that you were able to recognize, which were protists ?(1) Which belong to other kingdoms ?(2) Is there any evidence that different groups of microbes prefer different kinds of food substances? If so, what is the evidence ?(3) Which group of microorganisms was most widely distributed? What is a possible reason for this ?(4) In Chapter 3 we encountered the idea of succession. In this exercise, what evidence have we gathered for a small-scale succession within an individual bowl ?(5) What happens to the food materials as the growth of the microorganisms progresses ?(6) Why are most of the organisms observed in this exercise sometimes called decomposers ?(7)

REFERENCES TO AID IN IDENTIFYING "MICROORGANISMS"

FROBISHER, M. Fundamentals of Microbiology. 7th ed. Philadelphia: W. B. Saunders Company, 1962.
HENRICI, A. T. Molds, Yeasts, and Actinomycetes. 2nd ed. New York: John Wiley and Sons, Inc., 1947.
JAHN, T. L., and F. F. JAHN. How to Know the Protozoa. Dubuque, Iowa: William C. Brown Company, 1949.

FOR FURTHER INVESTIGATION

1. Some of the materials we have used as foods for microorganisms are also foods for us. We have seen what the microorganisms do to these foods. Clearly it is to our advantage to prevent our foods from becoming foods for microorganisms. Choose one food, and investigate the effects of various temperatures upon the growth of microorganisms on it. The Temperature Gradient Box, mentioned in Exercise 2.4, is a convenient piece of apparatus, but not essential.

2. Chemicals are often added to human food substances to discourage the growth of microorganisms. Commercial bread usually contains a "mold inhibitor." Commercial catsup usually contains a "preservative." The presence of these substances is mentioned on the label of the product. You can test their effectiveness by setting up cultures with and without them, but you may have to use homemade bread and catsup.

EXERCISE 6.2

EXPERIMENTS ON SPONTANEOUS GENERATION

INTRODUCTION

Leeuwenhoek discovered microorganisms in the latter half of the seventeenth century. Throughout the eighteenth century there was a growing belief that microbes were connected with the putrefaction (rotting) of meat and meat broths, and with the fermentation of fruit juices. There was also much speculation about the origin of the microorganisms observed in putrefying broths and fermenting juices. Do the microbes <u>cause</u> putrefaction and fermentation, or are the microbes the <u>result</u> of these processes? Do the microbes arise from the nonliving materials; that is, do they appear spontaneously? Or do the microbes come from pre-existing microorganisms? If the latter is true, where do the parent organisms come from? Such were the questions that led scientists into heated controversy—some believing, some not believing in the spontaneous generation of microbes. Because microbes are so small, it is difficult to answer these questions by simple observation.

At the time of the American Revolution, an Italian, Lazzaro Spallanzani, conducted experiments in an attempt to answer these questions and to refute (show to be wrong) the theory of spontaneous generation—the theory that microbes arise from nonliving materials. But his results and his interpretation of them failed to convince those who believed in the theory. Later Pasteur carried out more carefully designed experiments, which provided decisive answers.

In this exercise experiments similar to those of Spallanzani and Pasteur will be demonstrated. We shall not duplicate exactly the procedures used by them. The principles involved are the same, but we shall make use of techniques developed since their day. For example, we avoid some glassworking by using flasks with rubber stoppers; we use a pressure cooker or an autoclave instead of the more elaborate sterilization procedure that was necessary in Pasteur's day.

MATERIALS AND EQUIPMENT

1. Straight glass tubes (7-8 mm diameter), 30 cm long, 2
2. Bunsen burner with wing top, for bending glass
3. Triangle file
4. Rubber stoppers or corks, for flasks—3 with one hole each (to receive glass tubes), 2 without holes

5. Straight glass tube, 7-8 mm diameter, 8-10 cm long
6. Bouillon cube
7. Beaker, 1000 ml
8. Stirring rod
9. Glass funnel
10. Ring stand (to fit funnel)
11. Filter paper
12. Graduated cylinder
13. Erlenmeyer flasks, 250 ml, 7
14. Heat source, for boiling broth
15. Autoclave or pressure cooker
16. Paraffin or sealing wax
17. Beaker, 250 ml
18. Forceps and wad of cotton

PROCEDURE

Using the wing-top burner, bend the 30-cm lengths of glass tubing—one into a **J** shape and the other into an **S** shape (see Figure 6.2-1). Trim the tubes so that their lengths are similar to those in the illustration. Insert them into one-hole stoppers. Insert the straight piece of glass tubing into the third one-hole stopper.

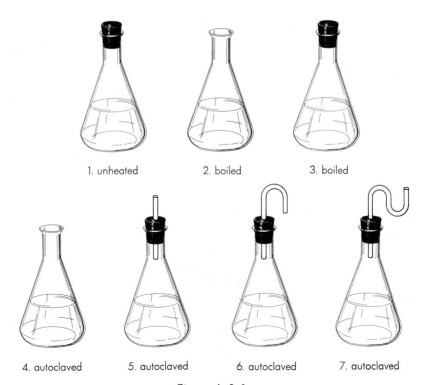

1. unheated   2. boiled   3. boiled

4. autoclaved   5. autoclaved   6. autoclaved   7. autoclaved

Figure 6.2-1

Dissolve one bouillon cube in 500 ml of warm water. When cool, filter. The broth must be sparkling clear. Pour 70 ml of the clear broth into each of seven flasks. Number the flasks with pencil. Treat them as follows:

Flask 1 — Overall Control
   Plug with solid stopper. Do not heat.
Flask 2 — Spallanzani's Control
   Add 10 ml of water. Boil gently for fifteen minutes. About 10 ml of water will boil off, making the level approximately the same as in the other flasks. Leave open.
Flask 3 — Spallanzani's Experiment
   Add 10 ml of water. Boil gently for fifteen minutes, with solid stopper resting at an angle in the mouth of the flask. At conclusion of boiling, plug immediately with stopper. Seal with wax or paraffin. To do this, melt paraffin in beaker. Apply with wad of cotton held by forceps.
Flask 4 — Pasteur's Control
   Heat in pressure cooker or autoclave for fifteen minutes at 15 lb pressure. Leave open.
Flask 5 — Modified Pasteur's Control
   Plug with a stopper through which the straight glass tube has been inserted. Heat in the pressure cooker or the autoclave as for Flask 4. Then seal with paraffin around the neck of the flask and around the tube where it comes through the stopper.
Flask 6 — Pasteur's First Experiment
   Plug with a stopper through which the J-shaped glass tube has been inserted. Heat in pressure cooker or autoclave as for Flask 4. Seal as for Flask 5.
Flask 7 — Pasteur's Final Experiment
   Plug with a stopper through which the S-shaped glass tube has been inserted. Heat in pressure cooker or autoclave as for Flask 4. Seal as for Flask 5.

Put all flasks on a laboratory table (not in direct sunlight or over a radiator).

Look for changes in the flasks each day for one week, then weekly for five weeks. In your data book, record the date on which the experiment is set up. Record changes in the clearness of the broth as they occur, noting the number of the flask and the date. Other observed changes in the broth (appearance of scum, mold colonies, etc.) may also be recorded. At the end of the experiment, open the flasks and note the odor of the broth in each.

STUDYING THE DATA

Consider Flasks 2 and 3, which represent Spallanzani's experiment. What difference did you observe in these flasks during the five weeks ?(1) How can you explain the difference ?(2) In your experiment Flask 3 may or may not have developed turbidity (cloudiness). In Spallanzani's case, the sealed flask developed no turbidity and no putrid odor. But biologists of his day denied that this showed microbes had to get into broth from outside; that is, they clung to the theory of spontaneous generation. How do you think they defended their point of view in the face of Spallanzani's evidence ?(3)

Now consider Flasks 4 to 7, representing some of Pasteur's work. In the experimental setup, what is the function of Flask 4 ?(4) Why did Pasteur provide openings in his flasks ?(5) How do you explain the result obtained in Flask 7 ?(6)

Compare your observations of Flask 1 with those of Flasks 2 and 4. Explain any likenesses and differences in these results.(7)

CONCLUSIONS

In the light of the results of these experiments, discuss the questions that were raised in the introduction to this exercise.

REFERENCES

CONANT, J. B., and L. K. NASH (eds.). Harvard Case Histories in Experimental Science. Cambridge, Mass.: Harvard University Press, 1957.

GABRIEL, M. L., and S. FOGEL (eds.). Great Experiments in Biology. Englewood Cliffs, N. J.: Prentice-Hall, Inc., 1955.

EXERCISE 6.3

MICROSCOPIC STUDY OF BACTERIA

INTRODUCTION

Bacteria are among the best known and most widespread of the protists. In 1676 Antony van Leeuwenhoek mixed peppercorns (unground pepper) with water, allowed the mixture to stand for a few days, and examined a drop of this <u>infusion</u> with his simple microscope. In the infusion he saw bacteria for the first time.

Today we use high-powered microscopes to observe bacteria. With such instruments we see bacteria magnified a thousand times or more. We may observe living bacteria in water mounts, as in Exercise 6.1. More often we kill and stain them so that certain structures that could not be observed in living bacteria become clearly visible.

PURPOSES

In this exercise we will prepare bacteria from a peppercorn infusion for microscopic examination by staining them. We will then observe the stained bacteria and record observed differences in shape, size, and arrangement.

MATERIALS AND EQUIPMENT

1. Peppercorn infusion (a few days old), from Exercise 6.1
2. Bunsen burner or alcohol lamp
3. Inoculating loop
4. Beaker or glass tumbler (5 to 7 cm diameter)
5. Crystal-violet stain
6. Medicine dropper
7. Microscope slide
8. Paper towels
9. Monocular microscope
10. Immersion oil (optional)
11. Monocular microscope with oil-immersion objective (optional)

PROCEDURE

A. Staining Bacteria

1. Gently heat a <u>clean</u> slide by passing it above the blue cone of a burner flame three times. When the slide is cool, place a loop of the peppercorn infusion on the slide, and use the loop to spread the liquid over an area the size of a nickel. Let the invisible film of bacteria dry in the air.

2. <u>Quickly</u> pass the slides <u>through</u> the flame three or four times, film side up. The slide should be just uncomfortably hot when touched

to the back of the hand.   Let the slide cool to room temperature.

3. Pour tap water into a beaker or glass tumbler until the water is about 3 cm from the top.   Place the slide across the top of the beaker with the film surface up, as shown in Figure 6.3-1(A).   Cover the film with several (three or four) drops of crystal-violet solution. Allow the dye to remain on the film for fifteen to thirty seconds. Then rinse off the stain by pulling the slide gently to one side until one end drops slowly into the glass of water, as shown in Figure 6.3-1(B).

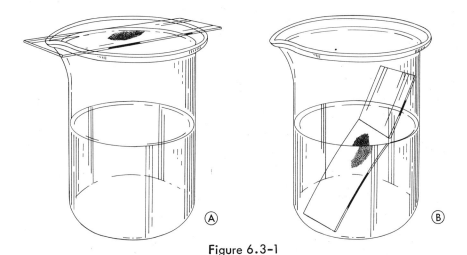

Figure 6.3-1

4. Remove the slide.   Empty the beaker, and refill it with clean water. Gently dip the slide in the beaker of clean water several times. Drain the water from the slide by holding it vertically and pressing a lower corner against a paper towel.   Remove the remaining water by blotting gently with a folded paper towel, as shown in Figure 6.3-2.

Figure 6.3-2

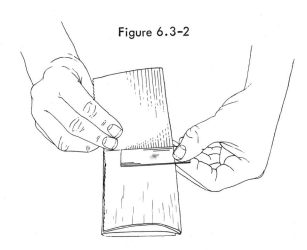

Place the slide in the fold of the towel, as shown, and close the towel upon it as you would the pages of a book. Do not wipe the slide. When the film is dry, it is ready to be examined microscopically. A cover slip is not necessary.

B. Microscopic Examination of Stained Bacteria

Use the low-power objective to focus on the stained bacteria. Many species of bacteria can barely be seen with low power. They may only appear as tiny colored specks, but when they are in clear focus, swing the high-power objective into place. If necessary, re-focus with the _fine_ adjustment.

Optional: Observations at a magnification close to X1000 may be made if microscopes with oil-immersion objectives are available. Swing the high-power objective to one side. Put one drop of immersion oil directly on the stained bacterial film. Slowly swing the oil-immersion objective into place, watching the end of the objective from the side. The tip of the objective should dip into the drop of oil but should not be allowed to touch the slide. Using the _fine_ adjustment, very carefully focus on the stained bacteria.

CAUTION: Use only the _fine_ adjustment, and turn it back and forth only a small fraction of a full turn at a time, until the stained organisms come into clear focus.

C. Recording Observations

A variety of bacteria should be visible on the slide. Observe differences in size, shape, staining, and arrangements of groups.

In your data book draw a circle about 6 cm in diameter to represent the field of the microscope. In the circle carefully draw the organisms you can observe on the slide. Try to show accurately their shape, the way they are grouped, and their size in relation to the diameter of the field of view. Refer to Exercise 1.4, subheading G, and to the record of that work in your data book. Then estimate the sizes (diameter of more or less round organisms; length and width of others) of the smallest and the largest bacteria on your slide. Record the dimensions in microns.

PATTERNS IN THE BIOSPHERE

CHAPTER 7

Patterns of Life
in the Microscopic World

————————————————————————

EXERCISE 7.1

DECOMPOSING ACTION OF SOIL MICROBES

PURPOSES

The purposes of this exercise are (1) to compare the decomposing effects of soil microorganisms on different organic materials, and (2) to compare rates of decomposition in different soils.

BACKGROUND INFORMATION

In this exercise parts of various dead organisms are converted to humus by the action of soil microorganisms. It is important to know something about the chief substances that are used as food by the microorganisms in this experiment. Most of these substances have been mentioned in the text. A cotton string is mostly cellulose. Cellulose also occurs in a twig or a leaf; there is a small amount in rolled oats. The twig and the leaf contain a considerable amount of lignins, and the leaf also contains some pectins. The rolled oats are mostly starch, with small amounts of protein and fat. An insect, too, contains proteins and fat, but its exoskeleton is mostly chitin. Nylon is included as an example of a man-made material; the elements in it are similar to those in natural organic substances, but no microorganisms ever had a chance to use nylon as a food until man added it to the environment about thirty years ago.

MATERIALS AND EQUIPMENT (for each team)

1. Flower pots, 4 inches in diameter, 4
2. Deep dishes, 4
3. Washed sand
4. Rich garden soil
5. Petri dish lids, 4
6. Dead leaves, 2
7. Dead insects, 2
8. Dead twigs, 2
9. Cotton string or twine, 2 pieces
10. Rolled oats, 4 cubic centimeters (abbreviated, cc)
11. Nylon fabric, 2 cm X 2 cm, 2 pieces
12. Glass-marking crayon, 1

PROCEDURE

Cover the holes in the bottoms of the flowerpots with small stones or pieces of broken pots. Fill two flowerpots with moist, washed sand to within 3 cm of the top, as shown in Figure 7.1-1. Press the sand down firmly. Mark off the surface of the sand into three equal sectors. In the middle of one sector, place a dead leaf that has been soaked in water until it is pliable; in another, place a dead insect; in the third area, place about 2 cc of rolled oats. Mark off the surface of the sand in the second pot into three equal sectors. In one sector place a dead twig; in a second, a piece of cotton string; in the third, a piece of nylon fabric.

Mark each pot with your team's symbol or number. Cover the materials with the lid of a petri dish (open side downward), gently but firmly pressing the edge of the lid into the sand. Set the pots in deep dishes, and fill each deep dish with water. The water will soak upward through the pot until the entire content of each pot is moist.

Repeat this procedure with the two remaining pots, using rich garden soil instead of sand. Put all four pots in a warm, dark place. Keep the soil moist at all times by adding water to the deep dishes, in which the pots were placed.

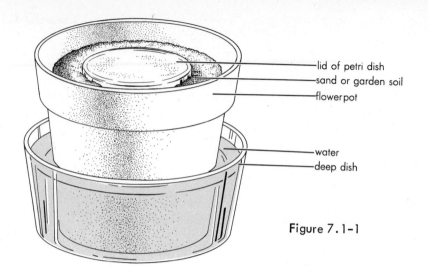

lid of petri dish
sand or garden soil
flowerpot

water
deep dish

Figure 7.1-1

OBSERVATIONS

In your data book copy the chart shown below. Your chart should extend across facing pages to allow wide columns under "Changes Observed." Fill in the principal substances by reference to the information at the beginning of this exercise. Make observations at the times indicated on the chart.

OBJECTS	SUBSTANCES	CHANGES OBSERVED				
		Second Day	First Week	Second Week	Third Week	Fourth Week

Note any odors. Compare the appearances of the materials. Look for masses of mold mycelium. Test the strength of the twine by pulling on it.

STUDYING THE DATA

On the sand, which <u>substance</u> seems to decompose most rapidly?(1) Most slowly?(2) On the garden soil, which substance seems to decompose most rapidly?(3) Most slowly?(4) What kinds of organisms were you able to observe during the experiment?(5)

CONCLUSIONS

What general statement can you make about the rate at which different substances are decomposed by soil organisms?(6) Do your data show any general difference between rates of decomposition on sand and those on garden soil? If so, what hypothesis can you suggest to explain the difference?(7)

FOR FURTHER INVESTIGATION

1. In the light of the results of this experiment, discuss problems involved in the preservation of fiber and wood products.
2. What effect would the warmth of a climate have on the formation of a humus? Can you investigate this problem experimentally?

EXERCISE 7.2

SOME MICROBIAL TECHNIQUES

INTRODUCTION

Much of what is known about the activities of microbes comes from studies of populations rather than from studies of individuals. Populations of microorganisms may be easily and quickly obtained by growing them in the laboratory. If a bit of soil or a few drops of pond water are placed in a suitable medium, a large, mixed population of microorganisms will quickly develop.

In studying such a mixed culture, a microbiologist will usually begin by separating the different kinds of organisms from one another. He will then grow "pure" cultures of each kind to determine their distinctive characteristics. Microbiologists are also interested in finding out how many organisms are present so that density of each kind in both mixed and pure cultures can be determined.

If we have a mixed population of horses, cattle, and pigs in a pasture, it is an easy matter to separate the three kinds of animals and determine the number of each. But how can we do the same with a mixed population of microorganisms consisting of millions of individuals, some of them so small that they are barely visible under the microscope? And there is another difficulty: Occasionally horses, cattle, and pigs may be dangerous, but at least we can see them coming. How can we protect ourselves from the dangerous kinds of microorganisms that perhaps are present in a mixed population? What precautions can be taken so that we can work with them safely?

The basic methods for studying microbes safely were developed between fifty and a hundred years ago, mostly by microbiologists who were working with bacteria. Of course, many improvements have been made in these methods, and some entirely new techniques—such as those involving radioactive materials—have been developed recently. But the beginning microbiologist must still learn the basic techniques for handling microscopic organisms.

PURPOSES

This exercise shows (1) how microorganisms, some of which may be dangerous, can be handled safely and efficiently; (2) how the density of a microbial population can be determined; (3) how pure cultures can be obtained from a mixed culture of microorganisms.

MATERIALS AND EQUIPMENT

A. For Preparation of Tubes of Sterile Medium and Sterile Distilled Water

1. Pipette, 10 ml
2. Test tubes, 19 mm X 150 mm, 8 per pair of students
3. Peptone, 4 g*
4. Beef extract, 2.4 g*
5. Agar, 12 g*
6. Distilled water, 800 ml*
7. Balance
8. Beaker, 1000 ml
9. Graduated cylinder, 500 ml
10. Ring stand
11. Heat source
12. Stirring rod
13. Funnel
14. Rubber tubing, to fit funnel tube
15. Pinch clamp or spring-compressor clamp
16. Nonabsorbent cotton
17. Wire test-tube basket or other suitable container
18. Autoclave or pressure cooker

*This quantity provides enough medium for 15 pairs of students.

B. For Preparing the Plates (per team)

1. Culture tubes, plugged, containing 15 ml of sterile nutrient agar, 5
2. Culture tubes, plugged, containing 5 ml sterile distilled water, 3
3. Test-tube rack
4. Beakers, 600 ml, 2
5. Ring stand
6. Bunsen burner
7. Thermometer, $0^{\circ}C$ to $100^{\circ}C$
8. Glass-marking crayon
9. Petri dishes (sterile), 5
10. Inoculating loop
11. Mixed culture of bacteria (Serratia marcescens and Sarcina lutea) in water
12. Paper towels

PROCEDURE

A. Preparations
(to be done for the whole class by a small group of students)

Each team will need five test tubes containing sterile agar medium and three test tubes containing sterile distilled water.

With the pipette, place 15 ml of water in a test tube and mark the water level with a glass-marking crayon. Pour out the water. Using this tube as a ruler, mark the 15-ml level on enough tubes to provide five for each team.

Following directions from your teacher, add the peptone, beef extract, and agar to the distilled water in the 1000-ml beaker. Mix thoroughly. Heat the mixture until it comes to a boil, stirring continuously. Use the funnel, pinch clamp, and rubber tube as directed by your teacher to pour this nutrient agar into the marked tubes (fill to the 15-ml mark). Plug the tubes with cotton.

Using the pipette, place 5 ml of distilled water in enough test tubes to provide three for each team. Plug each with cotton.

Place all the tubes in wire baskets, and sterilize in an autoclave at 15 lb pressure for fifteen minutes.

The directions given under Procedures B, C, and D, following, will be supplemented with demonstrations by the teacher. As you read the directions and observe the demonstrations, keep the following questions in mind: (a) How do these techniques prevent the escape of organisms from dishes and tubes? (b) How do these techniques prevent the entrance into dishes and tubes of unwanted organisms from the environment?

B. The "Pour-Plate" Method

Each team has five tubes of sterile medium and three tubes of sterile distilled water. Place the five tubes of medium belonging to your team in a 600-ml beaker, and add enough water to fill the beaker above the level of the medium in the tubes. Place the beaker on the ring stand, and heat. When the medium in the tubes has melted, transfer the tubes to a second 600-ml beaker containing water at 44°C. Check the temperature of the water carefully, using a thermometer. This beaker will have to be heated gently from time to time, to maintain (as closely as possible) the water temperature.

Wipe off the top of the laboratory table with a wet paper towel, place the three tubes of sterile distilled water in a rack, and number the tubes 1 through 3 with a glass-marking crayon. Place five sterile petri dishes on the table, and number them 1 through 5. Write the numbers on the bottoms of the dishes, close to the edge.

Refer to Figure 7.2-1 throughout the remainder of this procedure. Sterilize an inoculating loop in the flame of a Bunsen burner, and then transfer a loop of the mixed culture of Sarcina lutea and Serratia marcescens to Tube 1. (Observe carefully the way your teacher handles the plugs.) Reflame the loop as soon as the transfer has been completed. Mix thoroughly by rolling the tube between the palms, being careful to keep the plugged end upward so that the cotton remains dry. Again flame the loop. Transfer a loop of the material in Tube 1 to Tube 2. Mix in the same way you mixed Tube 1. Flame the loop. Transfer a loop of the material in Tube 2 to Tube 3. Mix.

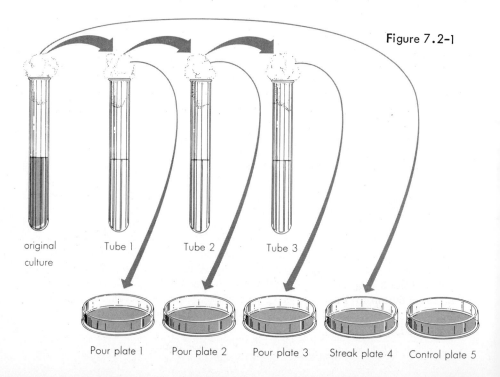

Figure 7.2-1

original culture   Tube 1   Tube 2   Tube 3

Pour plate 1   Pour plate 2   Pour plate 3   Streak plate 4   Control plate 5

Again flame the loop. Transfer a loop of the material in Tube 1 to the center of Dish 1 (Figure 7.2-2). Press the loop down firmly, making certain that the liquid in the loop is transferred to the bottom of the dish. Flame the loop. Transfer a loop of the material in Tube 2 to the center of Dish 2. Flame the loop. Transfer a loop of the material in Tube 3 to the center of Dish 3.

Figure 7.2-2

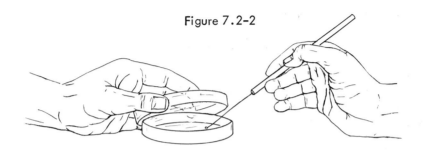

Remove a tube of medium from the 44°C water bath. Dry the tube with a paper towel, remove the plug, and flame the mouth of the tube. Pour the medium into Dish 1. Do not allow the tube lip to touch the inside of the dish (see Figure 7.2-3). Cover the dish (now a "plate") and move it gently with a circular motion, keeping the bottom of the dish on the tabletop. This motion should distribute the microorganisms uniformly in the plate. This completes the "pour-plate" method. Repeat the technique in preparing Plates (Dishes) 2 and 3.

Figure 7.2-3

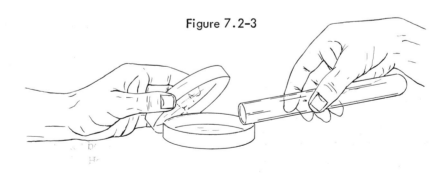

C. The "Streak-Plate" Method

Pour a tube of culture medium into Dish 4 and one into Dish 5. Dish 4 will be used for making a "streak plate"; Dish 5 is a control for the entire series of plates. Allow the medium to solidify. Flame the loop. Take a loop of the original mixed culture and streak the surface of the medium in Plate 4, using one of the patterns shown in Figure 7.2-4, as directed by the teacher. In your data book, record the pattern used.

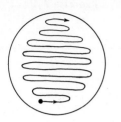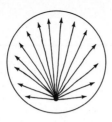

Figure 7.2-4

In a place designated by your teacher, incubate all the plates, up-side down and at room temperature. Observe daily until many bacterial colonies are clearly visible in some of the plates.

D. Counting the Colonies

Ignoring differences in appearance, count the number of separate colonies of bacteria that have developed on the medium in each of the "pour plates" (1, 2, and 3). Record the counts in your data book. Some of the plates may have hundreds of colonies growing in them. In some cases the colonies may be too crowded for any kind of count. In other cases you can estimate the number by using the following sampling technique:

With black ink draw a square 10 cm X 10 cm on a piece of white paper. Inside this square draw a series of straight lines parallel to its sides, forming a grid of 100 smaller squares—each 1 cm on a side. Position the plate on top of the paper so that the colonies of bacteria can be seen against the background of the grid. Choose five to ten of the small squares at random, and count the number of colonies in each. Add all the counts from any one plate, and divide the total by the number of small squares counted. This will give an average count per small square. Next, calculate the total surface of the culture medium in the plate. To do this, square the radius of the plate and multiply by pi (π; equals 3.14). To obtain an estimate of the number of colonies on the whole plate, multiply the average number of colonies per small square by the surface area (in cm^2) of the entire plate.

STUDYING THE DATA

When you have completed counts of all plates (except the "streak plate"), you are ready to estimate the population of organisms (number per cubic centimeter) present in the original mixed culture of bacteria. To do this, you will need the following information:

The volume of liquid held in an inoculating loop is approximately 5 mm^3. A loopful of the original mixed culture will therefore contain, on the average, $\frac{1}{200}$ of the number of bacteria present in each cubic centimeter of this culture. When this number of organisms is distributed in 5 cc of distilled water (Tube 1) and mixed, a loopful of this

dilution should contain $\frac{1}{200} \times \frac{1}{5 \times 200}$, or $\frac{1}{200,000}$, of the number orig-
inally present per cubic centimeter. This is the number of organisms that was introduced into Pour Plate 1. If we assume that each of these organisms gives rise to a visible colony, the number of colonies present in the plate represents the number of individual organisms. This number, multiplied by 200,000, will give the number of organisms per cubic centimeter in the original culture.

By transferring a loopful of the dilution in Tube 1 to Tube 2, a further dilution of $\frac{1}{1000}$ is obtained. Each colony developing in Plate 2 therefore represents a density of 200,000,000 organisms per cubic centimeter in the original culture. How many organisms per cubic centimeter of original culture does each colony in Plate 3 represent?

From the counts on each of the pour plates, carry out the calculations necessary to estimate the density of the population in the original culture. Make all calculations in your data book.

If it was possible to make estimates for all plates, you now have three separate estimates of the number of organisms present per cubic centimeter in the original culture. How closely do these compare with each other? It is thought that the best estimates can be made when the dilution results in a count of from 30 to 300 colonies per plate. Do you have a plate that falls in this range? If so, in your data book circle the population estimate made from it.

Examine Plate 5 (control). If colonies are present, count them and record the data. What correction in your original calculations is indicated if colonies are present in this control plate?(1) Make such a correction, if necessary.

Next examine Plate 4—the "streak plate." Compare the pattern of colonies with the pattern of streaking that you recorded in your data book. Are the patterns different, or are they similar?(2) How many kinds of colonies have developed? In what ways do they differ?(3) How many kinds of bacteria were in the original culture? What seems to be the principal way in which the colonies of these bacteria differ macroscopically?(4) Are any of the colonies well separated from each other? If so, suppose that you were to lift a part of one such colony on a sterile inoculating loop and streak it on a plate of sterile medium —how many kinds of colonies would you expect to develop?(5) What would you call such a culture (refer to Introduction)?(6)

Suggest a method for disposing of the cultures after you have finished studying them.

SUMMARY

From the instructions of the teacher and your own experience with this exercise, form a set of rules for working with microorganisms.(7)

In this exercise several different purposes were being pursued at the same time. Which are the principal steps involved in a procedure concerned only with determining the population density of microorganisms? (8) Which are the principal steps involved in a procedure concerned only with obtaining a pure culture? (9)

FOR FURTHER INVESTIGATION

1. The procedure for producing a pure culture was not completed in this exercise. Carry out the last step. How can you determine that you have been successful?
2. Use the method of this exercise to determine the population of microorganisms in a sample of stream or pond water. Your teacher may wish to suggest a different medium.

EXERCISE 7.3

INVESTIGATING AN INFECTIOUS DISEASE

INTRODUCTION

One of the first steps in the control of an infectious disease is to determine what specific microorganism "causes" it, that is, what microorganism must be present in the host to produce the symptoms of the disease. De Bary, Pasteur, and many others helped in developing the idea that the symptoms of infectious diseases are associated with the presence of microorganisms in the host; Koch was the first to set forth a method for determining that a particular disease results from the presence of a particular microorganism. This method is embodied in the following set of tests (known as Koch's postulates):

1. The organism suspected of producing the disease symptoms must be found constantly associated with those symptoms.
2. The suspected organism must be grown outside the host and in a pure culture.
3. When organisms from this pure culture are inoculated into a healthy individual of the host species, the symptoms of the disease in question must appear in the individual.

4. The suspected organism must then be taken from the experimental host, grown again in pure culture, and identified as the species present in the original culture.

For many years Koch's postulates were accepted as the only reliable way to determine the causative agent of an infectious disease. They cannot, however, be used to establish the cause of every type of infectious disease, because some microorganisms cannot be grown outside the body of the host (thus making postulates 2 and 4 impossible). Nevertheless, the postulates are still considered to be the basic tests for determining the causative agents of most infectious diseases.

In Chapter 7 the discussion centers on diseases of man, but the principles of infectious disease apply to all organisms. Because experimentation with animal diseases is difficult, in this exercise we shall investigate an infectious disease of plants—crown gall.

PURPOSE

This exercise is intended to illustrate some of the procedures used in the tests that make up Koch's postulates.

MATERIALS AND EQUIPMENT (for each team)

1. Potted plants of bean, tomato, or sunflower, 2
2. Pot labels, wooden, 2
3. Dissecting needle
4. Bunsen burner
5. Culture tube of Agrobacterium tumefaciens
6. Inoculating loop
7. Microscope slides, 3
8. Beaker, 5 to 7 cm in diameter
9. Crystal-violet solution
10. Medicine dropper
11. Paper towels, 3
12. Monocular microscope
13. Glass-marking crayon
14. Scalpel (or razor blade)
15. Forceps
16. Sodium hypochlorite solution, 1%
17. Sterile distilled water in plugged test tube
18. Petri dish, sterile
19. Culture tube of sterile dextrose agar

PROCEDURE

Choose two plants of approximately the same size and age. Label their pots A and B; then write your team's symbol on both labels.

Sterilize the dissecting needle by heating it in a flame. Allow the needle to cool; then use it to make several punctures (about 2 mm apart) on one side of the stem of Plant A, approximately midway between the points at which leaves are attached. Choose a part of the stem approximately 4 to 6 mm in diameter.

Again sterilize the dissecting needle. Dip the tip of the needle into the culture of Agrobacterium tumefaciens. Using the needle, puncture the stem of Plant B just as you did that of Plant A. Sterilize the needle. Place the plants in a well-lighted part of the laboratory, and keep them well watered.

Prepare a stained microscope slide of Agrobacterium tumefaciens, following the crystal-violet staining method outlined in Exercise 6.3. Examine under high power of a monocular microscope. In your data book, sketch a few of the bacteria, showing their shapes and arrangement. With a glass-marking crayon, label the slide 1, and store it for later use in this exercise.

Make observations of the potted plants every two or three days for a period of four or five weeks. In your data book record all changes and the dates on which they were first observed.

In time a knotlike growth, or gall, may appear on one of the plants. If this occurs, use a sharp scalpel to remove it. Wash the gall thoroughly. Using forceps, dip a clean microscope slide into a 1-percent solution of sodium hypochlorite for about twenty seconds. Rinse in sterile distilled water. Place the slide on a paper towel on the laboratory table and cover with the top of a sterile petri dish. Do not touch the upper surface of the slide, and do not allow it to touch anything in the laboratory.

Again using the forceps, dip the plant gall into the solution of sodium hypochlorite. Rinse in distilled water and place on the sterile microscope slide, near one end. Using a sharp scalpel sterilized in a flame, cut the gall in half. Cut a small piece (about 2 mm in diameter) from the center of the gall and place it in the middle of the slide. Discard the remaining gall tissue. Crush the small piece of tissue with the flat side of the scalpel blade.

With a sterile inoculating loop, transfer some of the juice from the crushed gall tissue to a sterile tube of dextrose agar. Label the tube and store it in a place designated by your teacher.

Examine the tube four or five days later. If colonies of microorganisms are present, take material from one of the colonies and prepare a slide as you did before (crystal-violet staining method). Label the slide 2.

Compare Slides 1 and 2 under high power of a monocular microscope. Draw a few of the organisms observed on Slide 2.

DISCUSSION AND CONCLUSIONS

Which of the two plants developed crown gall?(1) Which of the two plants was the control?(2) Why was a sterile needle used to puncture Plant A?(3) On the basis of your visual comparison of Slides 1 and 2, what conclusion may be drawn about the identity of the organisms in Slide 2?(4) Why is similarity of appearance insufficient evidence for concluding that the bacteria on the two slides are of the same species (see Chapter 6)?(5)

Do you believe that this experiment provides proof that Agrobacterium tumefaciens is the causative agent of crown gall? If so, explain how each of Koch's postulates is fulfilled in the experiment. If not, what additional steps should be taken to fulfill them?(6)

FOR FURTHER INVESTIGATION

1. Determine whether or not the bacteria taken from the galls you have cultured will produce new galls after they are inoculated into other plants of the same species.

2. The plants suggested for use in this experiment are dicots. Are other dicots susceptible to infection by Agrobacterium tumefaciens? Are monocots susceptible?

EXERCISE 7.4

NODULE-FORMING BACTERIA

PURPOSE

This exercise illustrates the relationship between a legume and a nitrogen-fixing bacterium.

MATERIALS AND EQUIPMENT

A. For Preparation of Medium

1. Bottle or test tube, about 30 ml, 1 per team
2. Aluminum foil, to cover bottle, 1 piece per team
3. Wire basket
4. Balance
5. Mortar and pestle
6. Potassium chloride (KCl), 5 g
7. Dibasic potassium phosphate (K_2HPO_4), 1.25 g
8. Calcium sulfate ($CaSO_4 \cdot 2H_2O$), 1.25 g
9. Magnesium sulfate ($MgSO_4 \cdot 7H_2O$), 1.25 g
10. Tribasic calcium phosphate ($Ca_3(PO_4)_2$), 1.25 g
11. Ferric phosphate (Fe_3PO_4), 0.01 g
12. Distilled water
13. Glass or porcelain container, 1.5 to 2.0 liters
14. Stirring rod
15. Agar, 8 g per liter of medium
16. Heat source
17. Ring stand
18. Test tubes (either 25 mm X 200 mm or 19 mm X 150 mm), 2 per team
19. Pressure cooker or autoclave

B. For Planting Seeds (per team)

1. Clover seeds, 3 or 4
2. Sodium hypochlorite solution (0.01%)
3. Forceps
4. Alcohol (isopropyl is satisfactory), about 10 ml
5. Bunsen burner
6. Bottle of sterile water
7. Test tubes of sterile Crone's nitrogen-free agar medium, 2
8. Glass-marking crayon
9. Commercial Rhizobium inoculum, 1

C. For Examining Nodules (per team)

1. Microscope slide
2. Medicine dropper
3. Forceps
4. Cover slip
5. Monocular microscope
6. Crystal-violet stain

PROCEDURE

A. Preparation of Medium
(to be done for the whole class by a small group of students)

Place 10 ml of water in each bottle, cover with aluminum foil, and place in a wire basket for sterilization.

Prepare Crone's nitrogen-free medium as follows: Mix and grind to a powder the chemicals listed as Items 6 through 11, under "MATE-RIALS AND EQUIPMENT: A. For Preparation of Medium." Place 1.5 g of the mixture in a liter of distilled water. Add 8 g of agar. Heat to boiling, to melt the agar; stir continuously to prevent burning. Pour 20 to 40 ml of the heated medium into the test tubes, and plug the tubes with cotton.

Sterilize the tubes along with the bottles of water.

B. Planting the Seeds

Place the clover seeds in the sodium hypochlorite solution, and allow them to soak for five minutes. This should kill mold spores and bacteria on the seed coats. Sterilize the forceps by dipping them into alcohol and igniting in the burner flame. Let the alcohol on the for-ceps burn off completely—then repeat this step. Using the sterilized forceps, remove the seeds from the sodium hypochlorite solution and place them in the bottle of sterile water. Shake the seeds in the water to rinse them thoroughly.

Resterilize the forceps, and remove one seed from the water. Place the seed in one of the tubes of Crone's nitrogen-free agar me-dium. The seed should be placed at the center of the agar surface. With a glass-marking crayon, mark this tube Control, and label it with your team symbol and the date.

Resterilize the forceps, and remove another seed from the water. Dip this seed into the commercial Rhizobium inoculum. Then place the seed at the center of the agar surface in a second tube. Mark this tube Test, and label with your team symbol and the date.

Set both the Test and the Control in a vertical position in a place designated by your teacher. Observe every two or three days at first; later, once a week. In your data book note all changes in the seeds and in the seedlings that develop from them. Record (with dates) the approximate length of stems, roots, and leaves as these appear. Be sure to watch for the formation of nodules (lumps or knotlike growths) on the roots.

C. Examination of Nodules (optional)

About five weeks after the planting, the teacher may want you to examine the nodules. If so, use the following procedure:

Remove the Test plant from the tube, and gently wash all excess agar from the roots. Look at all the roots carefully, noting the location of any nodules that have formed. If some are present, select one of the larger nodules (2 mm or more in diameter), remove it from the root with forceps, and place it on a clean microscope slide. Add a drop of water, and crush the nodule with the end of the forceps. Note the color of the inside of the nodule. Remove the larger pieces of the nodule, and cover the remainder of the crushed material with a cover slip. Observe under the high power of the microscope. In your data book describe what you see.

If you wish to see the bacteria in the nodule more clearly, stain with an aqueous solution of crystal violet, using the procedure outlined in Exercise 6.3.

CONCLUSIONS

Summarize any differences you observed between the Control and the Test plants. (1) Examine the composition of the medium in which you grew the plants. What were the possible sources of nitrogen for the plants? (2) Considering the design of the experiment, how might you account for the observed differences between the plants? (3) In coming to this conclusion, what assumptions are you making? (4)

FOR FURTHER INVESTIGATION

1. Will the Rhizobium culture that you used with clover form an equally efficient symbiotic relationship with other species of legumes? Answer this by experiment.

2. The amount of nitrogen compounds that is usable by plants can be measured in soils by simple methods involving color changes in certain chemicals. If your school has the necessary equipment, you might try to determine the increase of nitrogen in a particular soil after a crop of nodule-bearing legumes has been grown in it.

EXERCISE 7.5

GROWING SOIL MICROBES BY THE "MUD-PIE" TECHNIQUE

INTRODUCTION

Though soils abound with different kinds of microbes, the complexity of the mixtures of soil particles, dead organic substances, and living microbes makes it difficult to sort out the organisms. This difficulty may be overcome by encouraging microbial growth so that large numbers of microorganisms accumulate in masses, or colonies.

One way to grow soil microbes is by the "mud-pie" technique. On the smooth surface of a finely sifted soil that has been well moistened, the microbes will grow in easily visible colonies. The main kinds of microbes can then be recognized.

PURPOSES

The purposes of this exercise are (1) to culture soil microbes, and (2) to examine and identify some of the microorganisms thus grown.

MATERIALS AND EQUIPMENT (per team)

1. Sieve or food strainer
2. Loam soil from garden or greenhouse, about 200 g
3. Dish for sifted soil
4. Balance
5. Petri dishes or aluminum pie plates, 4
6. Calcium carbonate ($CaCO_3$), 3 g
7. Starch (corn or soluble), 2 g
8. Glucose or sucrose, 2 g
9. Glass-marking crayon
10. Spatula or broad-bladed knife
11. Aluminum foil, to cover plates (if pie plates are used)
12. Inoculating loop
13. Microscope slide
14. Monocular microscope (with oil-immersion objective, if it is available)
15. Medicine dropper
16. Beaker, 5 to 7 cm diameter
17. Methylene-blue stain
18. Paper towels

PROCEDURE

A. Preparation of "Mud-Pie" Cultures

The soil chosen for this experiment should be as fine in texture as possible. Using a sieve or a food strainer, remove the larger particles by sifting the soil into a dish. Discard the particles left in the sieve. Number the petri dishes (or aluminum pie plates) from 1 to 4.

Weigh out four portions of soil, 50 g each; put each portion into one of the petri dishes. Add nothing to Dish 1. To Dish 2 add 1 g of calcium carbonate ($CaCO_3$).

To Dish 3 add 1 g of $CaCO_3$ and 2 g of starch. To Dish 4 add 1 g of $CaCO_3$ and 2 g of glucose or sucrose.

Mix the materials in each dish thoroughly. Add just enough water to make a firm but easily shaped "mud-pie." With a spatula, press and smooth the materials in each dish to produce a glossy surface. The smoother the better! Cover the dishes (with aluminum foil if pie plates are used), and set them in a dark place, as directed by your teacher.

B. Observations

Examine the "mud-pie" cultures daily. It may be necessary to add a few drops of water from time to time, to maintain moistness. When microbial growth appears on the surface of the soil, pick up a small amount of the microbes with a sterilized inoculating loop and transfer to a microscope slide. Prepare a wet mount (see Exercise 1.4), and examine under high power. Note in your data book what you can see.

Next, prepare a stained mount by following the procedure given in Exercise 6.3, with the following exceptions: (1) When the slide has been prepared for the microbes, place a drop of water on it. Then, with a sterile inoculating loop, transfer a small amount of growth from one of the "mud-pie" colonies to the drop of water. (2) Use methylene-blue stain instead of crystal-violet, and stain for one to two minutes instead of for thirty seconds. Examine under high power. In your data book record any additional observations that the staining allows you to make.

Repeat these microscope observations for different kinds of colonies, as your teacher may direct.

Draw a few representative microorganisms taken from each culture. Try to identify each kind of organism (as closely as possible), using the "Catalogue of Living Things" (Appendix of the textbook) and Selman A. Waksman's Soil Microbiology (New York: John Wiley and Sons, 1952).

In your data book construct a chart with three columns. In the left-hand column, list the four types of "mud-pie" cultures; in the middle column describe the macroscopic appearance of each "mud-pie" culture; in the right-hand column, list the kinds of microorganisms observed in each culture.

DISCUSSION AND CONCLUSIONS

Calcium carbonate neutralizes acidity. What group of soil organisms is favored by the addition of calcium carbonate (see Chapter 7 in text)?(1) Compare the kinds of organisms found in Dish 1 with those in the other dishes. Do your results agree or disagree with the statements in the text? If they disagree, try to develop a hypothesis that might explain the disagreement.(2)

What was the function of the starch and glucose?(3) What is the normal source of such substances in soils?(4) Which dish developed the least microbial growth? Why?(5)

Although this exercise was designed primarily to provide opportunity for observing soil microorganisms, it has some experimental aspects. What hypotheses were involved in the design of the exercise?(6) Which dish served as a control in the experimental design?(7)

FOR FURTHER INVESTIGATION

Suggest a hypothesis concerning the effect of light on the growth of soil microorganisms by the "mud-pie" technique. Set up an experiment to test your hypothesis.

EXERCISE 7.6

SOIL NEMATODES

INTRODUCTION

The nematodes in the soil are not quite microscopic; under favorable circumstances they can be seen with the naked eye. And they are not "microorganisms," according to the microbiologist's use of the word (see Introduction to Exercise 6.1). But nematodes certainly are important members of the soil community.

Many soil nematodes attack the outside layers of plant roots. In some cases molds infect the plants through the openings made by the nematodes. In other cases the plants themselves react to nematode attack by producing growths that resemble galls (see Exercise 7.4). In either case the plant does not reach its full growth. Nematodes seriously damage such crops as cotton, sugar beets, lettuce, citrus fruits, cabbage, and carrots. Chemical companies now offer the farmer a number of <u>nematocides</u> in an effort to control the problem.

PURPOSE

In this exercise nematodes are separated from different soil samples, and the numbers of nematodes in these soils are compared.

MATERIALS AND EQUIPMENT

1. Soil samples (3 or more), 250 cc each
2. Plastic bags, 1 per soil sample
3. Rubber bands, 1 per soil sample
4. Glass-marking crayon
5. Glass funnels, 100-mm diameter (preferred), 1 per soil sample
6. Rubber tubing (10-cm lengths), to fit funnel tubes, 1 length per soil sample
7. Spring-compressor clamps or screw clamps, 1 per soil sample
8. Wire cloth (as in window screens), in squares a little larger than the top of the funnel, 1 square per soil sample
9. Ring stands, 1 per soil sample
10. Cleansing tissues (a brand that does not disintegrate rapidly when wet)
11. Beakers, 50 ml, 1 per soil sample
12. Medicine droppers, 1 per student
13. Microscope slides, 1 per student
14. Cover slips, 1 per student
15. Monocular microscopes, 1 per student

PROCEDURE

The soil samples should be obtained from a variety of places in which plants are growing: a meadow, a greenhouse, a garden, the pot of a houseplant, etc. For this exercise samples from a depth of 10 to

20 cm are better than samples from the surface. Place the soil samples in plastic bags, and close tightly with rubber bands. Mark each bag with a symbol identifying the sample.

The setup for separating nematodes from the soil is relatively simple (Figure 7.6-1). You will need as many of these devices as you have soil samples. Attach a length of rubber tubing to a funnel, and close the tubing with a clamp. Label the funnel with a symbol indicating the soil sample it will contain. Support the funnel with a ring stand (not shown in figure).

Fill the funnel with water, release the clamp, and allow the water to run off until its level is 6 to 8 cm below the rim. From the wire cloth construct a basket that fits in the top of the funnel and extends about 6 cm below the upper rim. Place two cleansing tissues in the basket, and lay the edges back so that they hang over the sides of the funnel. Place enough soil on the tissue to fill the basket within 2 cm of the funnel rim. Fold the ends of the tissue inward, over the soil sample.

Slowly add warm water (35°C) until the soil sample is covered to a depth of 1 cm. If the paper tissue becomes torn, repeat the procedure, using new tissue.

Allow this setup to stand for forty-eight hours. Then open the clamp and run about 3 ml of the water into a small beaker or test tube.

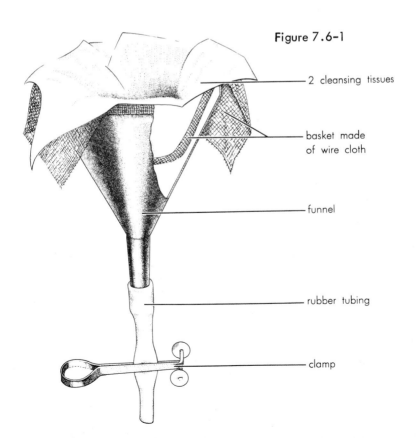

Figure 7.6-1

2 cleansing tissues

basket made of wire cloth

funnel

rubber tubing

clamp

If the water still contains soil particles or looks muddy, proceed as follows: Attach rubber tubing and a clamp to a clean funnel. Fold a piece of cleansing tissue as you would a piece of filter paper, and place it in this funnel. Fill the funnel with water. Release the clamp and drain off water until there is only about 1 cm in the tapered part of the funnel. Pour water collected from the first extraction into the funnel, raising the level 2 or 3 cm. Allow this to stand for a few hours. The nematodes will pass through the tissue, but the soil particles will not.

With a medicine dropper, take water from either the first or the second extraction, and place one drop of it on a clean microscope slide. Add a cover slip and examine with a microscope, using low power.

When nematodes are found, make a count of the number in each of five different microscope fields (see Figure 2.2-2). Calculate the average number and record it in your date book. Be sure to record which soil sample the nematodes came from. The counts made by other students will be recorded on the chalkboard, and a general average can be calculated for each soil sample.

You may also observe mites and active soil protists in addition to the nematodes. If present, how do they compare in abundance with the nematodes?(1)

CONCLUSIONS

What characteristic of nematodes makes it possible to separate them from the soil by the method used in this exercise?(2) Which of the soils used in your study had the most nematodes?(3) What hypotheses can you propose to explain the results?(4)

FOR FURTHER INVESTIGATION

1. How long will nematodes live in the water in which they were collected?

2. What is the effect of temperature on nematodes? Using the same kinds of soil samples, vary the temperature at which the nematodes are collected by placing funnels in the refrigerator, in a box heated by an electric heater, and in the classroom.

3. What concentration of a particular nematocide kills the nematodes you collect?

EXERCISE 7.7

THE ABUNDANCE OF AIRBORNE MICROORGANISMS IN VARIOUS SCHOOL ENVIRONMENTS

INTRODUCTION

Coughing and sneezing may spread droplets of materials from the mouth and nose to a distance of 3 m or more. The water in these droplets evaporates rapidly, leaving bits of dry materials (dust particles) that contain dormant bacteria. Other dust particles in the air carry dormant microbes derived from many sources. Thus dust particles may be vectors for disease organisms. Fortunately, most of the dormant microbes in the air are not disease organisms.

There are several ways to determine the number of microorganisms present in a given volume of air. But this exercise will not involve actual measurements of density. Instead, it will be concerned with a comparison of the abundance of microorganisms in several different places.

The exposed-petri-dish method of capturing microorganisms in the air will be used.

PURPOSE

This exercise is an attempt to compare the numbers of airborne microorganisms present at different places in your school.

MATERIALS AND EQUIPMENT

1. Test tubes, 19 mm X 150 mm, 10
2. Peptone, 1 g
3. Beef extract, 0.6 g
4. Agar, 3 g
5. Water (preferably distilled), 200 ml
6. Beaker, 400 ml
7. Balance
8. Stirring rod
9. Graduated cylinder, 25 ml
10. Ring stand
11. Heat source
12. Pressure cooker or autoclave
13. Petri dishes, 10
14. Glass-marking crayon

PROCEDURE

A. Preparation of Plates

Prepare nutrient agar by following the directions given in Exercise 7.2. Pour 15 ml of nutrient agar into each of the ten test tubes, and plug the tubes with cotton. Sterilize the tubes and ten petri dishes in the pressure cooker for fifteen minutes at 15 lb pressure.

Again following the directions in Exercise 7.2, pour the agar from the tubes into the ten sterile petri dishes—one tube per dish. Allow the agar to solidify.

B. Exposing and Incubating the Plates

Each team is responsible for one petri plate. Each team will be assigned a place where its plate is to be exposed. On the bottom of each petri dish, write the place where it is to be exposed and the number of the team. Some suggested areas are: biology laboratory, chemistry laboratory, industrial arts shop, social studies room, English room, auditorium, gymnasium, lunchroom, corridor.

When your team's plate is in its assigned place, remove the cover and expose the agar for six minutes. Replace the cover. After the plates are returned to the laboratory, they should be turned upside down and incubated in a place designated by your teacher.

C. Counting Colonies and Compiling Data

After three or four days, count the colonies of microorganisms in your team's plate. You can distinguish mold colonies by their cottony or fuzzy appearance and their large size. In your data book record the number of mold colonies and the number of bacteria colonies. Also record your counts on a master chart that includes the counts from all plates. A form similar to the one shown below may be used:

WHERE THE PLATE WAS EXPOSED	NUMBER OF COLONIES		
	Bacteria	Molds	Total
biology laboratory			
English room			

CONCLUSIONS

According to the data collected by your class, which location had the largest population of microorganisms? What explanation can you suggest for the high microbe population in this location?(1) According to your data, which place had the smallest population of microorganisms? What explanation can you give to account for the low population of microbes in this location?(2)

How reliable do you think your results are? (In other words, how likely do you think it is that a repetition of the experiment would give you the same results?) Depending on your answer to this question, suggest factors that make your results reliable or unreliable. (3) Would the count vary if you used a different medium in the plates or incubated them at a different temperature? Why or why not?(4) Why is it especially important to dispose of these plates, using proper bacteriological techniques (Exercise 7.2)?(5)

CHAPTER 8

Patterns of Life on Land

EXERCISE 8.1

LIMITING FACTORS IN DISTRIBUTION

INTRODUCTION

Under natural conditions bald cypress rarely grows on elevated ground (text pages 211, 214). There is evidence that this pattern of distribution is at least partly a result of the intolerance of bald-cypress seeds for relatively dry soil. Likewise, the absence of most other tree species in the swamps of the southeastern United States may be a result of the intolerance of their seeds for flooded soils. In any case, it is certain that the environmental requirements of seeds are important in determining the geographical distribution of seed-bearing plants (gymnosperms and angiosperms).

Moisture is, of course, a basic distributional factor, but it is difficult to maintain and measure different amounts of moisture in experimental situations. Light and temperature, on the other hand, are important factors of distribution that can be investigated more easily. And seeds are a convenient form of organism to use for experiment, especially since we can draw upon experience gained in Exercise 1.2.

PURPOSE

In this exercise the effects of light and temperature on the germination of different kinds of seeds are examined in an effort to draw conclusions about the natural distribution of the organisms involved.

MATERIALS AND EQUIPMENT

1. Beakers, 50 ml, 4 per team
2. Seeds of radish, vetch, tomato, and lettuce, 50 each per team
3. Fungicide, about 150 ml per team
4. Petri dishes, 5 per team
5. Filter paper or paper toweling, cut to fit petri dishes, 20 pieces per team
6. Cardboard dividers, cut to fit petri dishes, 20 per team
7. Forceps, 1 per team
8. Glass-marking crayon, 1 per team
9. Clear plastic bags, each large enough to contain 1 petri dish, 5 per team
10. Rubber bands, 5 per team
11. Shallow cardboard boxes, with covers, 2
12. Refrigerator
13. Incubator
14. Centigrade thermometers, 2

PROCEDURE

Label the beakers tomato, radish, vetch, and lettuce. In each, place 50 seeds of the species named. Add fungicide, and allow to soak for a period of time recommended by the teacher.

Place 4 disks of filter paper (or paper toweling) in each of the 5 petri dishes. Moisten them thoroughly. Divide each dish into quarter sections by inserting cardboard dividers, as shown in Figure 8.1-1.

Pour the fungicide solution from the beakers; rinse the seeds with water. Using forceps, place the seeds in the petri dishes—10 of one kind to each quarter section. Label the dishes with the team symbol, and number from 1 to 5. Place each dish in a clear plastic bag and close the bag with a rubber band.

Place each dish in a different environment, as follows:

Dish 1. Continuous light and cold (refrigerator)
Dish 2. Continuous dark and cold (box in refrigerator)
Dish 3. Continuous light and warm (incubator)
Dish 4. Continuous dark and warm (box in incubator)
Dish 5. Variable light and temperature (windowsill)

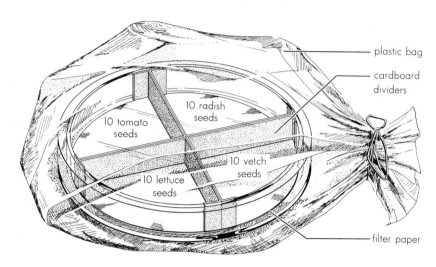

Figure 8.1-1

The lighted, cold environment in the refrigerator (Dish 1) should be maintained at 10° to 12°C, with the refrigerator light adjusted to remain on when the door is closed. The dark, cold environment (Dish 2) can be provided by placing a box in the refrigerator. Check the temperatures inside and outside the box with a thermometer. The warm environments should be maintained at 30° to 35°C. Place a light in the incubator (for Dish 3). A box in the incubator will provide a dark, warm environment (Dish 4). Check temperatures with a thermometer. A windowsill will provide a variable environment (Dish 5).

Each day count the number of seeds that have germinated (see Exercise 1.2 for definition). Remove the seeds with forceps as they germinate. Add the number counted each day to the total counted on previous days; that is, the counts are to be cumulative. Record the counts in your data book, using the following form (one for each dish):

Dish No. _____   Environment _____

KIND OF SEED	NUMBER GERMINATED				
	Day 1	Day 2	Day 3	←—→	Day 10
Tomato					
Radish					
Vetch					
Lettuce					

STUDYING THE DATA

Combine the data of all teams so that chance variations are smoothed out (Exercise 2.2, page 35, and Chapter 3, pages 64-65). We can measure success either by the speed of germination or by the proportion of seeds that have germinated at the end of the period of observation. Neither of these methods can be used for comparison between species, because there are hereditary differences between species—that is, differences that are independent of environmental factors. Such hereditary differences may be considered, however, when we judge the outcome of competition between two species in the same environment.

First, consider the proportion of seeds that germinated. In which environment did the greatest proportion of tomato seeds germinate?(1) Of radish seeds?(2) Of vetch seeds?(3) Of lettuce seeds?(4) Second, consider the speed of germination. Is there any case in which the seeds of one species germinated more rapidly in one environment but germinated in larger proportion in another? If so, which species and which environments are involved?(5)

Now consider the environmental factors separately. The germination of which kind of seed (if any) seems to be affected most by the amount of light?(6) By temperature?(7) Does any of the kinds of seeds germinate similarly in all the experimental environments?(8)

CONCLUSIONS

On the basis of the experimental results, describe the biome in which each species would have an advantage during germination. (9)

FOR FURTHER INVESTIGATION

In markets it is possible to obtain seeds of plants from many places. Such seeds as those of avocado, date, grapefruit, orange, pomegranate, lentil, many kinds of beans, etc., can be collected in the kitchen. These can be tested for germination in experimental environments, just as in this exercise.

EXERCISE 8.2

TEMPERATURE, RAINFALL, AND BIOME DISTRIBUTION

INTRODUCTION

Chapter 8 includes six examples of climatograms—grids on which averages (in these examples, monthly) of precipitation and temperatures at a particular location are plotted together. These climatograms show variations in only two important climatic factors during a year. Other factors may greatly affect climate, but a climatogram does give a rough idea of climate in the location from which the data were obtained.

Biomes are closely associated with climate. You can easily associate the climate of your own locality with the biome found there. Only by extensive travel, however, can the close relationship of particular climates with particular biomes be learned on a worldwide basis. This exercise is a poor substitute for such travel; but if it is carried out thoughtfully and with frequent reference to the description of biomes in Chapter 8, it can help you to visualize the association of climates with biomes. It can also help you to understand the biological relationships that make up the diversity of the biotic communities found on land.

PURPOSE

This exercise provides practice in associating climates (as expressed in monthly averages of precipitation and temperature) with biomes.

MATERIALS

1. Graph paper, 3 to 17 sheets per student

PROCEDURE

First, obtain monthly averages of precipitation and temperature from the weather station closest to your school. These data will be expressed as inches and as degrees Fahrenheit—units of the British system of measurement. (The U.S. Weather Bureau is one of the very few still using these units; even the British have adopted the centigrade temperature scale.) You will need to convert the data to centimeters of precipitation and degrees centigrade before making comparisons with the data given in this exercise. Draw a climatogram from the local data. The heading of the climatogram should include the name of the biome in which the data were recorded and the location of the weather station.

Second, draw climatograms from the data in Group 1, below. When these are completed, you will have eleven climatograms (six being in Chapter 8). And in this group you will have at least one representative climatogram from each of the major land biomes.

GROUP 1

T = temperature (in degrees centigrade);   P = precipitation (in centimeters)

a. Tropical Deciduous Forest: Cuiabá, Brazil

	J	F	M	A	M	J	J	A	S	O	N	D
T	27.2	27.2	27.2	26.7	25.6	23.9	24.4	25.6	27.8	27.8	27.8	27.2
P	24.9	21.1	21.1	10.2	5.3	0.8	0.5	2.8	5.1	11.4	15.0	20.6

b. Chaparral (Scrub Forest): Santa Monica, California

	J	F	M	A	M	J	J	A	S	O	N	D
T	11.7	11.7	12.8	14.4	15.6	17.2	18.9	18.3	18.3	16.7	14.4	12.8
P	8.9	7.6	7.4	1.3	1.3	0.0	0.0	0.0	0.3	1.5	3.6	5.8

c. Tropical Grassland: Moshi, Tanganyika

	J	F	M	A	M	J	J	A	S	O	N	D
T	23.2	23.2	22.2	21.2	19.8	18.4	17.9	18.4	19.8	21.4	22.0	22.4
P	3.6	6.1	9.2	40.1	30.2	5.1	5.1	2.5	2.0	3.0	8.1	6.4

d. Tropical Desert: Aden, Aden

	J	F	M	A	M	J	J	A	S	O	N	D
T	24.6	25.1	26.4	28.5	30.6	31.9	31.1	30.3	31.1	28.8	26.5	25.1
P	0.8	0.5	1.3	0.5	0.3	0.3	0.0	0.3	0.3	0.3	0.3	0.3

Third, draw climatograms from the data in Group 2, below, as assigned by the teacher.

GROUP 2

		J	F	M	A	M	J	J	A	S	O	N	D
a.	T	1.1	1.7	6.1	12.2	17.8	22.2	25.0	23.3	20.0	13.9	7.8	2.2
	P	8.1	7.6	8.9	8.4	9.2	9.9	11.2	10.2	7.9	7.9	6.4	7.9
b.	T	10.6	11.1	12.2	14.4	15.6	19.4	21.1	21.7	20.0	16.7	13.9	11.1
	P	9.1	8.9	8.6	6.6	5.1	2.0	0.5	0.5	3.6	8.4	10.9	10.4
c.	T	25.6	25.6	24.4	25.0	24.4	23.3	23.3	24.4	24.4	25.0	25.6	25.6
	P	25.8	24.9	31.0	16.5	25.4	18.8	16.8	11.7	22.1	18.3	21.3	29.2
d.	T	12.8	15.0	18.3	21.1	25.0	29.4	32.8	32.2	28.9	22.2	16.1	13.3
	P	1.0	1.3	1.0	0.3	0.0	0.0	0.3	1.3	0.5	0.5	0.8	1.0
e.	T	-3.9	-2.2	1.7	8.9	15.0	20.0	22.8	21.7	16.7	11.1	5.0	-0.6
	P	2.3	1.8	2.8	2.8	3.2	5.8	5.3	3.0	3.6	2.8	4.1	3.3
f.	T	19.4	18.9	18.3	16.1	15.0	13.3	12.8	13.3	14.4	15.0	16.7	17.8
	P	0.0	0.0	1.5	0.5	8.9	14.7	12.2	8.1	2.0	1.0	0.3	0.8
g.	T	-22.2	-22.8	-21.1	-14.4	-3.9	1.7	5.0	5.0	1.1	-3.9	-10.0	-17.2
	P	1.0	1.3	1.8	1.5	1.5	1.3	2.3	2.8	2.8	2.8	2.8	1.3
h.	T	11.7	12.8	17.2	20.6	23.9	27.2	28.3	28.3	26.1	21.1	16.1	12.2
	P	3.6	4.1	4.6	6.9	8.1	6.9	6.4	6.6	8.9	5.1	5.6	4.6
i.	T	23.3	22.2	19.4	15.6	11.7	8.3	8.3	9.4	12.2	15.1	18.9	21.7
	P	5.1	5.6	6.6	5.6	2.8	0.9	2.5	4.1	5.8	5.8	5.1	5.3
j.	T	17.2	18.9	21.1	22.8	23.3	22.2	21.1	21.1	20.6	19.4	18.9	17.2
	P	0.3	0.5	1.5	3.6	8.6	9.2	9.4	11.4	10.9	5.3	0.8	0.3
k.	T	-20.0	-18.9	-12.2	-2.2	5.6	12.2	16.1	15.0	10.6	3.9	-5.6	-15.0
	P	3.3	2.3	2.8	2.5	4.6	5.6	6.1	8.4	7.4	4.6	2.8	2.8
l.	T	-0.6	2.2	5.0	10.0	13.3	18.3	23.3	22.2	16.1	10.6	4.4	0.0
	P	1.5	1.3	1.3	1.0	1.5	0.8	0.3	0.5	0.8	1.0	0.8	1.5

STUDYING THE DATA

Compare the climatogram based on data from the weather station nearest your school with the climatogram (in the text or in Group 1) representing the same biome. In what ways are the two climatograms similar?(1) What characteristics distinguish them from the climatograms representing other biomes?(2) What characteristics of the climate (as represented by monthly precipitation and temperature averages) seem to be related to characteristics of the biome? How are the two sets of characteristics related?(3) Relate the characteristics of each biome with the characteristics of its climate shown on the climatograms.(4)

DISCUSSION

You should now be able to decide which biomes are represented in the data given in Group 2. From each set of climatic data, you are to predict the biome that the data represent. In doing this, you are testing generalizations made from studying the known data. Write your prediction (the name of a biome) at the top of each graph.

It is well to keep in mind that all predictions are subject to error. Some predictions—for example, that night will follow day—are rather certain; others, as that tomorrow will be warmer than today, are less certain. Here you are working with only two variables. You have no data concerning winds or cloudiness, and you can only judge humidity indirectly. So you are predicting with a lower expectation of success than if you were considering more variables. Nevertheless, you can make predictions of some value even from a consideration of these two variables alone. Not all climatic variables are of equal importance. Because precipitation and temperature are more important than other climatic factors in distinguishing biomes, they provide a good basis for determining which biome is represented.

FOR FURTHER INVESTIGATION

1. A biome is not uniform. While traveling through any biome, we can observe gradual changes in biotic and abiotic factors. Thus the ecologist can distinguish subdivisions of biomes. Often these subdivisions can be correlated with slight changes in climate. The middle-latitude grassland of North America illustrates this relationship well. As we travel from east to west, we pass through tall-grass prairie, mid-grass prairie, short-grass plains, and finally (in some places) bunch grass before reaching mountains or desert. The climatic changes that accompany these biotic changes can be illustrated with climatograms prepared from the data given on the next page.

a. Tall-Grass Prairie: Dubuque, Iowa

	J	F	M	A	M	J	J	A	S	O	N	D
T	-6.7	-5.0	1.7	9.4	15.6	21.1	23.9	22.2	17.8	11.1	2.8	-3.9
P	3.8	3.6	5.6	6.6	9.9	11.4	9.4	8.6	10.2	6.4	4.8	3.8

b. Mid-Grass Prairie: Kearney, Nebraska

	J	F	M	A	M	J	J	A	S	O	N	D
T	-4.6	-1.9	2.6	9.9	15.8	21.8	25.7	24.4	18.9	12.2	3.3	-2.2
P	1.3	1.6	2.8	6.1	9.9	10.3	6.5	5.2	6.1	3.0	2.1	1.5

c. Bunch Grass: Laramie, Wyoming

	J	F	M	A	M	J	J	A	S	O	N	D
T	-6.1	-5.6	-1.7	3.3	7.8	12.8	16.7	16.7	11.1	5.0	-1.1	-5.6
P	1.3	0.8	2.0	2.5	3.8	3.1	4.3	3.0	2.5	2.3	1.3	1.3

2. In the study of climates, the relationship between temperature and precipitation is more important than the measurement of either. This can be illustrated with data from the middle-latitude grassland of North America. Draw climatograms from the three sets of data below (arranged in a series from south to north). How do you explain the presence of these different climates in one biome (grassland)?

a. Coastal Prairie: Galveston, Texas

	J	F	M	A	M	J	J	A	S	O	N	D
T	12.2	13.3	17.2	21.1	24.4	27.8	28.9	28.3	26.7	22.8	17.2	13.9
P	8.6	7.6	7.4	7.9	8.6	10.7	10.2	11.9	14.5	10.9	9.9	9.4

b. Mid-Grass Prairie: Omaha, Nebraska

	J	F	M	A	M	J	J	A	S	O	N	D
T	-5.6	-3.9	2.8	10.6	17.2	22.2	25.0	23.9	18.9	12.8	3.9	-2.8
P	1.8	2.3	3.3	7.1	10.4	11.9	10.2	8.1	7.6	5.8	2.8	2.3

c. Prairie-Aspen Border: Winnipeg, Manitoba, Canada

	J	F	M	A	M	J	J	A	S	O	N	D
T	-20.0	-17.8	-9.4	3.3	11.1	16.7	18.9	17.8	12.2	5.0	-6.1	-14.4
P	2.3	1.8	3.3	3.6	5.1	7.9	7.9	5.6	5.6	3.6	2.8	2.3

3. A kind of climatogram much used by ecologists is shown in Figure 8.2-1. Two sets of data are plotted on the same grid. A comparison can then be easily made between the two. With a little practice, you can associate the shape of such a climatogram with climates that are characteristic of different world regions. In the example, the shapes of the two graphs are similar, though their positions on the grid differ. The shape is characteristic of climates in middle latitudes of the Northern Hemisphere.

The details of the graphs can be associated with particular biomes. Paris is in a middle-latitude deciduous-forest biome; Denver is in a middle-latitude grassland biome. What characteristics in the graph can you associate with the difference in these biomes?

Figure 8.2-1

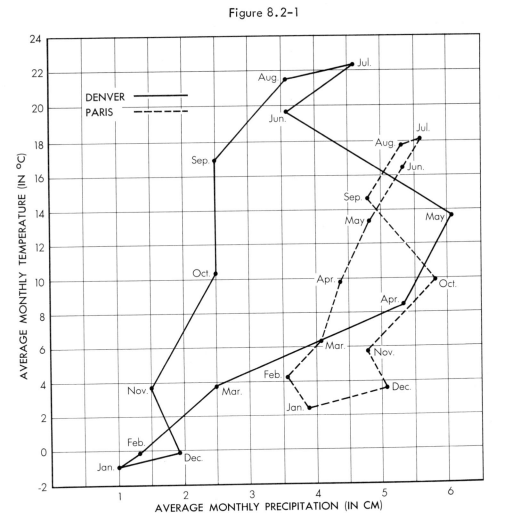

Collect data from other pairs of biomes or use some of the data in this exercise, and plot the data in the manner shown in Figure 8.2-1. Discuss the relationship between differences in the graphs and differences in the biomes represented by the graphs.

EXERCISE 8.3

EFFECTS OF FIRE ON BIOMES

INTRODUCTION

"It is a difficult thing, sir, to describe, but I will do my best.... We were sound asleep one night in a cabin about a hundred miles from this, when, about two hours before day, the snorting of the horses and lowing of the cattle which I had ranging in the woods suddenly awakened us....

"On going to the back of the house, I plainly heard the crackling made by the burning brushwood, and saw the flames coming towards us in a far extended line. I ran to the house, told my wife to dress herself and the child as quick as possible, and take the little money we had, while I managed to catch and saddle the two best horses....

"Intent on striving to the utmost to preserve our lives, I thought of a large lake some miles off, which might possibly check the flames.

"The heat of the smoke was insufferable, and sheets of blazing fire flew over us in a manner beyond belief. We reached the shores, however, coasted the lake for a while, and got round to the lee side. There we gave up our horses, which we never saw again. Down among the rushes we plunged by the edge of the water, and laid ourselves flat, to wait the chance of escaping from being burnt or devoured. The water refreshed us, and we enjoyed the coolness.

"On went the fire, rushing and crashing through the woods. Such a sight may we never see! The heavens, themselves, I thought were frightened, for all above us was a red glare mixed with clouds of smoke, rolling and sweeping away....

"The day passed on and we became hungry. Many wild beasts came plunging into the water beside us, and others swam across to our side and stood still. Although faint and weary, I managed to shoot a Porcupine, and we all tasted its flesh. The night passed, I cannot tell you how. Smouldering fires covered the ground, and trees stood like pillars of fire, or fell across each other. The stifling and sickening smoke still rushed over us, and the burnt cinders and ashes fell thick about us. How we got through that night I really cannot tell, for about some of it I remember nothing....

"Towards morning, although the heat did not abate, the smoke became less, and blasts of fresh air sometimes made their way to us. When morning came, all was calm, but a dismal smoke still filled the air, and the smell seemed worse than ever....

"By this time the blaze of the fire was beyond our sight, although the ground was still burning in many places, and it was dangerous to go among the burnt trees. After resting awhile, and trimming ourselves, we prepared to commence our march. Taking up the child, I led the way over the hot ground and rocks; and, after two weary days and nights, during which we shifted in the best manner we could, we at last reached the 'hard woods' which had been free of the fire. Soon after we came to a house, where we were kindly treated for a while."

—from the Journal of John James Audubon

The above quotation is from an account of a forest fire that occurred in Kentucky about 150 years ago. Evidence such as this from many observers, as well as scars on the landscape itself, indicates that large fires have long been commonplace occurrences. Fires may be caused by man deliberately or accidentally; but fires also start from natural causes—lightning and volcanoes, for example. By whatever means they may begin, fires have many effects upon the organisms in their paths.

Though all organisms are affected by fire, the most immediate and easily observed effects are seen in the vegetation. Repeated fires can affect the vegetation to such an extent that they may be an important factor in modifying the characteristics of biomes.

PURPOSE

In this exercise, evidence concerning the effects of fires on three kinds of communities is presented in pictures. This evidence will be studied in relation to a general question: How does fire affect vegetation in different biomes?

PROCEDURE

As you read each of the following sections, base your answers to the questions upon study of the pictures.

A. Fire in a Middle-Latitude Grassland

Figures 8.3-1 to 8.3-4 picture a situation that is often found in the southern part of the North American grassland. Study Figures 8.3-1 and 8.3-2. Which population is increasing in size?(1) Roots of the shrub (mesquite) have been found in mine shafts many meters below the surface of the soil. What competitive advantage might this give mesquite over grasses?(2) If the trend shown in Figures 8.3-1 and 8.3-2 continued, what kind of community might eventually occupy this region?(3)

Figure 8.3-1

Figure 8.3-2

Now refer to Figures 8.3-3 and 8.3-4. In these figures the plant parts shown in white at or below ground level represent unharmed tissue. Do both kinds of plant survive a fire?(4) Which kind of plant has lost the most growing tissue?(5) Grasses usually reach maturity and produce seeds in one or two years; mesquite usually requires four to ten years. Which kind has lost most in terms of growing time?(6) In Figure 8.3-4, which kind of plant occupies most of the land?(7) Using the information you now have, how do you explain the result shown in Figure 8.3-4.(8) What might you expect this area to look like four or five years after a fire?(9)

Now you can make a generalization on the effect of fire in this community. What would be the appearance of the landscape if fires occurred every few years?(10) Describe the probable landscape if fires did not occur at all.(11) What environmental factor seems to be necessary for maintaining grassland in this region?(12)

Figure 8.3-3

Figure 8.3-4

B. Fire in a Forest of the Great Lakes Region

The Great Lakes region of North America is an <u>ecotone</u>—a region of transition, a region in which there is a gradual change from one biome to another. The natural forests of the Great Lakes region show a mixture of the characteristics of the middle-latitude deciduous-forest biome and the taiga biome (Figure 8.3-5). But early in the settlement of the region, man brought about a great change in the landscape (Figure 8.3-6). Previously fires had apparently been rare in this region, but they became more frequent after this change. What factors might have brought about the increase in the number of fires ?(13) If fire did not occur, what might the area shown in Figure 8.3-6 look like

Figure 8.3-5

Figure 8.3-6

in later years ?(14) What characteristic of jack pines gives that species a competitive advantage whenever there is a fire (Figures 8.3-7 and 8.3-8)?(15) Describe the area shown in Figure 8.3-8 ten to twenty years later.(16)

Jack pines produce cones in eight to ten years but do not live to a very great age. The seedlings do not thrive in shade. Suppose no further fires occurred for two hundred years. What changes in appearance might take place in this area during that period (see discussion of succession in text, page 243)?(17) Suppose fires occurred about once every twenty years. What might the area look like at the end of two hundred years?(18)

Figure 8.3-7

Figure 8.3-8

C. Fire in a Forest of the Southeastern United States

In the southeastern United States there are extensive forests in which longleaf pine is almost the only large tree, though seedlings and saplings of deciduous trees often occur. Until they are from three to seven years old, young longleaf pines look somewhat like clumps of grass (Figure 8.3-9). While in this "grass stage" the young trees develop deep roots in which a reserve supply of food is stored.

Fires in these forests generally are confined to the ground, where they burn grasses and the sparse growth of deciduous shrubs and saplings. Why do you think fires in this kind of forest are confined to the ground?(19) What is the effect of fire on longleaf pines in the "grass stage"?(20) What is the effect on the deciduous plants?(21) Which plants have a competitive advantage after a fire?(22) After the "grass stage" the longleaf pines grow rapidly in height and develop a thick bark that resists scorching. What is the effect of ground fires

Figure 8.3-9

Figure 8.3-10

Figure 8.3-11

Figure 8.3-12

at this stage in the development of the pines (Figure 8.3-11)?(23) Which plants have a competitive advantage when fires do not occur (Figure 8.3-12)?(24) What combination of factors seems to maintain a longleaf-pine forest within the deciduous-forest biome?(25)

DISCUSSION

Knowledge of the ecological effect of fire on biomes can be useful to man. If you were interested in raising cattle in the region described in Procedure A, would occasional fires be an advantage or a disadvantage? Why?(26) If you were interested in growing deciduous trees in the region described in Procedure B, would fire be an advantage or a disadvantage? Why?(27) If you were interested in maintaining a longleaf-pine forest to obtain turpentine (a product of longleaf pines), would ground fires be an advantage or a disadvantage? Give reasons for your answer.(28)

Suppose that you wanted bobwhites (game birds that nest on the ground) in your turpentine forest. What effect might this have on your management of the forest?(29) What things must ecologists know before deciding whether to recommend fire as a method of management to a land owner?(30)

FOR FURTHER INVESTIGATION

This exercise is based on an article by Charles F. Cooper, "The Ecology of Fire," in Scientific American, April, 1961. The article also discusses fire in Douglas-fir forests of the Northwest and in ponderosa-pine forests of the Southwest. Other information may be found in books on forestry, range management, and plant ecology. Prepare a comprehensive report on fire as a factor in land ecosystems.

CHAPTER 9

Patterns of Life in the Water

EXERCISE 9.1

FIELD AND LABORATORY STUDY OF A POND COMMUNITY

INTRODUCTION

Ponds have many advantages for the study of aquatic communities. They furnish a variety of habitats, have many relationships with the surrounding land, and are available to schools in many parts of the country. Natural ponds usually show the most complex relationships, but man-made ponds are both simpler to study and most widely distributed geographically. If your class has studied a land community (Exercise 3.1), that experience ought to increase your ability to investigate a pond.

MATERIALS AND EQUIPMENT

A. Field Work (for the entire class)

1. Glass-marking crayons, 4
2. Jars (wide-mouth, screw-top), 1 liter, 2
3. Jars (wide-mouth, screw-top), 4 liter, 7
4. Jars (wide-mouth, screw-top), 0.5 to 1 liter, 13
5. Plankton net

6. Can (No. 3), lid smoothly removed
7. Sieve (No. 8 mesh)
8. Forceps, 2
9. Plastic bags, 6
10. Rubber bands, 6
11. Plant-grappling bar
12. Trowels
13. Dip net
14. Wire-cloth seine
15. Boat (optional)
16. Waders or swim suits (optional)

B. Laboratory Work
  (by teams: quantities depend upon size of teams)

1. Medicine droppers
2. Monocular microscopes
3. Stereomicroscopes
4. Hand lenses
5. Microscope slides
6. Cover slips
7. Forceps
8. Scalpels
9. Finger bowls or porcelain pans
10. Reference books (Some good ones are listed at the end of this exercise.)
   Figure 9.1-1 shows some collecting equipment that can be made in the school.

PROCEDURE

A. Field Work

Four teams are needed: one to study plankton organisms, a second to study the organisms on the bottom of the pond, a third to study the larger water plants, and a fourth to study the larger animals of the pond.

All teams must be careful not to disturb the environment more than is absolutely necessary. This should present no problem for Team 1; it will be more difficult for the others. Remember that only a few specimens of each species are needed.

Team 1: Before leaving the laboratory use a glass-marking crayon to label two wide-mouth, 1-liter jars as follows: Surface-water Zone, and Deep-water Zone.

Take the jars and the plankton net to the collecting boat or to a place on shore from which the plankton net can be cast into the water. Fill each jar about one-third full of clear pond water.

Cast the net into the water and pull it through the open-water zone. If the net is pulled rapidly, it will stay near the surface of the water. Pull the net through the water several times; then raise it. You may be able to see a number of tiny organisms in the bottle. Untie the bottle from the net and empty its contents into the jar labeled <u>Surface-water Zone</u>. Repeat the surface collecting three or four times.

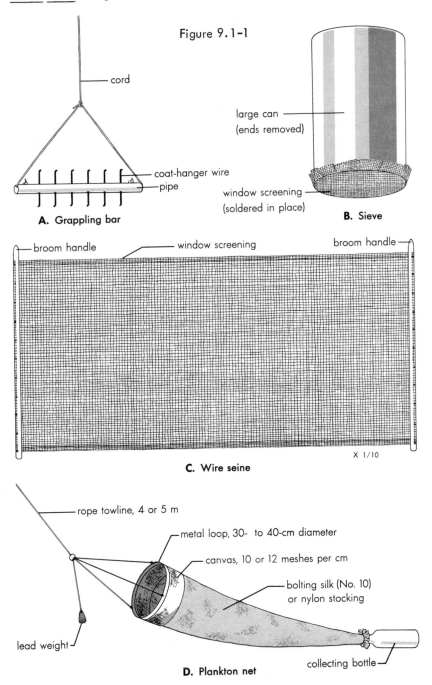

Figure 9.1-1

cord

large can
(ends removed)

coat-hanger wire
pipe

window screening
(soldered in place)

A. Grappling bar

B. Sieve

broom handle   window screening   broom handle

X 1/10

C. Wire seine

rope towline, 4 or 5 m

metal loop, 30- to 40-cm diameter

canvas, 10 or 12 meshes per cm

bolting silk (No. 10)
or nylon stocking

lead weight

collecting bottle

D. Plankton net

To collect organisms in the deep-water zone, allow the net to sink to the desired depth and then pull slowly. Place collections from the deep water in the second jar. If you must wait for other teams after finishing your work, put the jars in the shade until you are ready to leave. If jars are left in sunlight, the temperature in them will rise and many of the organisms will die.

Team 2: Before leaving the laboratory select three 0.5-liter jars and three 4-liter jars. Use a glass-marking crayon to label one of each size as follows: <u>Bottom</u>: <u>Emergent-plant Zone</u>, <u>Bottom</u>: <u>Submerged-plant Zone</u>, and <u>Bottom</u>: <u>Open-water Zone</u>.

Take the jars, a sieve, and a can to the pond. Fill each jar about one-half full of clear pond water. With the can, scoop up some mud from among the emergent plants. Dump this mud into the sieve; then shake the sieve in the water until the mud is washed out. Remove dead leaves and sticks by hand. Pick out whatever organisms you find, and put these into the appropriate 4-liter jar. Then carefully scoop up a small sample of the mud and place it in the appropriate 0.5-liter jar.

Repeat this procedure in the other two zones.

Team 3: Before leaving the laboratory use a glass-marking crayon to label six large plastic bags. Label two <u>Emergent Plants</u>, two <u>Floating Plants</u>, and two <u>Submerged Plants</u>.

Take the labeled bags, six rubber bands (to fasten the bags shut), a trowel, and a plant-grappling bar to the pond.

In each of the three plant zones collect a specimen of each kind of plant found. Whenever possible the specimen should consist of a whole plant. Roots and underground stems are often important for identification. If the whole plant is too large, collect leaves and flowers or fruits. Put the plants of each zone into separate plastic bags.

Team 4: Before leaving the laboratory select ten jars varying from 0.5 to 1 liter in capacity. Using a glass-marking crayon, label five of the jars <u>Emergent-and-floating-plant Zone</u>, and the other five <u>Submerged-plant Zone</u>. Select four 4-liter jars, and label two of them <u>Emergent-plant Zone</u> and the other two <u>Submerged-plant Zone</u>.

Take all the jars, a dip net, and a seine to the pond. One member of the team should be assigned to record animals seen but not collected. This should include all animals that seem to be a part of the pond community, whether they live <u>in</u> the pond or not. (For examples, see text Figures 9.7 and 9.8.)

Use the dip net or the seine to collect the larger animals—for example, fish, crayfish, some of the larger insect larvae, turtles, and snakes. The smaller ones will go through the holes in the collecting equipment.

First catch the animals in the emergent-plant zone, near the edge of the pond. Put them into the labeled jars. Insect larvae may be placed together in the same jar, with some sticks and leaves for shelter. Only a few fish should be placed together in one jar. Use the smaller jars for specimens that might injure one another. Be careful in handling animals; some of the insects, as well as larger animals, can inflict painful bites.

In a similar manner collect organisms in the submerged-plant zone. Do not collect more than one or two specimens of each of the larger animals.

Upon returning to the laboratory, place the jars in the lower part of a refrigerator or in some other cool place. This will make the organisms less active and will help to keep the large ones from eating the smaller ones.

B. Laboratory Work

Each team will study its own collections and report its findings to the class.

The organisms must be identified. First, use the illustrations at the end of this exercise; then use whatever other guides are available in your classroom. The key in Exercise 4.3 should be helpful in identifying insects. Most organisms should be identifiable to the phylum level; many will be identifiable to lower levels. Specific identification is not necessary.

This exercise is not designed as a quantitative study, but some idea of the relative abundance of different kinds of organisms will be useful in forming an understanding of the community. Whenever possible, record your observations with respect to numbers of identified organisms in the pond community. Listing kinds of organisms in order of abundance might be one method.

Team 1: The plankton organisms are mostly microscopic; use medicine droppers for handling the organisms, slides and cover slips for mounting them, and monocular microscopes for observing them.

Team 2: Hand lenses or stereomicroscopes can be used to observe organisms washed from the mud. The organisms will be more easily seen if placed in a finger bowl over a piece of white paper, or in a white porcelain pan. Handle the larger organisms with forceps, the smaller ones with medicine droppers. Samples of mud in the small jars should be examined by placing a small bit of the mud in a drop of water on a microscope slide under a monocular microscope.

Teams 3 and 4: Hand lenses, forceps, and finger bowls (or porcelain pans) are the only tools needed for examining the collections of these two teams.

SUMMARY

When all the data have been exchanged between teams, each student should write a description of the pond community, attempting to relate all the data.

Consider the niches of the various organisms. To begin with, you can assume that macroscopic green plants are producers. Microscopic organisms are more difficult to decide about: some consumers may be

colored green by algae they have eaten, and the green of some producers may be obscured by other pigments. First-order and higher-order
consumers can sometimes be separated on the basis of their structure—
predators, for example, are clearly higher-order consumers. Can
you see any relationship between the size of organisms and their relative abundance? If so, what is the relationship, and how can you explain it? Finally, consider the relationships between the pond and
surrounding communities on the land. How does energy received from
the sun flow from the pond community into land communities? Is there
any reverse flow of energy? If so, how does it occur?

GUIDE TO SOME COMMON FRESHWATER ORGANISMS

Figure 9.1-2. Microscopic Organisms

AMEBOIDS: Pseudopods present. (a) Actinosphaerium (spherical, with
stiff radiating projections); (b) Amoeba (pseudopods, no shell); (c) Arcella
(shell present)

CILIATES: Cilia on all or part of body. No flagella. Some have chlo-
rophyll.   (a) Colpoda; (b) Vorticella; (c) Paramecium; (d) Stentor;
(e) Euglena intermedia; (f) Euglena intermedia (contracted); (g) Euglena
ascus; (h) Spirostomum; (i) Tetrahymena; (j) Didinium; (k) Prorodon

UNICELLULAR FLAGELLATES: One or more long whiplike flagella.
With or without cilia. Colorless.   (a) Spironomas; (b) Collodictyon;
(c) Colponema

COLONIAL FLAGELLATES: (a) Codonodendron; (b) Volvox (constantly
rotating); (c) Pandorina

ROTIFERS: Bands of cilia near mouth.   Colorless.   (a) Synchaeta;
(b) Asplanchna; (c) Philodina; (d) Keratella

SIMPLE BLUE-GREEN ALGAE: Dark green or blue-green clusters in gelatinous sheaths. (a) Chroococcus; (b) Gloeocapsa

FILAMENTOUS BLUE-GREEN ALGAE: (a) Gloeotrichia (in gelatinous
sheaths that often run together); (b) Rivularia (tapering filaments in
sheaths); (c) Nostoc (firm sheaths); (d) Anabaena (cells of different sizes,
in chains); (e) Lyngbya (thin sheaths); (f) Oscillatoria (no sheaths)

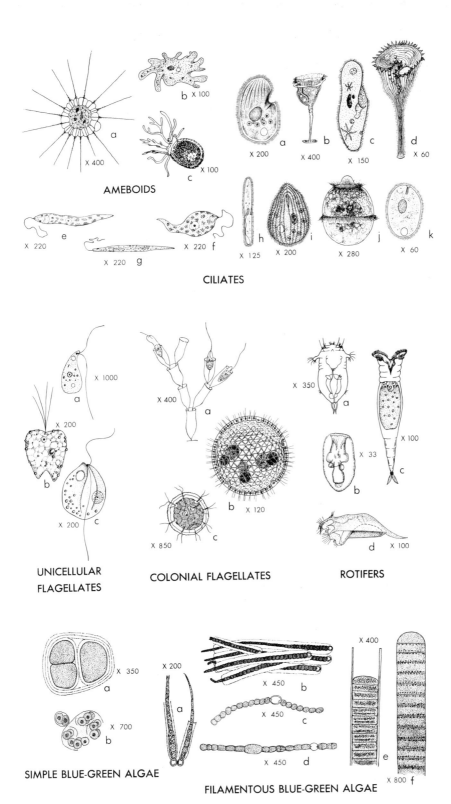

AMEBOIDS

CILIATES

UNICELLULAR FLAGELLATES

COLONIAL FLAGELLATES

ROTIFERS

SIMPLE BLUE-GREEN ALGAE

FILAMENTOUS BLUE-GREEN ALGAE

Figure 9.1-2

Figure 9.1-3. More Microscopic Organisms

SINGLE-CELLED GREEN ALGAE: (a) Ankistrodesmus; (b) Protococcus;
(c) Euastrum; (d) Cosmarium; (e) Chlorella; (f) Staurastrum; (g) Selenas-
trum; (h) Xanthidium; (i) Treubaria; (j) Micrasterias

COLONIAL GREEN ALGAE: (a) Sphaerocystis; (b) Dictyocphaerium;
(c) Hydrodictyon; (d) Coleochaete; (e) Scenedesmus; (f) Pediastrum;
(g) Sorastrum; (h) Chaetophora

FILAMENTOUS GREEN ALGAE: (a) Mougeotia; (b) Oedogonium; (c) Ulo-
thrix; (d) Zygnemopsis; (e) Desmidium; (f) Microspora; (g) Spirogyra

GOLDEN ALGAE (DIATOMS):   Unicellular or loosely colonial algae.
Walls of silica, consisting of two overlapping halves that fit together like
the halves of a petri dish. (a) Stephanodiscus; (b) Navicula gracilis;
(c) Navicula rhynocephala; (d) Diatoma elongatum; (e) Diatoma hiemale
(girdle view); (f) Diatoma hiemale (valve view); (g) Cymbella; (h) Pin-
nularia; (i) Asterionella; (j) Tabellaria

OTHER GOLDEN ALGAE: (a) Monocilia (branching filaments); (b) Leu-
venia (ovoid or pear-shaped, solitary); (c) Tribone (cells cylindrical,
joined end-to-end); (d) Chrysidiastrum (amoeboid cells joined in free-
floating colonies); (e) Botrycoccus (compact, irregular, gelatinous, semi-
opaque masses)

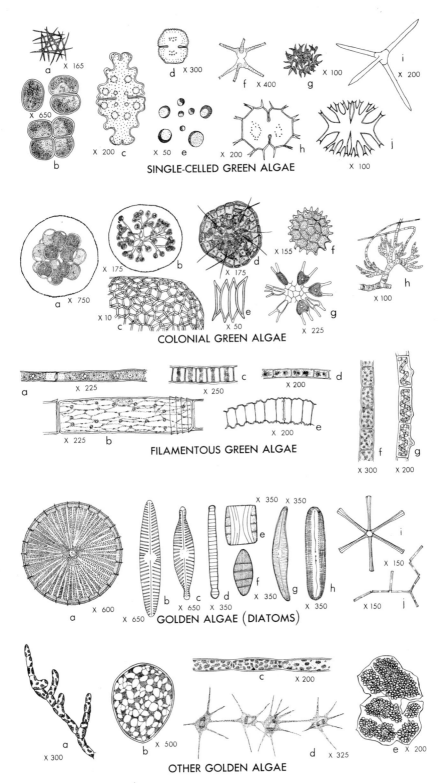

SINGLE-CELLED GREEN ALGAE

COLONIAL GREEN ALGAE

FILAMENTOUS GREEN ALGAE

GOLDEN ALGAE (DIATOMS)

OTHER GOLDEN ALGAE

Figure 9.1-3

Figure 9.1-4. Macroscopic Plants

MOSSES: Submerged or emergent. Erect, feathery stalks.

LIVERWORTS: Flat and ribbon-like. Rootlike structures on undersurface.
Above: Ricciocarpus; below: Riccia

SMARTWEEDS: Emergent. Small flowers in dense clusters.

SEDGES: Emergent. Stems triangular in cross section.

ARROWHEAD: Emergent. Leaves shaped like broad spearheads.

CHARA: Submerged. An alga with whorled branches.

BUR REED: Emergent. Long grasslike leaves may be submerged.

DUCKWEED: Floating. Roots hang in water. Frequently forms extensive mats.

COONTAIL: Submerged. Leaves stiff, hairlike, branched in whorls.
No roots.

RUSHES: Emergent.   Leaves grasslike.   Clusters of small fruiting
structures.

CATTAILS: Emergent.   Tall grasslike leaves.   Long brown fruiting
structures.

TAPE GRASS: Submerged. Leaves ribbon-like. Plant rooted to bottom.
Flowers break off and float to surface.

MARE'S-TAIL: Submerged. Leaves small, simple, in whorls.

PICKERELWEED: Emergent.   Leaves heart-shaped.   Flowers (purple)
tightly clustered on slender spike.

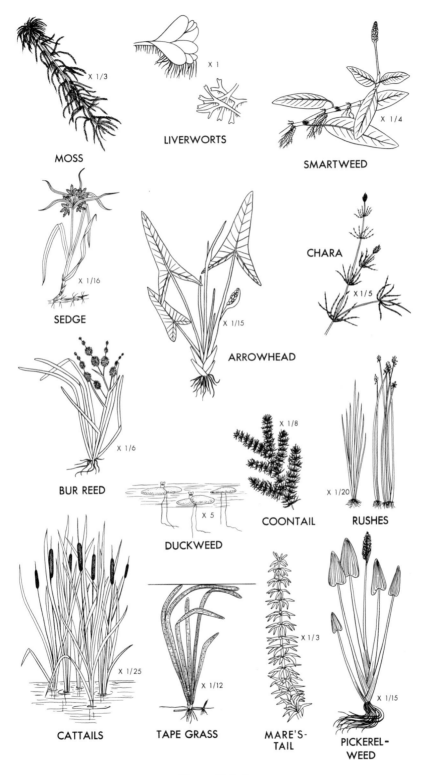

MOSS X 1/3

LIVERWORTS X 1

SMARTWEED X 1/4

SEDGE X 1/16

ARROWHEAD X 1/15

CHARA X 1/5

BUR REED X 1/6

DUCKWEED X 5

COONTAIL X 1/8

RUSHES X 1/20

CATTAILS X 1/25

TAPE GRASS X 1/12

MARE'S-TAIL X 1/3

PICKEREL-WEED X 1/15

Figure 9.1-4

Figure 9.1-5. Arthropods

COPEPODS: Small crustaceans with several hairlike spines at tip of abdomen. Body elongated. (a) Halicyclops; (b) Diaptomus (a larval stage); (c) Diaptomus (adult)

OSTRACODS: Small crustaceans with no spines. Body covered by a jointed carapace, somewhat resembling small clam shells.

CLADOCERANS: Small crustaceans with no spines at tip of abdomen or a single spine only. Body short. (a) Daphnia (female); (b) Daphnia (male); (c) Ceriodaphnia

OPOSSUM SHRIMP: Carapace covers most of thorax. All limbs of thorax similar. Eyes stalked. No gills in most species.

WATER MITE: Body not jointed. Eight jointed legs.

SCUD: No carapace. Limbs of thorax different from each other. Eyes not stalked. Body compressed laterally. Gills present.

CRAYFISHES: Carapace not jointed. Pincers on anterior legs.

MAYFLIES: Adults usually have clear, narrow wings. Wings usually held vertically when at rest. Larvae aquatic. Adults and larvae with three "hairs" at end of abdomen.

CADDIS FLIES: Adults have clear, broad wings. Larvae aquatic, wingless, and usually live within a case composed of pebbles or debris.

DRAGONFLIES: Adults large, usually clear-winged. Wings extend horizontally when at rest. Large eyes. Larvae aquatic. End of abdomen without "hairs."

MOSQUITOES: Adult has only one pair of wings. Larvae small, without legs, float at surface of water, and breathe air through tubes.

BEETLES: Adult has a pair of hard wing covers, not overlapping. Larvae wingless. Example: water scavanger

BUGS: Adult has a pair of overlapping wings. No hard wing covers. Larvae wingless. Example: giant water bug

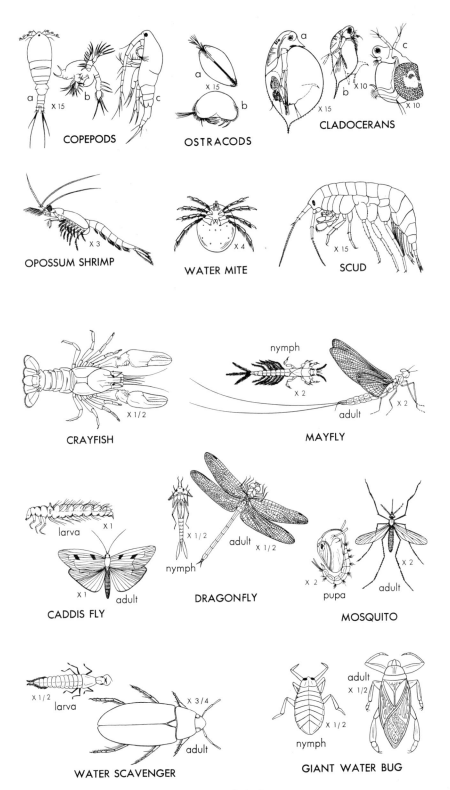

COPEPODS

OSTRACODS

CLADOCERANS

OPOSSUM SHRIMP

WATER MITE

SCUD

CRAYFISH

MAYFLY

nymph

adult

CADDIS FLY

larva

adult

DRAGONFLY

nymph

adult

MOSQUITO

pupa

adult

WATER SCAVENGER

larva

adult

GIANT WATER BUG

nymph

adult

Figure 9.1-5

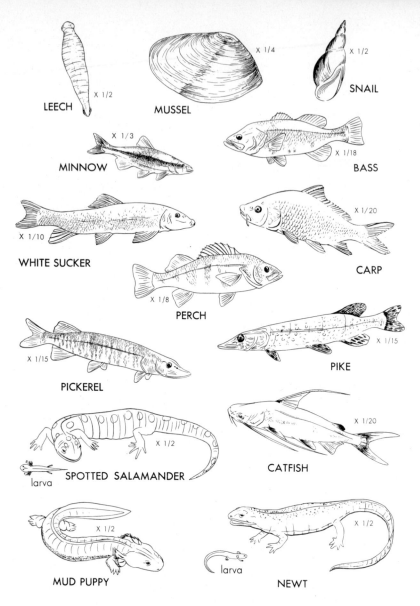

Figure 9.1-6. Annelids, Mollusks, and Vertebrates

LEECHES: Segmented worms with flat bodies. Usually with suction disks at both ends.

MUSSELS: Mollusks with shells in two parts, hinged together.

SNAILS: Mollusks with shells in one part, usually coiled.

BONY FISHES: Vertebrates with paired fins. Gills concealed beneath a single covering, the operculum. Examples: minnow, bass, white sucker, carp, perch, pickerel, pike, catfish

SALAMANDERS: Tailed amphibians with paired appendages and toes. Gills (when present) without a covering. Examples: spotted salamander, mud puppy, newt

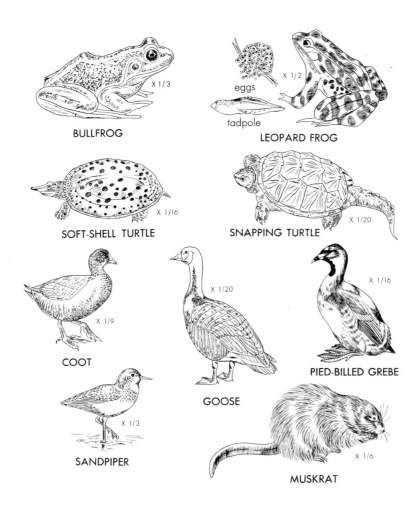

eggs

tadpole

BULLFROG

LEOPARD FROG

SOFT-SHELL TURTLE

SNAPPING TURTLE

COOT

GOOSE

PIED-BILLED GREBE

SANDPIPER

MUSKRAT

Figure 9.1-7. More Vertebrates

FROGS: Tailless amphibians. Posterior pair of appendages longer than anterior pair; used in leaping. Examples: bullfrog, leopard frog

TURTLES: Reptiles with a broad, flat form. Usually with an armor of bony plates. Examples: soft-shell turtle, snapping turtle

BIRDS: Vertebrates with feathers. Examples: coot, goose, pied-billed grebe, sandpiper (Birds of freshwater habitats are of many kinds; see text for illustrations of ducks, herons, plovers, and gulls.)

MAMMALS: Vertebrates with hair. Feed young with milk. Example: muskrat (See text for illustrations of other mammals important in freshwater habitats—mink, beaver, moose, etc.)

REFERENCES

CONANT, R. Field Guide to Reptiles and Amphibians. Boston: Houghton Mifflin Company, 1958.

EDDY, S. How to Know the Freshwater Fishes. Dubuque, Iowa: William C. Brown Co., 1957.

JAHN, T. L., and F. F. JAHN. How to Know the Protozoa. Dubuque, Iowa: William C. Brown Co., 1950.

MORGAN, A. Field Book of Ponds and Streams. New York: G. P. Putnam's Sons, 1930.

MUENSCHER, W. Aquatic Plants of the United States. Ithaca, N. Y.: Comstock Publishing Associates, Inc., 1944.

NEEDHAM, P. Guide to the Study of Freshwater Biology. San Francisco: Holden-Day, Inc., 1962.

PENNAK, R. W. Fresh-water Invertebrates of the United States. New York: The Ronald Press Co., 1953.

WARD, H. B., and G. C. WHIPPLE. Fresh-water Biology, editor, W. T. EDMONDSON. 2nd ed. New York: John Wiley and Sons, Inc., 1959.

See also references listed at the ends of Chapters 4, 5, and 6 in the text.

FOR FURTHER INVESTIGATION

1. The study of the pond ecosystem is more difficult than the study of the pond community. It requires measurement of abiotic factors such as temperature at different depths, distance to which light penetrates, amount of dissolved oxygen, etc. If you are interested in extending your study to the whole pond ecosystem, you will find descriptions of limnological methods in Needham, Guide to the Study of Freshwater Biology (listed above).

2. Compare the organisms found in the stream that leads out of your pond with the organisms in the pond. Can you account for differences between the pond and stream biotas? How?

EXERCISE 9.2

SUCCESSION IN FRESHWATER COMMUNITIES:
A LABORATORY STUDY

INTRODUCTION AND PURPOSE

Ecological succession (see text pages 64-66) occurs in all kinds of communities. In most communities it is difficult to study because it occurs so slowly. In some freshwater communities, however, it may take place rather rapidly. Furthermore, it is possible to set up fresh-water communities on a small scale in the laboratory. Thus, within the laboratory, we can combine a study of the kinds of organisms that occur in fresh water with a study of ecological succession.

MATERIALS AND EQUIPMENT

1. Wide-mouth jars (about 1-liter capacity), 3
2. Glass-marking crayon
3. Debris from ditch or pond
4. Sterilized pond water, about 6 liters
5. Aquarium gravel
6. Pond organisms (e.g., algae, small crayfish, snails, water beetles, duckweed, etc.)
7. Glass plates (somewhat larger than mouths of jars), 3
8. Distilled water, about 1 liter
9. Microscope slides
10. Cover slips
11. Medicine droppers
12. Monocular microscopes
13. Stereomicroscopes or hand lenses

PROCEDURE

With the glass-marking crayon, label the three wide-mouth jars A, B, and C. On each jar place a water-level mark two-thirds of the distance from bottom to top. Also label each jar with the date. In Jar A place an assortment of twigs, dead leaves, and small stones ob-tained from a ditch, puddle, or pond that has dried up; then gently add sterilized pond water until it reaches the marked level. Into Jar B pour sterilized pond water to the marked level. In Jar C place enough aquarium gravel to form a layer about 2 cm deep; then add about 2 liters of unsterilized pond water and a number of small organisms collected from a pond.

Cover each jar with a glass plate.   Each cover should be held up on one side by a matchstick or piece of cardboard so that air can circulate in and out of the jars. Place the jars in a location where they will receive plenty of strong light—but not direct sunlight. Maintain the water level in all jars throughout the study by adding distilled water, as needed.

Examine the jars daily during the next three or four days. Watch for any appearance of cloudiness in the water and for scum on the surface of the water or on the objects in it. All observations should be recorded in your data book with the date and letter of the jar.

When a scum appears, examine a drop of it under the monocular microscope. If organisms are observed, make sketches of them in your data book. Remember to record the date and letter of the jar from which the scum came.

After the first few days examine the jars weekly for five or six weeks. Examine water samples under the monocular microscope. Stereomicroscopes or hand lenses should be used to examine small macroscopic organisms. At each examination list the kinds of organisms, the date, and the jar letter. Use the illustrations in Exercise 9.1 and the references given there to aid in identification of organisms.

STUDYING THE DATA

Arrange the data in a chart, listing the three jars vertically and the dates of observation horizontally. In discussing the data, elapsed time should be expressed in number of days rather than by dates. How soon were organisms noted in Jar A?(1) Where did these organisms probably come from?(2) How soon were organisms noted in Jar B?(3) Where did these organisms probably come from?(4) After Jar C was set up, what organisms were first noted in it?(5) Where did these organisms come from?(6) Did any organisms originally in Jar C disappear during the time of study? If so, what were they, and how can you account for their disappearance?(7) Did any organisms that appeared in Jars A and B later disappear? If so, what were they, and how can you account for their disappearance?(8)

CONCLUSIONS

Which jar most closely resembles a permanent pond?(9) Which jar most closely resembles a temporary pond or puddle?(10)

Has ecological succession occurred? If so, in which jar was it

most evident?(11)   According to your results, in which kind of natural freshwater community would succession be likely to occur most
rapidly?(12)

EXERCISE 9.3

EFFECTS OF SALINITY ON LIVING ORGANISMS

INTRODUCTION

Salinity is an abiotic environmental factor that is of great importance to aquatic organisms.   The salinity of natural waters varies
greatly; it is usually least in headwater streams, greatest in lakes that
have no outlets.   And tolerance to salinity varies widely among different species of organisms.
Sodium chloride is by far the most abundant salt in natural waters;
it is used in this exercise to make solutions of differing salinities. Although oceanographers express salinities as parts of salt per thousand
parts of water (by weight), we shall express salinities as percentages
(by weight).

PURPOSE

In this exercise the effects of solutions of various salinities on different kinds of small aquatic organisms are determined and compared.

MATERIALS AND EQUIPMENT (per pair of students)

1. Medicine dropper
2. Microscope slides
3. Cover slips
4. Living specimens of small aquatic organisms
5. Monocular microscope
6. Paper towels
7. Watch or clock
8. Sodium chloride solutions (1%, 3%, and 5%)
9. Distilled water or tap water

PROCEDURE

Using a medicine dropper, place a drop of water containing the organism you are to study on a slide; add a cover slip. Observe the organism for a few minutes to determine its normal appearance and actions. You may slow down the movement of some kinds of protists by adding a few wisps of cotton or a bit of shredded paper towel. In your data book record the name of the organism.

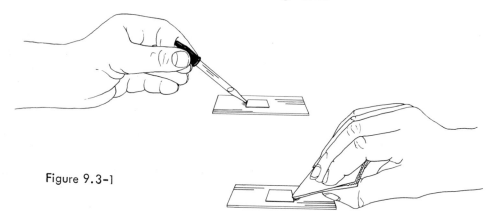

Figure 9.3-1

At one edge of the cover slip, add a drop of 1-percent salt solution. Record the time. Draw the salt solution under the cover slip by placing a small piece of paper towel (or other absorbent paper) at the opposite edge of the slip, as shown in Figure 9.3-1. As the salt solution moves under the cover slip, observe carefully the reaction of the organism. Notice changes in movements and changes in shape. Record in your data book the concentration (percentage) of the solution, the reactions observed, and the time at which the reactions began. Continue observations until no new responses are observed. Replace the salt solution with tap water in the same way in which you added the salt solution. Record the time required for recovery, if recovery occurs.

Repeat the procedure, using 3-percent salt solution. Observe and record results. Repeat the procedure using 5-percent salt solution.

STUDYING THE DATA

First, each student should consider his own data. Did the kind of reaction differ with different salt solutions? Try to explain any differences.(1) If the organism failed to recover, how can you explain this?(2) What kind of aquatic habitat do you think the organism normally inhabits?(3)

Next, all students who worked with the same organism should discuss their results together. Variability among different individuals of a species in response to the same environmental factor is common in biology. At each salinity, what were the maximum and the minimum reaction times observed for the organism? What was the average?(4) What were the maximum and minimum recovery times at each salinity? What was the average?(5) Did all the individuals react in the same way? If not, what differences were noted?(6)

Finally, comparisons should be made between different organisms. Data may be summarized on the chalkboard in a table like the following:

ORGANISM	SALINITY	KIND OF RESPONSE	AVERAGE TIME	RECOVERY	AVERAGE TIME

Which organism was most tolerant to change in salt concentration?(7) Which organism was least tolerant?(8) Is there any relationship between speed of response and failure to recover? If so, try to explain the relationship. (9) On the basis of these data, which of the organisms would you expect to find most widely distributed in the waters of the world?(10) What other environmental factors (for which you do not have data) might modify your answer to the previous question?(11)

FOR FURTHER INVESTIGATION

Many larger animals regularly move from marine water into fresh water (or vice versa), apparently without harm; others cannot tolerate much change in salinity. You can devise means of testing the salinity tolerance of aquatic animals such as crayfish, goldfish, guppies, or snails, using the principles employed in this exercise. CAUTION: It is not necessary to kill the animals used in your experiments. Whenever they show signs of discomfort, return them to a less concentrated salinity. How would you proceed if you were using a marine species (for example, a clam worm) in your experiments?

EXERCISE 9.4

EXPLORING MARINE COMMUNITIES

INTRODUCTION

The oceans are vast. Of all ecosystems, marine environments are the least explored and their living inhabitants the least known. To penetrate the depths and search the wide reaches of the seas, expensive vessels with elaborate equipment are necessary. But the edges of the sea are more accessible. Littoral communities can provide many indications of the richness and diversity of marine life.

PURPOSE

This exercise is intended for schools that are located near the ocean. It provides guidance for exploring the marine communities that lie close to the shore.

MATERIALS AND EQUIPMENT (approximate quantities for a class)

1. Plankton net
2. Boat (optional)
3. Petri dishes, 8
4. Stereomicroscopes, 2
5. Reference books (Some suggested titles are listed at the end of this exercise.)
6. Medicine droppers, 8
7. Microscope slides, 8
8. Cover slips, 16
9. Monocular microscopes, 2
10. Jars, 50- to 200-ml capacity, 24
11. Graduated cylinder, 100 ml
12. Formaldehyde solution (40%), 0.5 liters
13. Plastic buckets, at least two per habitat
14. Glass-marking crayon
15. Plastic beakers or glass jars, 500- to 1000-ml capacity, 20
16. Shovels, 4
17. Sieves, 4
18. Rakes, 2

19. Heavy knives or chisels, 8
20. Face masks (optional), 2
21. Wire-cloth seines (see Figure 9.1-1), 2
22. Seine   about 1.2 m X 6 m

PROCEDURE

Divide the class into teams, each to investigate the organisms of one part of the shallow ocean waters near the shore.

Before beginning the collecting of marine organisms, each student should become familiar with the following precautions:

1. Always work in pairs—never alone.
2. Beware of slipping on alga-covered rocks. One of the gravest dangers is slipping and falling on a jar or knife. Be extremely careful with these items.
3. Never go barefoot. The most dangerous "species" normally encountered are broken bottles, rusty cans, boards with nails, and fishhooks.
4. Collect unfamiliar animals with caution. Bites and stings are painful and may be dangerous.
5. Do not put your hand into a dark cave or deep hole among rocks and expect to get it back in the same condition.
6. Do not dive into the water with a face mask on; wade in, holding the face mask in place.
7. Do not disturb the environment more than is absolutely necessary. Fill in any holes left in the sand or mud after digging. Replace all rocks and driftwood.

As far as possible, organisms collected should be studied in the field while still alive. Marine organisms are difficult to transport alive to a laboratory. If you find organisms that you wish to identify more carefully than field conditions will permit, make sketches of them in your data book. If you wish to take preserved specimens back to the laboratory, place such specimens in small jars containing 93 parts seawater and 7 parts 40% formaldehyde solution.

A. Studying the Plankton

Suspend the plankton net in the sea from a piling or pier, making sure that the net extends into the current and is not likely to become snagged on any obstructions. Attach the towline firmly to the pier, and allow the net to remain in the water for thirty minutes if the current is normal, fifteen minutes if the current is swift. In areas where there is little or no current, the net can be towed behind a small boat. (Plankton samples can also be obtained by pouring seawater through the net, but this method takes more time.) Haul in the net and remove the collecting bottle. Pour its contents into petri dishes. Wash the net in fresh water, and set it out for further collecting.

Observe the living plankton in the petri dishes through a stereomicroscope. Identify as many organisms as you can. The illustrations in Exercise 9.1 may be of use, since many freshwater plankton organisms are similar to those of the sea. The larval organisms in Figure 9.4-1 are likely to be abundant among marine plankton at certain times of the year. Also use the references listed at the end of this exercise.

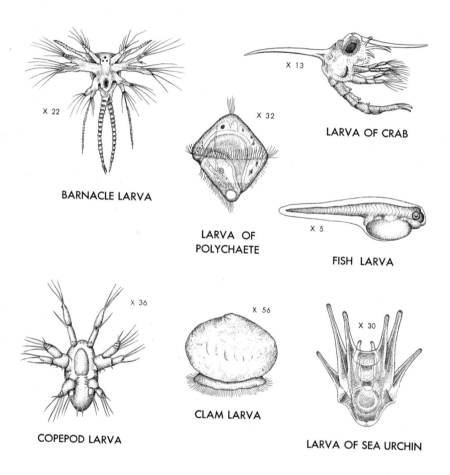

X 22

BARNACLE LARVA

X 13

LARVA OF CRAB

X 32

LARVA OF POLYCHAETE

X 5

FISH LARVA

X 36

COPEPOD LARVA

X 56

CLAM LARVA

X 30

LARVA OF SEA URCHIN

Figure 9.4-1. Some larvae common in marine plankton

Many organisms may be too small to be seen with the stereomicroscope. Transfer one or two drops of the water from a petri dish to a slide, add a cover slip, and observe under a monocular microscope.

B. Studying Other Habitats

The edge of the sea includes a variety of habitats; which ones are to be studied by your class will depend upon the kind of shore that is available.

Label the buckets with the names of the habitats in which you expect to collect. Fill the buckets about two-thirds full of seawater and place them in a shaded spot. As organisms are collected (in small containers such as plastic beakers or glass jars), bring them to the appropriate buckets. Collect only one or two specimens of each species. Do not crowd the organisms in the bucket. Every hour or so, replace the water in each bucket with fresh seawater.

Sandy beach: This kind of shore may be divided into a spray zone, an intertidal zone, and a subtidal zone. In the first, use a shovel to dig for organisms that live buried in the sand. In this zone there is usually a line of debris cast up beyond the usual high-tide line by storms. Turn over the debris to find animals that hide in it. The shovel is a useful tool in the intertidal zone, too. Where the water rolls up on the beach, turn sand into a sieve and allow the water to wash away the particles of sand. A rake is useful for collecting larger organisms that live in the sand of shallow water. In coves and estuaries where there is little surf, a seine may be used to collect swimming organisms of the subtidal zone. Several students are needed to operate the seine. An effective method is to fasten one end of the seine near the edge of the water, carry the other end out into the water, and then swing it in an arc back toward shore.

Rocky shore: The three zones that occur on sandy shores also occur here, but they are likely to be narrower. Most of the organisms are sessile; some are fixed permanently to one spot, others move about from time to time. Use a knife with a heavy blade or a light chisel to pry the organisms loose. This collecting technique applies in all zones. In the subtidal zone it may be necessary to use a face mask to see under water. CAUTION: Jagged rocks will cut; smooth rocks are slippery.

Mud flat: Shovels, rakes, and sieves are the most efficient tools for collecting on mud flats.

Marsh: Small organisms may be picked up by hand from the grasses and sedges of the marsh. In the small channels that thread through the marsh and often retain water even at low tide, the wire-cloth hand seine is a useful tool for scooping up small crabs or fishes.

SUMMARY

When all the possible identifications have been made (either in the field or in a later laboratory session), the data gathered by each team should be distributed to the whole class. From the combined data it should be possible to make some generalizations.

Which groups (you may consider phyla, classes, orders, or families) occur in the greatest number of habitats?(1) Which groups are found in a single habitat only?(2) What adaptations can you find that fit species in the wide-ranging groups to different habitats?(3) What hypotheses can you suggest to explain the occurrence of some groups in one habitat only?(4)

Of the organisms you have been able to identify to the level of genus or species, which occur in more than one habitat?(5) What kinds of tolerance seem to be associated with the ability of these organisms to live in a variety of habitats?(6)

Compare the organisms from two habitats that differ as much as possible (for example, intertidal rocks and mud flats). What adaptations seem to fit organisms of the same taxonomic group for life in the two different habitats? For example, how do the adaptations of mollusks inhabiting intertidal rocks differ from those of mollusks inhabiting mud flats?(7) In which habitats are most of the producers found?(8) Where does the energy for organisms in the other habitats come from?(9)

REFERENCES

ABBOTT, R. T. How to Know the American Marine Shells. New York: New American Library of World Literature, Inc.

——————. Sea Shells of the World, ed. H. S. ZIM. New York: Golden Press, Inc., 1962.

DAWSON, E. Y. How to Know the Seaweeds. Dubuque, Iowa: William C. Brown Co., 1956.

HAUSMAN, L. A. Beginner's Guide to Seashore Life. New York: G. P. Putnam's Sons, Inc., 1949.

MINER, R. W. Field Book of Seashore Life. New York: G. P. Putnam's Sons, Inc., 1950.

RICKETTS, E. F., and J. CALVIN. Between Pacific Tides. 3rd ed. rev. by J. W. HEDGPETH. Stanford, Calif.: Stanford University Press, 1962.

ZIM, H. S., and L. INGLE. Seashores. New York: Simon and Schuster, Inc., 1955.

——————, and H. H. SHOEMAKER. Fishes. New York: Simon and Schuster, Inc., 1957.

FOR FURTHER INVESTIGATION

1. Your data in this exercise consist of the names of organisms associated with the marine habitat in which the organisms were found. This is the kind of data that must always be gathered first in any community study. The next step is to obtain quantitative data: How abun-

dant are the different organisms? To determine this, sample spaces must be marked off, measured, and the number of organisms within the space counted. Densities can then be calculated. Refer to Exercise 3.1 for methods that can be adapted to some kinds of shore habitats. However, in studying shore communities, volumes rather than areas often need to be measured.

2. None of the procedures in this exercise permit the detection of bacteria, which are important members of marine communities. Marine bacteria can best be cultivated in a medium made up of about 20 g agar and 980 ml seawater.

EXERCISE 9.5

MEASUREMENT OF pH IN AQUATIC ECOSYSTEMS

INTRODUCTION

On text pages 176-177 we discussed ions and the acidity and alkalinity that result from the ionization of water. Just as these characteristics of water solutions greatly affect organisms that live in soil water, so they also affect organisms that live in inland and marine waters. They are abiotic factors of aquatic environments that rank with temperature, salinity, and current flow in importance. To analyze an aquatic environment—that is, to understand an aquatic ecosystem—the ecologist must measure variations in such factors.

PURPOSES

This exercise (1) shows a method by which acidity and alkalinity may be measured and (2) uses this method in an investigation of some aquatic ecosystems.

BACKGROUND INFORMATION

Hydrogen ions (H^+) and hydroxyl ions (OH^-) both result from the ionization of water (H_2O—which can also be written HOH). Since water molecules produce both hydrogen (acid) ions and hydroxyl (alkaline) ions, in any water solution a change in the concentration of either kind of ion brings about a change in the concentration of the other. Therefore, it is possible to use a single scale of numbers to measure acidity-alkalinity in water solutions. This scale is called the pH scale, and the numbers in it indirectly express the concentration of hydrogen ions.

At any particular moment $\frac{1}{10,000,000}$ of the molecules in chemically pure water are ionized. This number can be written as 10^{-7}, and the pH of such water is said to be 7. Since the number of hydrogen and hydroxyl ions is equal, such water is neither acid nor alkaline; it is neutral. If hydrogen ions are added to chemically pure water so that their concentration is increased tenfold, the concentration will then be $\frac{1}{1,000,000}$, or 10^{-6}, or pH 6; this is an acid solution. If enough hydroxyl ions are added to reduce the proportion of hydrogen ions to $\frac{1}{100,000,000}$, or 10^{-8}, then the pH is 8. This is an alkaline solution. Thus, the pH scale runs from 1 to 14, with numbers below 7 indicating an acid solution (the lower the number, the stronger the acid) and numbers above 7 indicating an alkaline solution (the higher the number, the stronger the alkali).

Many soluble pigments (coloring substances) change chemically when there is an increase or a decrease in the pH of the water in which they are dissolved. Often the chemical change in the pigment involves a loss of color or a shift to a different color. For many such pigments the pH range in which the color change occurs is known. Therefore, if both the pigment and the pH range within which it changes color are known, the pigment can be used as an indicator to determine the pH of an unknown solution. One such indicator was used in Exercise 1.3.

MATERIALS AND EQUIPMENT (per team)

A. For Studying the Action of Indicators

1. Beakers, 50 or 100 ml, 6
2. Glass-marking crayon
3. Graduated cylinder
4. Distilled water, 100 ml
5. Glass stirring rods, 6
6. Methyl red solution
7. Bromthymol blue solution

8. Phenolphthalein solution
9. Hydrochloric acid
10. Sodium hydroxide solution

B. For Studying the pH of Different Water Samples

1. Water samples, 3 or more
2. Test tubes, 1 per sample
3. Glass-marking crayon
4. Glass stirring rods, 1 per sample
5. Microscope slides, 1 per sample
6. Wide-range pH test paper, 1 cm per sample

PROCEDURE A: THE ACTION OF INDICATORS

Mark the six beakers as follows: A-1, B-1, A-2, B-2, A-3, B-3. Into each beaker pour 15 ml of distilled water, and add a stirring rod. To beakers A-1 and B-1 add a drop of methyl red solution; to beakers A-2 and B-2 add a drop of bromthymol blue solution; to beakers A-3 and B-3 add a drop of phenolphthalein solution. In your data book record the color in each beaker. To each of the three A beakers add a drop of hydrochloric acid and stir; to each of the B beakers add a drop of sodium hydroxide solution (a base, or alkali) and stir. If no color changes occur, continue to add acid, one drop at a time, to each A beaker, stirring after each addition. Be sure to keep each stirring rod in its own beaker. In the same way, add base to each B beaker. If, after stirring, a color change remains in any beaker, record the new color next to the old and the number of drops of acid or base added. When a color change has occurred in either beaker of any pair, your work with that pair is finished. Continue the procedure until a color change has occurred in one beaker of each pair.

STUDYING THE DATA

According to the background information given above, approximately what pH should distilled water have? (1) As acid is added to the A beakers, what happens to the pH value? (2) As base is added to the B beakers, what happens to the pH value? (3) Keeping these ideas in mind and referring to your data, arrange the indicator colors in order of increasing pH. (4) Your teacher will give you the pH range in which each indicator changes color.

With a whole series of such indicators, the approximate pH of solutions can be worked out. More accurate pH determinations can be

made with electrically operated instruments, but <u>colorimetric</u> determination of approximate pH remains useful. Often, however, it is
convenient to use indicator papers. These are prepared by soaking
porous paper in a pigment solution and then allowing the paper to dry.
A number of pigments may be combined in the same paper so that different ones do not have to be tried separately. The next part of this
exercise makes use of such an indicator paper.

PROCEDURE B: THE pH OF DIFFERENT WATER SAMPLES

Obtain samples of water from different aquatic environments.
Among these should be tap water, aquarium water, and water from a
pond or stream. Water might also be obtained from a swamp or bog,
from a polluted stream, from a roadside ditch, etc. If seawater is not
available, a solution approximating it can be made up in the chemistry
laboratory (consult your teacher).

Arrange test tubes on a table, one tube for each water sample.
Pour water from each sample into a separate test tube, and mark the
tubes so that you can identify the source of the water.

Place one microscope slide in front of each test tube. Mark each
slide with the symbol of the test tube behind it. Place a small piece
of test paper on each slide. Dip a glass stirring rod into the first
sample, and transfer a drop of the liquid to the test paper. Repeat if
not enough liquid has been obtained. Note the color of the test paper
where the drop has been placed, and compare with the color scale that
comes with the paper. Record the pH of the sample. Repeat this
procedure for each sample, using a different stirring rod and slide in
each case.

SUMMARY

What is the pH range discovered in your samples?(5) According
to your evidence, are natural waters more likely to be acid, or are
they more likely to be alkaline?(6) Can you think of any reason for
this? If so, state it.(7) What was the source of the sample that is
farthest from neutral?(8) Can you explain why it is so acid or so
alkaline?(9)

FOR FURTHER INVESTIGATION

This exercise relates pH to ecosystems in only a general way.
Using the same technique, you can explore the effects of pH on specific aquatic organisms by experimentally varying the pH in their environments. Do populations of laboratory animals have any effect on
the pH of their environments?

CHAPTER 10

Patterns of Life in the Past

EXERCISE 10.1

PALEONTOLOGICAL COMPARISON

INTRODUCTION

The work of the paleontologist involves more than hunting for fossils, digging them out, and preparing them for exhibition in museums. Determining the changes in living things through geological time requires careful study of large numbers of fossils (often, mere fragments) and detailed comparison between the remains of different species. You know that scientific results must be verifiable—that is, they must be recorded in a form that will permit other investigators to get the same results from the same procedures. Therefore, the paleontologist usually records his observations and comparisons in the form of measurements. For this reason, much of the work of the paleontologist must be performed in the laboratory.

PURPOSE

This exercise illustrates one of the methods used by paleontologists for determining the relationships within a group of organisms.

BACKGROUND INFORMATION

The earliest animals that can be considered as belonging to the horse family (Equidae) are members of the early Eocene genus <u>Hyraco-therium</u> (text Figure 10.38). In rocks of the late Eocene and of succeeding epochs of the Cenozoic, fossil remains of the family Equidae are abundant. Paleontologists have classified the animals represented by these fossils into about twenty genera. The present understanding of relationships among seventeen of these genera is shown in Figure 10.1-1.

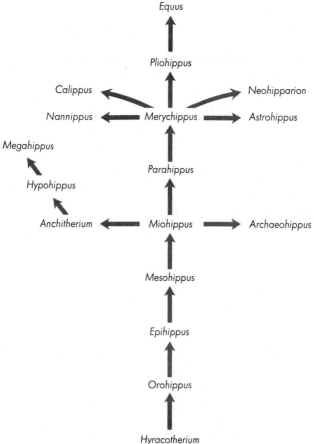

Figure 10.1-1.   Relationship of seventeen genera of horses, based on evidence from many characteristics

Since the fossil material is abundant, paleontologists have a great many structural characteristics to consider when working out relationships within the family Equidae. Text Figure 17.12 illustrates two of these; another will be treated in this exercise.

In the horses the grinding teeth are in the back part of the mouth, separated from the front teeth by a toothless space. On each side of each jaw the grinding teeth (cheek teeth) consist of three premolars and three molars (Figure 10.1-2). The structural characteristic to be studied in this exercise is the <u>distance</u> spanned by the cheek teeth.

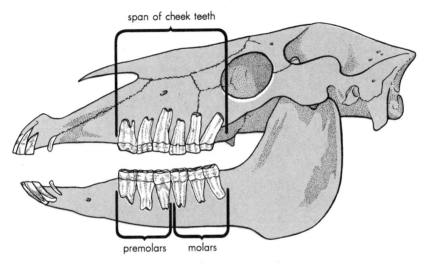

Figure 10.1-2. Skull of modern horse, showing position of teeth

MATERIALS

    1. Graph paper, 1 sheet per student

PROCEDURE

    The span of the cheek teeth has been measured in many fossil specimens of horses. The data for the genera considered in this exercise are presented in Figure 10.1-3. These data suggest certain relationships when plotted on a graph. Construct the graph by using the span of the cheek teeth as the ordinate and geological time as the abscissa (see Exercise 2.1 for these terms). Figure 10.1-4 shows the most convenient kind of grid; it should be made as large as possible so that the plotted points will not be crowded. As each point is plotted on the graph, place beside it the number (from Figure 10.1-3) of the genus it represents.

GENERA OF EQUIDAE	TIME OF EXISTENCE	SPAN OF CHEEK TEETH (in cm)
1. Hyracotherium	Early Eocene	4.3
2. Orohippus	Middle Eocene	4.3
3. Epihippus	Late Eocene	4.7
4. Mesohippus	Early Oligocene	7.2
	Middle Oligocene	7.3
5. · Miohippus	Late Oligocene	8.4
	Early Miocene	8.3
6. Parahippus	Early Miocene	10.0
7. Anchitherium	Early Miocene	11.3
8. Archaeohippus	Middle Miocene	6.5
9. Merychippus	Middle Miocene	10.2
	Late Miocene	12.5
10. Hypohippus	Late Miocene	14.2
11. Megahippus	Early Pliocene	21.5
12. Pliohippus	Early Pliocene	15.5
	Middle Pliocene	15.6
13. Nannippus	Early Pliocene	11.0
	Late Pliocene	10.7
14. Calippus	Early Pliocene	9.3
15. Neohipparion	Middle Pliocene	13.1
16. Astrohippus	Middle Pliocenė	11.8
	Late Pliocene	11.8
17. Equus	Late Pliocene	18.8
	Pleistocene	17.6

Figure 10.1-3

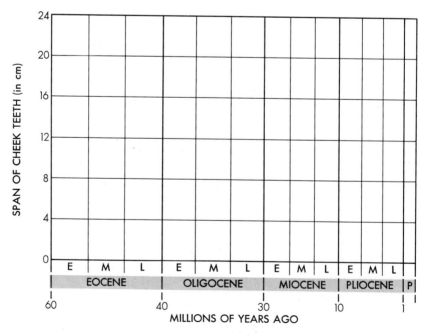

Figure 10.1-4

Connect the points representing the genera Hyracotherium, Orohippus, Epihippus, Mesohippus, and Miohippus. What seems to have been the trend of evolution in the span of cheek teeth in the Equidae during Eocene and Oligocene times?(1) Is it possible to continue a single line farther to the right on the grid?(2) Without drawing such a line, describe the trend of evolution in cheek-teeth span during the Miocene, Pliocene, and Pleistocene.(3)

Now you need to find out whether the data on cheek-teeth span fit the relationships among the equid genera—relationships worked out by paleontologists from the evidence provided by other structural characteristics. To do this, draw lines between the dots on your grid to correspond to the arrows on Figure 10.1-1. For example: Draw a line from the dot for Miohippus to that for Anchitherium, continuing through that for Hypohippus to that for Megahippus; draw another line from the dot for Miohippus to that for Archaeohippus; draw a third line from Miohippus to Parahippus, etc.

CONCLUSIONS

If data on any single characteristic conflict with relationships worked out from other characteristics, the data will produce a set of crossing lines when graphed. Do the data on cheek-teeth span support the relationships shown in Figure 10.1-1, or do they conflict with the relationships?(4)

What was the approximate average change in cheek-teeth span per million years from Hyracotherium to Miohippus?(5) What was the average change from Miohippus to Megahippus?(6) From Miohippus to Equus?(7) From these results, what generalization can you make about the rate of evolution within a taxonomic group?(8)

What evidence do you have that the direction of an evolutionary change can be reversed?(9)

CHAPTER 11

The Geography of Life

EXERCISE 11.1

THE EFFECTS OF BARRIERS ON DISPERSAL

INTRODUCTION

The study of the effects of a natural barrier on dispersal is often a long-term task; months or even years may be needed to obtain adequate data. In this exercise an experimental situation requiring much less time will be used to study the effects of barriers on dispersal.

PURPOSE

This exercise tests the effects of barriers on the dispersal of three species of motile aquatic organisms.

MATERIALS AND EQUIPMENT

1. Soft glass tubing, 8-mm diameter, 29-cm lengths, 6
2. Bunsen burners (with wing tips), 6
3. Squares of wire gauze, about 10 X 10 cm, 6

4. Soft glass tubing, 8-mm diameter, 30-cm lengths, 12
5. Black plastic (or cloth) adhesive tape, about 2 cm wide, 6 m
6. Glass culture dishes, 8 cm high, 20-cm diameter, 6
7. Beakers, 250 ml, 18
8. Euglena culture, 3 liters
9. Pond water or aged aquarium water, 12 liters
10. Beakers, 30 ml, 6
11. Planaria, 75
12. Small pond snails, 75

PROCEDURE

A. Setting Up the Experiment

There are six setups in this experiment; they can best be handled by six teams. The following directions are to be followed by each team.

Each team needs three lengths of glass tubing—one 29 cm long (called A), two 30 cm long (called B and C). Using a Bunsen burner with a wing tip, heat Tube A at a point equidistant from its ends. Hold the axis of the tube at a right angle to the axis of the flame. Rotate the tube constantly so that its walls are heated uniformly. When the tubing becomes soft, pull gently on the ends to form a constriction that has about half the original diameter of the tubing (Figure 11.1-1).

Figure 11.1-1. Tube A (before bending)

The length of the tube should then be approximately 30 cm. Keep the tube straight until the constriction has hardened; then put it aside, on a piece of wire gauze, to cool. Next, heat Tube B, and make a right-angle bend about 6 cm from one of its ends. In making the bend, the axis of the tube should be parallel to the axis of the flame. Make similar bends in Tubes C and A (A last, so that it will have had more time to cool). After making each bend, place the tube on the wire gauze to cool. Now make a similar bend 6 cm from the other end of Tube B. Be sure that the bends at the two ends are in the same plane (Figure 11.1-2). Do the same with Tubes C and A. When both ends of the

Figure 11.1-2.
Tube B, with right-angle
bends at each end

Figure 11.1-3.
Tube <u>C</u>, with wrapping
of black adhesive tape

tubes have cooled, carefully wrap Tube <u>C</u> with black adhesive tape along the straight portion so that all light is excluded (Figure 11.1-3).

Arrange the six culture dishes (one per team, each marked with the team number) on a table or along a shelf in the laboratory so that environmental conditions are as uniform as possible. The dishes should be located so that they receive daylight from one side but are not exposed to direct sunlight.

(Directions now resume for each team.) Place three beakers or jars next to the culture dish, between the light and the dish (Figure 11.1-4). Place each of the three bent tubes so that one arm extends into the large culture dish and the other arm extends into one of the beakers. The ends of the tubes should be a few centimeters above the bottoms of the dish and beaker. If necessary, place small pieces of wood on the rims of the containers to support the tubes at the right height. Place the beakers so that they are all the same distance from the large culture dish. Now remove all the tubes, placing each one next to its beaker.

Fill the culture dish to a level 2 cm from the top, as follows:

Team	Liquid in Culture Dish
1	Euglena culture
2	Pond water
3	Pond water
4	Euglena culture
5	Euglena culture
6	Pond water

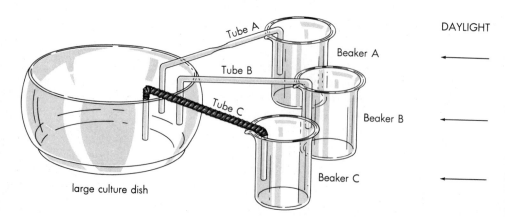

Figure 11.1-4

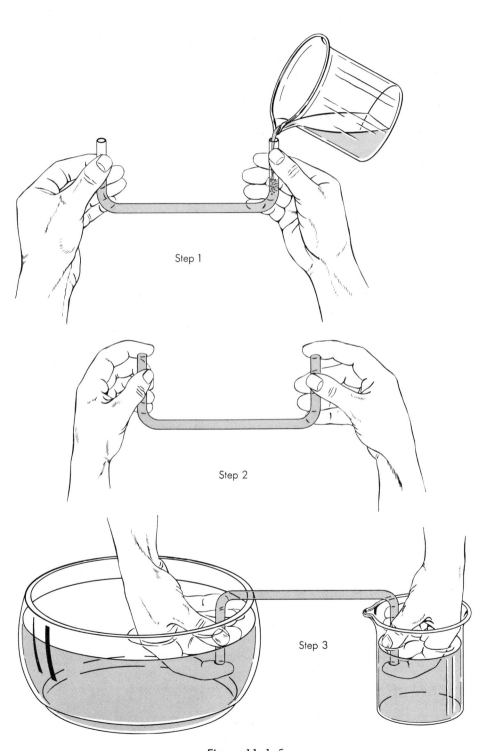

Step 1

Step 2

Step 3

Figure 11.1-5

Then pour pond water into each of the three beakers to a level equal to that in the culture dish. Working in pairs, fill each of the bent tubes with pond water. One student holds the tube (one hand at each end) so that the bends of the tube point upward; the other student carefully pours pond water from a small beaker into one end of the tube (Figure 11.1-5). When it is completely filled and begins to overflow, the student holding the tube places the tips of his forefingers over the ends of the tube. Keeping his fingers in position, he inverts the tube and places the ends under the surface of the liquid in the culture dish and the beaker. The fingers are then removed from the ends of the tubes. If this procedure has been carried out properly, there will be no air bubbles in the tube, and it will form a liquid-filled bridge connecting the culture dish and the beaker.

When all the tubes have been filled and placed in position, introduce animals into the culture dishes, as follows:

Team	Animals Introduced into Large Culture Dish
1	none
2	25 Planaria
3	25 snails
4	25 Planaria
5	25 snails
6	25 Planaria and 25 snails

B. Recording the Data

Each team will observe its setup daily for one week. Determine the number of organisms of each kind that have passed from the culture dish through the glass tubes into the beakers. Counts of Planaria and snails present no problem. The number of Euglena can be estimated by observing the color of the pond water in the beakers. The following system should be used in recording observations of Euglena.

  o   no green color in beaker
  +   slight green color in beaker
  ++   moderate green color in beaker
  +++   green color as intense in beaker as in culture dish

In your data book record observations on a chart similar to the one shown below. Members of Teams 1, 2, and 3 will need to make only

Name of Organism	DAYS				
	1	2	3		7
Beaker A					
Beaker B					
Beaker C					

one copy of the chart, since they will be making observations of only a single kind of organism. Members of Teams 4, 5, and 6 will need to make two copies of the chart, one for each organism.

STUDYING THE DATA

When observations have been completed, the data from each team must be gathered together for study by all students. This may be done on the chalkboard or by exchanging duplicated data among teams.

What kind of barrier is represented by each of the three tubes?(1) Is there any kind of barrier in the experiment in addition to the ones represented by the tubes? If so, what is it?(2)

For each organism, list the barriers in the order of their effectiveness. Use the time required for the organism to appear in the beakers as a measure of effectiveness—the shorter the time, the less effective the barrier.(3) Did any of the barriers completely bar the dispersal of any of the three kinds of organisms? If so, which barrier, which organism, and how did the barrier prevent the dispersal?(4) In comparing one organism with another, can time be considered a measure of the effectiveness of a barrier? Why or why not?(5) Is any barrier equally effective in hindering the dispersal of all the species of organisms? If so, which barrier?(6)

It is possible that a barrier may be effective in hindering the dispersal of a species when the species is alone, but less effective when the species is living with another species. Does the experiment provide any evidence for this hypothesis? If so, what is the evidence?(7)

CONCLUSIONS

On the basis of your results, what generalizations can you make about barriers and dispersal?(8) Does each generalization apply to natural as well as laboratory situations? Why or why not?(9)

FOR FURTHER INVESTIGATION

Can you devise a similar experiment using other organisms (for example: ants, cockroaches, earthworms) and other barriers (for example: temperature, water currents, ditches, etc.)?

EXERCISE 11.2

BARRIERS AND ADAPTIVE RADIATION

INTRODUCTION

The separation of the Australian realm from Asia near the end of the Cretaceous period produced one of the most effective barriers known in biogeography. Apparently the separation occurred before the placental mammals (text pages 322-324) evolved. Few of these were able to cross the ocean barrier; therefore, in the Australian realm adaptive radiation of mammals has occurred chiefly among the marsupials, whose ancestors were already present when the ocean barrier developed.

PURPOSE

Adaptive radiation among placental mammals has been described (text pages 322-325) and that of the marsupials has been discussed more briefly (text pages 362-364). The purpose of this exercise is to provide a broader understanding of adaptive radiation among mammals and to introduce a related principle of biogeography.

BACKGROUND INFORMATION

The structural adaptations of mammals to particular ecological niches are many, but it is possible to group them roughly. One such grouping makes use of five general headings related to habitats, as follows:

Aquatic (living in water)
1. Body streamlined
2. Tail flattened
3. Legs short or lacking
Fossorial (burrowing in soil)
1. Forelegs with large claws
2. Legs short
3. Eyes and ears small
4. Snout lengthened and provided with sensitive whiskers

Cursorial (running, usually in grassland)
    1. Eyes and ears large
    2. Legs long
    3. Tail long
    4. Toes only (not whole foot) supporting the body
Arboreal (living in trees)
    1. Tail long and often prehensile (grasping)
    2. Toes with claws
        (or)
    3. Toes separated, adapted to grasping
Aerial (living in air)
    1. Skin spread between legs, between toes, or between both
    2. Size usually small

PROCEDURE

In your data book prepare a table as follows:

AQUATIC		FOSSORIAL		CURSORIAL (etc.)	
Marsupial	Placental	Marsupial	Placental	Marsupial	

In a museum or zoo examine as many mammals as possible. Consider each species with respect to the adaptations listed above. Not all species of mammals will fit into the five groups; there are other possible groups, and many groups overlap. When you come upon a species that clearly fits one of the groups, find out whether it is a marsupial or a placental mammal, enter its name in the correct column, and below its name write the numbers of the adaptations (listed above) that appear in the species.

STUDYING THE DATA

The placental mammals are classified into many different orders; the marsupials are placed in a single order (see Appendix of text).

Does any one order of placental mammals have species in as many of the adaptational groups as does the marsupial order? If so, which one? If not, which placental order appears in the most groups?(1) Would you say that the adaptive radiation of the marsupials has been as great as that of the placentals? What evidence do you have to support your answer?(2) Can you suggest a reason for your conclusions in this comparison? If so, state it.(3)

Adaptive radiation in different taxonomic groups often results in species that appear somewhat alike. Such superficial resemblances may be striking, even though an investigation of internal structure clearly shows that the similar organisms are correctly classified in separate groups and not together. The process that leads to this situation is called convergent evolution. Text Figures 11.24 and 11.26 show two examples of convergent evolution between marsupials and placentals. Can you find other examples of this process among the mammals listed on your chart? If so, what are they?(4) What is your explanation for convergent evolution?(5)

FOR FURTHER INVESTIGATION

Adaptive radiation is conspicuous among the birds of the Neotropical realm. Of course their habitats and structural adaptations are quite different from those of mammals. When the birds of the Neotropical realm are compared with those of the Ethiopian and Oriental realms, many examples of convergent evolution can be found—often on the family rather than the species level. You can make a study of these matters if you have available a museum or zoo with a large collection of birds.

WITHIN THE INDIVIDUAL ORGANISM

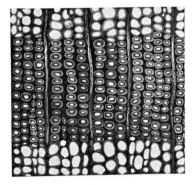

CHAPTER 12

The Cell

EXERCISE 12.1

DIVERSITY IN CELL STRUCTURE

INTRODUCTION

From as far back as Exercise 1.1 you have been observing cells—or, at least, organisms consisting of a single unit of protoplasm. Yeast organisms usually consist of single cells; and some of the protists, such as bacteria, are single cells.

Up to this point, however, we have not been concerned with cells as such. Now, in exploring the internal structure of organisms, it is necessary to look at some of the various kinds of cells—just as we investigated diversity among individual organisms in Section Two. It makes no difference whether the cells to be examined occur in plants, animals, or protists; in this exercise, however, attention is concentrated on plants and animals, since many protists have already been observed (Exercises 1.5, 6.3, 9.2, for example).

PURPOSE

This is an observational exercise in which the structures of a number of different kinds of living cells are compared.

MATERIALS AND EQUIPMENT (for each student or pair of students)

1. Onion, cut into pieces about 1 cm^2
2. Forceps (fine-pointed)
3. Microscope slide
4. Scalpel
5. Medicine droppers, 3
6. Cover slips.
7. Monocular microscope
8. Iodine—potassium-iodide solution (I_2KI)
9. Paper towels
10. Stamens of <u>Tradescantia</u>
11. Elodea leaves
12. Toothpicks (sterile)
13. Methylene blue solution
14. Dissecting needles, 2
15. Frog blood
16. Frog skin
17. Frog muscle
18. Ringer's solution

PROCEDURE

Note: Be sure to clean slides thoroughly with water and paper towels before placing another kind of material on them.

A. Epidermal Cells of Onion

You will be provided with small pieces of onion. On the inner (concave) side the "skin" (epidermis) may be readily peeled off with forceps. Place a small piece of epidermis (much smaller than a cover slip) on a slide. If the piece you have is too large, trim it with a scalpel. The epidermis is a single layer of cells; try to avoid over-lapping or wrinkling it. Add one or two drops of water and a cover slip.

Examine the onion epidermis under the low power of the micro-scope. Look for the boundaries of cells. In your data book draw a small section of the field of view to show how the cells are arranged.

Place a drop of stain (iodine—potassium-iodide) along one edge of the cover slip. Draw it under the cover slip, using the technique given in Exercise 9.3. Note in your data book any changes that occur as the stain spreads across the onion epidermis. Then switch to high power and draw a single cell, including as much detail as you can see. Label all the parts you can identify (text pages 379-382). Even with the high power of your microscope, you will be able to see only a few of the parts known to occur in cells.

B. Hair Cells of Tradescantia

The stamens of the Tradescantia flower have many small hairs that are visible to the naked eye. With fine-pointed forceps, pick off some of these hairs and place them in a drop of water on a slide. Gently add a cover slip so that it does not crush the hairs.

Examine under low power. Draw the cells of one hair to show their arrangement. Is there evidence that the cells are living? If so, what is the evidence?(1) Switch to high power and draw a single cell, including as much detail as you can see. Label all the parts you can identify.

C. Cells of Elodea Leaf

With forceps remove a young leaf from near the tip of an elodea plant. Place it on a slide in a drop of water and add a cover slip.

Observe the leaf with low power. By slowly turning the fine adjustment back and forth, determine the number of cell layers in the leaf.(2) Switch to high power. Select an average cell, focus on it carefully, and make a drawing of it, including as much detail as you can see. Label all the parts you can identify.

D. Cells of the Human Cheek

Using a sterile toothpick, scrape the inside surface of your cheek. Do not dig a hole in your cheek; you should obtain a barely visible mass of material. Rub this material on a clean slide. Add one drop of water and stir thoroughly with the toothpick. Add a drop or two of methylene blue and a cover slip.

Examine under low power. When you have found several cells well separated from the others, center them in the field of view and switch to high power. By carefully using the fine adjustment, try to discover the three-dimensional shape of the cells. Would you describe them as spherical, disk-shaped, or neither?(3) Draw one or two cells, including as much detail as you can see. Label all the parts you can identify.

E. Cells of Frog Blood

Place a drop of diluted frog blood on a clean slide. Add a drop of methylene blue and a cover slip. Most of the cells to be seen are red blood cells. Find a portion of the slide where the cells are neither too crowded nor too scarce, and center it in the field of view. Switch to high power. Draw one or two cells, including as much detail as you can see. Label all the parts you can identify.

F. Cells of Frog Skin

Place scrapings from a frog's skin on a clean slide. Add a drop of Ringer's solution and a cover slip. Locate cells with low power and then switch to high power. Draw one or two cells, including as much detail as you can see. Label all the parts you can identify.

G. Cells of Frog Muscle

Place a bit of frog muscle on a clean slide. Add a drop of Ringer's solution. Tease (pick) the sample apart, using two dissecting needles. Add a drop of methylene blue and a cover slip. Examine under low power. Find material that is as thin as possible and switch to high power. Draw a small portion of the material, including as much detail as you can see. Label all the parts you can identify.

SUMMARY

On the basis of your observations, which kinds of cells (plant or animal) seem to have more angular, less rounded shapes?(4) Which have more clearly defined boundaries?(5) What cell structure may be involved in these characteristics?(6)

In your data book draw a table like the following, allowing a column for each kind of cell structure observed:

SOURCE OF CELL	CYTOPLASM	CELL WALL	NUCLEUS	
Onion epidermis				
Tradescantia stamen				
Elodea leaf				

Review your sketches and notes. For each kind of cell examined, place an X beneath the name of each cell structure observed. Does the lack of an X indicate that the structure was not present in the cells observed? Why or why not?(7)

EXERCISE 12.2

IDENTIFYING SOME SUBSTANCES FOUND IN PROTOPLASM

INTRODUCTION

How can the biochemist tell what substances occur in protoplasm? How can he identify the substances present in such a complicated and ever changing material? As a result of more than a century of study, biochemists have accumulated a wide variety of tests by which they can identify many substances found in protoplasm. Some of these tests identify specific chemical substances; others identify groups or classes of substances.

The processes involved in identifying substances usually kill the living matter. Therefore, even though he can identify the substances, the biochemist is faced with a further question: Are the substances in the dead remains the same as those that existed in the living protoplasm? In other words, has the killing of the protoplasm changed the substances in it? While definite answers cannot always be given to these questions, the combination of evidence from many different kinds of procedures has allowed biochemists to come to reasonably firm conclusions about many substances.

PURPOSE

In this exercise we shall attempt to identify substances from three of the four chemical groups that (together with water) make up almost 100 percent of protoplasm (text page 395). There is no convenient test for carbohydrates as a group; but there is a chemical test for starches, and there are chemical tests for certain sugars (including glucose). There are chemical tests for proteins as a group. And there are physical tests (those that do not involve chemical reactions) for fats. We shall not attempt to identify nucleic acids.

MATERIALS AND EQUIPMENT

1. Test tubes, 16 X 125 mm, 20
2. Glass-marking crayon
3. Glucose solution
4. Starch solution

5. Egg albumen solution
6. Vegetable oil
7. Medicine droppers, 4
8. Test-tube rack
9. Benedict's or Fehling's solution
10. Test-tube holder
11. Bunsen burner
12. Iodine solution
13. Millon's reagent
14. Sudan IV
15. Food samples (several kinds)
16. Scalpel
17. Glass rod
18. Paper towel

PROCEDURE

A reagent is any substance used to convert one substance into another by means of the reaction it causes. The first step in any testing procedure is to "validate the reagents"—that is, to show that each reagent reacts in a characteristic way with the substance we are testing for and does not react in the same way with other substances.

Mark four test tubes S (for sugar), four St (for starch), four P (for protein), four F (for fat), and four W (for water). Then arrange the tubes in four sets, each set consisting of S, St, P, F, and W tubes. Into each of the twenty tubes pour 5 ml of water. To each S tube add 2 drops of glucose solution; to each St tube add 2 drops of starch solution; to each P tube add 2 drops of egg albumen solution; to each F tube add 2 drops of vegetable oil.

To each of the five tubes of the first set add about 1 ml of Benedict's or Fehling's solution. Heat each tube gently over the Bunsen burner. (CAUTION: Be sure the mouth of the tube is not directed toward yourself or any other person!) In your data book record any changes that occur in the color of the reagent; be sure to record the symbols of tubes in which change occurs.

To each of the five tubes of the second set add 1 drop of iodine solution. Record any changes.

To each of the five tubes of the third set add 10 drops of Millon's reagent. Heat the tubes gently over the Bunsen burner. Record any changes.

To each of the five tubes of the fourth set add 1 drop of Sudan IV solution. Shake the tubes and allow them to stand a few minutes. Record the symbol of each tube in which the characteristic color of Sudan IV collects in the substance being tested.

You now have methods with which you can test for four different classes of substances that occur in protoplasm. You will use these methods to test several samples of materials. Since man obtains his

food from the protoplasm of other organisms, foods contain the substances of protoplasm. It is therefore convenient to use foods as the
test materials.

Chop the sample you are given into small pieces. Divide the
chopped sample among four test tubes. Add a small amount of water
to each tube, and stir with a glass rod. If possible, use the rod to
break up the sample further, but be careful not to break the rod or test
tube. Rinse and wipe off the glass rod after use in each tube.

Apply a different one of the four testing methods to the sample in
each tube. Unless the sample contains a large amount of fats, results
from the test for these substances will not be clear. Fats may be concentrated to bring about a clearer test by gently heating the tube containing the sample. (A supplementary test involves rubbing the sample
on a piece of paper. Permanent translucent spots on the paper indicate fats; water in the sample will make translucent spots also, but
these will disappear as the water evaporates.)

SUMMARY

On the chalkboard assemble the results obtained by all members
of the class in a table like the following:

SAMPLE	SUGARS	STARCHES	PROTEINS	FATS

In the first column list the samples tested. For each substance found
in a particular sample place an X in the appropriate column. After
you have studied all the results, try to make some general statements
about the relationship between the source of each sample (whether animal or plant) and the abundance of the four groups of substances in it.

EXERCISE 12.3

DIFFUSION THROUGH A MEMBRANE

PURPOSE

The purpose of this exercise is to demonstrate the action of a differentially permeable membrane.

MATERIALS AND EQUIPMENT

1. Cellulose tubing, 20-cm lengths, 2
2. Soluble starch solution
3. Rubber bands, 2
4. Glucose solution
5. Iodine solution
6. Beaker, 600 or 1000 ml, 2
7. Glass-marking crayon
8. Tes-tape or piece of Clinitest tablet in test tube

PROCEDURE

The cellulose tubing may be opened by moistening and then rubbing it between the thumb and forefinger. Tie a tight knot about 1 cm from one end of each piece of tubing.

Into one tube pour soluble starch solution to within about 5 cm of the top. Pinch the top of the tube together tightly, and rinse the tube under running water to remove any starch on the outside. Fasten the top of the tube with a rubber band, and place the tube in a beaker of water (Figure 12.3-1). Mark the beaker A. Add enough iodine solution to give the water a distinct yellowish color.

Into the second tube pour glucose solution to within about 5 cm of the top, and repeat the procedure given in the previous paragraph—but do not add iodine solution to the water in the beaker. Mark this beaker B.

Allow the tubes to stand about twenty minutes. Then dip a piece of Tes-tape into the water in Beaker B (or pour a small quantity of the water into a test tube containing a fragment of a Clinitest tablet). Record the color in your data book.

iodine solution —

cellulose tubing
containing
starch solution —

water in beaker —

Figure 12.3-1

Observe the tube in Beaker <u>A</u>. Record any color change observed in either the tube or the water in the beaker. .

Let Setup B stand overnight. The next day, record any change observed in the tube.

STUDYING THE DATA

On the basis of the chemical test for starch, what must have happened to the iodine molecules in Setup A ?(1) On the basis of the chemical test for glucose, what must have happened to the glucose molecules in Setup B ?(2) Which material did not pass through a membrane ? How do you know ?(3) From the evidence obtained by allowing Setup B to stand overnight, what other substance must have passed through the membrane ?(4)

CONCLUSIONS

By various methods, physicists can measure the size of molecules. They show that iodine molecules and water molecules are very small, glucose molecules are considerably larger, and starch molecules (synthesized from many glucose molecules—text page 396) are very large. On this basis suggest a hypothesis to account for the observations made in this exercise. (5) In this hypothesis what assumption must you make about the structure of the membrane? (6)

EXERCISE 12.4

MITOSIS

INTRODUCTION

When a tissue is quickly killed and preserved, the structure of its cells remains very much as it was at the moment of death. If the tissue contains many dividing cells, it will probably contain cells in various stages of mitosis. But when we examine such a tissue with the microscope, we find it very difficult to determine which stage comes first, which second, third, and so on. Yet, even before the phase microscope made it possible to observe mitosis as a continuous process, painstaking study over a period of many years had enabled cytologists to work out the sequence of steps that occurs in the dividing cell.

PURPOSE

In this exercise you will prepare material for the study of mitosis. Plant material will be used, so that you can compare your observations with the description and illustrations of mitosis in animal cells (text pages 402-404).

MATERIALS AND EQUIPMENT

1. Onion bulb or garlic clove
2. Scissors
3. Small beaker or wide-mouth bottle
4. Round toothpicks (optional)
5. Black paper
6. Fixative solution, in small wide-mouth bottle
7. Solution of one part concentrated hydrochloric acid and one part 95% ethyl alcohol solution
8. Carnoy's fluid (with chloroform)
9. 70% alcohol
10. Forceps
11. Microscope slide
12. Scalpel
13. Iron-acetocarmin solution
14. Cover slip

15. Paper towels
16. Heat source
17. Beaker, 100 ml
18. Monocular microscope

PROCEDURE

Select a fresh firm onion (or garlic clove) and cut off the old dried roots close to the base of the bulb. Choose a beaker (or wide-mouth bottle) of the proper size to support the bulb on its rim. (If the mouth of the beaker is too large for this, insert three or more toothpicks into the bulb and suspend it over the mouth. See Figure 12.4-1.) Pour water into the beaker until it just touches the root end of the onion.

Wrap the beaker with black paper and place it in dim light at room temperature for several days. Watch for new roots to appear. Keep the base of the onion wet by adding water as needed.

When the new roots are 1.5 to 2.5 cm in length, snip off 1 to 2 cm at the end of each root with a pair of small scissors. Drop the roots into a small wide-mouth bottle of fixative solution. The roots should remain in this solution twelve to twenty-four hours. The fixative kills the cells and preserves cell structures.

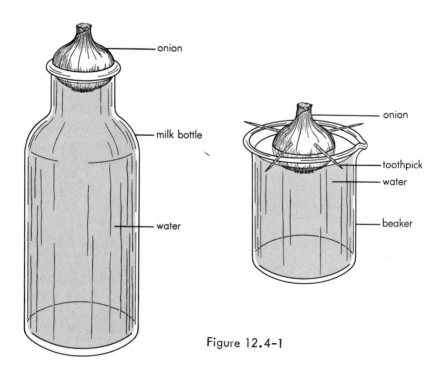

Figure 12.4-1

Pour off the fixative solution. Then add a solution of one part 95-percent ethyl alcohol and one part concentrated hydrochloric acid. (CAUTION: Do not get solution on fingers!) Allow the roots to remain in this solution five to ten minutes. This dissolves the pectins that hold the cells together. Pour off this solution, and add Carnoy's fluid. (CAUTION: Carnoy's fluid is poisonous and inflammable; keep it off your fingers and away from flame!) Let the roots soak five to ten minutes. This reagent hardens the tissues after the acid treatment has softened them. Drain off the Carnoy's fluid and add 70-percent alcohol as a preservative. In this the roots can be stored indefinitely.

Using forceps, pick out a root and place it on a clean slide. With a scalpel, cut off the tip (the last 2 mm or less of the root). Discard the rest. Immediately add one or two drops of iron-acetocarmin solution. Using the scalpel, cut the tip into fine pieces. Do not allow the preparation to dry out. Quickly place a cover slip over it. Lay a folded piece of paper towel—a little larger than the slide—over the cover slip. Now place your left thumb on the towel, directly over the cover slip. With your right thumb press down firmly on the top of your left, crushing the cells on the slide. Do not twist the bottom thumb—the aim is to crush the cells without disrupting their position under the cover slip. Remove the paper towel. This is known as a "squash preparation."

Place the slide across the top of a small beaker in which water is boiling. Leave the slide over the boiling water one minute. This gentle heating clears the stain from the cytoplasm, increasing the contrast with the chromosomes. Remove the slide and wipe off the water vapor that has condensed on the bottom.

OBSERVATIONS

With the microscope, examine the slide under low power. Scan the entire preparation. Look for cells in which the nucleus appears to be broken up into distinct threadlike parts. These cells were undergoing mitosis at the time they were killed. Locate the area where cells in stages of mitosis are most numerous. Where is this area in relation to the end of the root tip?(1) Using high power, examine this area carefully. You may have to adjust the diaphragm of your microscope to see detail. In your data book draw at least five cells, showing different stages in plant mitosis. In each case be sure to draw the whole cell. Arrange the stages in the order in which you think they occur during mitosis. Use the illustrations of animal mitosis in the text (page 403) as a guide.

EXERCISE 12.5

SOME CHARACTERISTICS OF LIVING MATTER

INTRODUCTION

In most organisms the living matter (protoplasm) is divided into small units called cells. In some, however, masses of protoplasm that have many nuclei and no internal divisions occur. Among such acellular organisms, the slime molds (text pages 165-166) are especially convenient for study. They are easily cultured and produce large masses of protoplasm that show up well under the microscope.

PURPOSE

In this exercise some of the characteristics of living matter are examined in the slime mold <u>Physarum</u> <u>polycephalum</u>.

MATERIALS AND EQUIPMENT

1. Culture of slime mold (<u>Physarum</u> <u>polycephalum</u>)
2. Monocular microscope
3. Dissecting needle
4. Bunsen burner
5. Powdered oatmeal
6. Scalpel
7. Acetic acid
8. Glass rod
9. Glass-marking crayon

PROCEDURE

You will receive a petri dish containing a thin layer of nonnutrient agar on which the slime mold is growing. Remove the lid from the petri dish and examine the pattern of growth. In your data book sketch the growth pattern of the slime mold.

Observe the activity of the protoplasm with the low power of the microscope. In your data book describe what you see. (1)

With a dissecting needle, tear or puncture the edge of the proto-plasm. Observe for several minutes. What happens? (2) Heat a needle, and bring it close to the edge of the slime mold—but <u>do not</u> <u>touch</u> the organism. Observe with the low power of the microscope. How does the organism react? (3) Sprinkle a small amount of powdered oatmeal close to the outer edge of the protoplasm. Observe for several minutes. Describe any reaction that you see. (4)

Cut off several small pieces of the protoplasm, and leave them close to the main body. With a glass rod that has been dipped in weak acetic acid (vinegar will do) touch the surface of the agar about 1 cm from the slime mold. With a glass-marking crayon mark an <u>X</u> on the outside of the dish, beneath the point touched. Place the lid on the petri dish and store in a cool, moderately lighted place. Observe on the following day. Describe the result of separating pieces of the slime mold. (5) Is the main body of protoplasm an individual? Explain your answer. (6) How does the slime mold react to the presence of acid on the agar medium? (7)

SUMMARY

Using the observations you have made in this exercise plus the text materials on slime molds (Chapter 6) and cells and protoplasm (Chapter 12), discuss the following: (a) the appearance of living matter to the naked eye and under magnification; (b) the behavior of living matter; (c) the relationships between living matter and the environment.

EXERCISE 12.6

A STUDY OF ENZYME ACTION

INTRODUCTION

The study of enzymes that function within cells (<u>intra</u>cellular enzymes) is difficult. But many others (<u>extra</u>cellular enzymes) are secreted by cells into the environment, where they carry on their functions. The action of extracellular enzymes is relatively easy to study, and we have no reason to suppose that it is greatly different from that of intracellular enzymes.

PURPOSE

In this exercise the action of an extracellular enzyme is studied under varying conditions.

BACKGROUND INFORMATION

In Chapter 12 of the text the discussion of enzymes centers on those that are involved in energy release and on those that are involved in synthesis. In this exercise we shall study an enzyme that acts in the chemical breakdown of starch. The general name for such enzymes is amylase, but other names have been applied to them, depending upon the kind of organism and the kind of tissue in which the enzyme occurs. We shall use the starch-splitting enzyme produced in cells of the human salivary glands—ptyalin (salivary amylase). Ptyalin, in saliva, is secreted into the mouth cavity, where it converts the starch of foods into maltose, a disaccharide sugar. Maltose reacts to Benedict's or Fehling's solution in the same way that glucose does (see Exercise 12.3). When a food contains no sugar and much starch, these solutions can be used to detect the change that is brought about in the starch by the enzyme.

MATERIALS AND EQUIPMENT

A. For Establishing the Presence of the Enzyme

1. Unsweetened cracker
2. Test tubes, 4
3. Thermometer (-10°C to 110°C range)
4. Funnel and support
5. Filter paper, 2 sheets
6. Iodine solution
7. Benedict's or Fehling's solution
8. Test-tube holder
9. Bunsen burner
10. Paraffin

B. For Varying the Conditions of Enzyme Action

1. Test tubes, 7
2. Paraffin
3. Glass rod
4. pH test paper
5. Beakers, 7
6. Starch solution
7. Ring stands, 7
8. Bunsen burners, 7

9. Test-tube holders, 7
10. Benedict's or Fehling's solution
11. Thermometers (-10°C to 110°C range), 5
12. Ice
13. Diluted hydrochloric acid, pH 6
14. Diluted hydrochloric acid, pH 3
15. Sodium hydroxide solution, pH 8
16. Sodium hydroxide solution, pH 11

PROCEDURE

A. Establishing the Presence of the Enzyme

The first step is to determine the normal action of the enzyme. Crush a piece of cracker (about 1 cm^2) into a test tube. Add warm water (about 37°C) to a depth of about 5 cm. Shake, and pour into a funnel lined with filter paper. Collect part of the filtrate (the liquid that seeps through the filter paper) in a second test tube to a depth of about 1 cm, and another part in a third test tube to a depth of about 2 cm. Test the first portion of the filtrate for starch and the second portion for sugar. If the test for sugar is positive (that is, if it indicates the presence of sugar) try another brand of cracker.

Chew a piece of paraffin and spit the accumulated saliva into a test tube. When a few milliliters have been collected, test for sugar. If the test is positive, try another student.

A student that has saliva testing negative for sugar should then chew a piece of cracker (about 9 cm^2) testing negative for sugar. After thorough chewing (two or three minutes), deposit the mass of cracker and saliva into a funnel lined with filter paper. Add about 5 ml of warm water (37°C), and collect about 3 ml of the filtrate in a test tube. Test the filtrate for sugar. Considering the procedure used, what conclusion can be drawn from a negative test? From a positive test? (1)

B. Varying the Conditions of Enzyme Action

In part A of this Procedure, the enzyme action occurred in the mouth, in its normal situation (in vivo: Latin: in a live [condition]). To test the effectiveness of ptyalin under other conditions, the enzyme action must take place outside the mouth (in vitro: Latin: in glass— that is, in a test tube, beaker, etc.). We shall test the effects of varying temperature and different pH's (see Exercise 9.5) on the ability of ptyalin to catalyze the change of starch to maltose.

Using paraffin, collect saliva from the students who provided the saliva used in part A. You will need seven test tubes, each containing saliva to a depth of about 2 cm. Using a wide-range pH test paper, determine the approximate pH of the collected saliva.

1. Place the first test tube in a beaker containing water at 37°C. Add a few drops of starch solution to the tube. Allow the tube to remain in the water bath ten minutes. Then remove and test for sugar.

2. Place the second test tube in a beaker containing boiling water. Add a few drops of starch solution to the tube. Allow the tube to remain in the water bath ten minutes. Then remove and test for sugar.

3. Place the third test tube in a beaker containing crushed ice. Add a few drops of starch solution to the tube. Allow the tube to remain in the ice ten minutes. Then remove and test for starch.

4. To the fourth test tube add an equal volume of hydrochloric acid solution, pH 6. Mix by rolling the tube between the palms of the hands. Place the tube in a beaker containing water at 37°C. Add a few drops of starch solution. Allow the tube to remain in the bath ten minutes. Then remove and test for sugar.

5. To the fifth test tube add an equal volume of hydrochloric acid solution, pH 3. Mix by rolling the tube between the palms of the hands. Place the tube in a beaker containing water at 37°C. Add a few drops of starch solution. Allow the tube to remain in the bath ten minutes. Then remove and test for sugar.

6. To the sixth test tube add an equal volume of sodium hydroxide solution, pH 8. Mix, and place in a beaker containing water at 37°C. Add a few drops of starch solution. Allow the tube to remain in the bath ten minutes. Then remove and test for sugar.

7. To the seventh test tube add an equal volume of sodium hydroxide solution, pH 11. Mix, and place in a beaker containing water at 37°C. Add a few drops of starch solution. Allow the tube to remain in the bath ten minutes. Then remove and test for sugar.

STUDYING THE DATA

If the work has been divided among teams, assemble the data on the chalkboard. Under which conditions of temperature and pH does the enzyme work in vivo? (2) Which (if any) results show that the enzyme also works in vitro if the conditions of temperature and pH are similar to those in the mouth? (3)

Use the data to work out a general statement concerning the effect of temperature variation on the action of the enzyme. (4) Use the data to work out a general statement concerning the effect of pH variation on the action of the enzyme. (5) Would you expect intracellular enzymes to be more sensitive or less sensitive to variations in temperature and pH than is the extracellular enzyme? Why? (6)

CHAPTER 13

The Functioning Plant

EXERCISE 13.1

SEPARATION OF THE PIGMENTS THAT OCCUR IN LEAVES

INTRODUCTION

How does the biochemist know that the green color of leaves is the result of a mixture of several kinds of pigments? Obviously he cannot know unless he has some method of separating the pigments from the leaves and from each other. The separation from one another of the multitude of substances found in protoplasm is the first step in any biochemical study. Many methods are used to accomplish this. Substances that are soluble in water (sugars, for example) are easily separated from substances that are insoluble in water (fats, for example). But many substances found in organisms are so much alike that the usual methods of separation employed by chemists fail.

In the late nineteenth century chromatography was discovered by a Russian chemist. At first this method was used (as its name implies) only to separate substances that have color—pigments. By the 1930's, however, ways of applying chromatography to the separation of colorless substances had been developed. And to the original technique— which involved separation on paper—had been added techniques involving separation on other materials. Many new lines of investigation were opened to biochemists by the development of the chromatographic techniques. During the past thirty years great progress in biochemistry has resulted.

PURPOSE

In this exercise we shall use the simplest kind of chromatography to separate some of the pigments that occur in leaves.

MATERIALS AND EQUIPMENT (for each team)

1. Paper clip
2. Cork (to fit the larger test tube)
3. Filter paper
4. Scissors
5. Test tube, 25 X 200 mm
6. Solvent (8% acetone, 92% petroleum ether)
7. Test-tube rack
8. Spinach leaves
9. Fine sand
10. Acetone
11. Mortar and pestle
12. Cheesecloth
13. Cleansing tissue
14. Funnel
15. Funnel support
16. Test tube, 18 X 150 mm
17. Pencils, 2
18. Pipette, with a very fine tip

PROCEDURE

Assemble the apparatus shown in Figure 13.1-1; but do not add the solvent yet. Bend a paper clip into the shape of a long J and force the long end into the bottom of a cork. Cut a strip of filter paper so that its width is slightly less than the inside diameter of the larger test tube and its length is such that it will hang as shown in the figure. Cut notches in the strip, as shown. Pour solvent into the test tube to a depth of about 1.5 cm. Place the cork with the hook attached (but without the strip of filter paper) in the test tube. Place the tube in an upright position in a rack.

Place two or three spinach leaves, a little fine sand, and about 5 ml of acetone in a mortar, and grind thoroughly. Place a layer of cheesecloth in a funnel, and add a layer of cleansing tissue. Pour the acetone (which now contains the extracted pigment) into the funnel, and collect the filtrate in the smaller test tube. What is the color of the filtrate? (1) Is there any evidence that more than one pigment is dissolved in the acetone? (2)

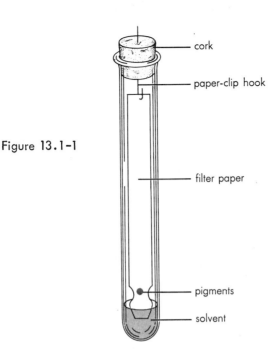

Figure 13.1-1

cork

paper-clip hook

filter paper

pigments

solvent

Support the strip of filter paper across two pencils so that the portion between the notches does not touch the table. Using a fine-pointed pipette, place a drop of the pigment extract on the paper, between the notches. Allow the drop to dry. Add another drop in the same place, and allow it to dry. Repeat until a total of four drops have been placed on the paper—one on top of another. When the final drop has dried, remove the cork from the test tube, hang the strip on it, and place it in the test tube. The level of the solvent must be well below the spot—about 1 cm below. Be sure the cork is tight. Watch the solvent rise in the filter paper. When the upper edge of the solvent almost reaches the hook, remove the cork (with the filter paper attached) from the tube and hold it until the solvent has dried.

STUDYING THE DATA

Examine the chromatogram. How many bands of color can you see? (3) How many of the bands might be made up of chlorophylls? (4) What other colors can you see in the chromatogram? (5) Why can't you see these pigments in the leaf? (6) Suggest a hypothesis to explain the change of color that often occurs when a leaf dies. (7)

Now consider the process by which the pigments were separated. How do you know that all the pigments were soluble in the solvent you used? (8) From what point did all the pigments start as the solvent began to rise? (9) What can you say about the time in which all the pigments were moving? (10) In what characteristic, then, must the pigments have differed? (11)

FOR FURTHER INVESTIGATION

1. Why were the leaf pigments studied in Exercise 13.1 extracted with acetone? Why was water not used? What liquids besides acetone can be used to extract these pigments from the leaf?

2. Are there any leaf pigments that are not extracted by acetone? If so, what are they, and how can they be extracted?

3. What effect does the nature of the solvent have on the success of chromatography? Try 100-percent acetone, 100-percent petroleum ether, different mixtures of these two, alcohol, and various mixtures with alcohol. Does the nature of the pigments you are trying to separate affect the success of chromatography? Using some of the solvents listed above, try separating other pigments, such as those in the black or blue inks of ball-point pens.

EXERCISE 13.2

LOSS OF WATER BY PLANTS

PURPOSE

The purpose of this exercise is to measure the effect of one environmental factor upon transpiration from a leafy shoot.

MATERIALS AND EQUIPMENT (for each team)

1. Two-hole stopper (to fit flask)
2. Glass tubing, bent to a right angle
3. Large battery jar or bowl
4. Rubber tubing, about 20 cm long
5. Leafy shoot (all teams but one)
6. Solid glass rod (one team only)
7. Scalpel
8. Erlenmeyer flask, 500 ml
9. Water at room temperature
10. Collodion or warm paraffin
11. Pipette, 1 ml or 5 ml
12. Cork (with hole to fit pipette)
13. Burette clamp

14. Ring stand
15. Watch
16. Graph paper, 1 sheet per student
17. Pencils, 3 colors

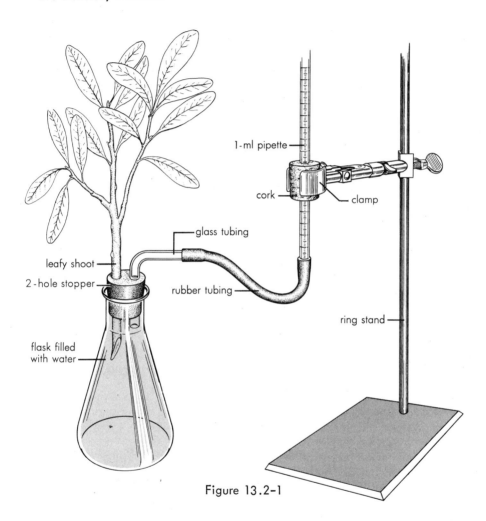

1-ml pipette

cork

clamp

glass tubing

leafy shoot

2-hole stopper

rubber tubing

ring stand

flask filled
with water

Figure 13.2-1

PROCEDURE

Set up the apparatus shown in Figure 13.2-1, as follows: Into one
hole of à two-hole stopper insert a length of glass tubing bent to a right
angle. Attach a length of rubber tubing to the glass tubing. Hold the
leafy shoot under water and cut off about 2 cm of the stem. Keep the
cut end of the shoot under water while inserting it in the second hole
of the stopper. (One of the teams should substitute a piece of solid
glass rod for the leafy shoot.) The stem should fit snugly in the hole.
Fill a flask to the brim with water at room temperature. Quickly in-

sert the stopper—with the shoot (or glass rod) and the tubing—into the flask. (CAUTION: Remove books and papers from the table; inserting the stopper will cause some overflow.) It is necessary to have the flask full in order to force water upward into the tubing. Seal the apparatus—especially where the stem and stopper are joined—with collodion or paraffin.

Insert a pipette through a cork. Slide the cork about halfway up the length of the pipette. Fill the pipette with water. Hold your index finger over the top of the pipette and insert the lower end into the rubber tubing that is connected to the flask. Seal connections with collodion or paraffin. Clamp the cork containing the pipette to a stand, for support.

As soon as the apparatus is assembled, note the position of the top of the water column in the pipette. In your data book record the position and the time at which the reading was taken. Two minutes later again note the position of the water column, and record. Continue to take readings at two-minute intervals until you have five readings.

As soon as the fifth reading has been taken, begin to fan the air near the leafy shoot. Members of the team should take turns fanning. At two-minute intervals record the position of the water column in the pipette until five readings have been made.

As soon as the fifth reading (tenth since the beginning) has been made, cover the leafy shoot loosely with a plastic bag. Gather the mouth of the bag together and tie it shut around the base of the stem. At two-minute intervals record the position of the water column in the pipette until five readings have been made.

STUDYING THE DATA

Considering the design of the apparatus, at what points may water have been lost from it? (1) Considering the results from the team that operated the control setup, what happened to the water in the apparatus? (2) Does the plastic bag provide any confirmation of this? If so, how? (3) How can you determine the amount of water lost from the apparatus? (4)

Plot your data in the form of a graph. Plot time along the abscissa and the pipette readings along the ordinate. As you draw the line, use a different color to represent each of the three conditions of the leafy shoot: (a) uncovered and air still, (b) uncovered and air fanned, and (c) covered.

What is the variable in this set of data? (5) How can you account for any changes in the slope of your graph line? (6)

CONCLUSIONS

You did not participate in the design of this experiment, but judging from the apparatus it should be easy to state the hypothesis that the designer had in mind.   What do you think it was?(7)   Do your data confirm the hypothesis? If so, how?(8)

EXERCISE 13.3

CHEMICAL ACTION IN A PLANT

PURPOSE

The purpose of this exercise is to demonstrate the presence in living plant tissues of a substance that brings about a chemical change.

MATERIALS AND EQUIPMENT (for each team)

1. Corn grains, 6
2. Paper towels, 2
3. Beakers, 2
4. Formalin-acetic alcohol (FAA)
5. Glass-marking crayon
6. Petri dishes containing sterile starch agar, 3
7. Petri dish containing sterile plain agar
8. Scalpel
9. Forceps
10. Iodine solution
11. Medicine dropper
12. Tes-tape

PROCEDURE

Day 1

Soak a paper towel in water. Wrap three corn grains in the towel. Place an inverted beaker over the towel.

Day 3

Remove the grains from the towel and place them in formalin-acetic alcohol (FAA), a fluid that kills and preserves the grains. Soak another paper towel in water. Wrap three more corn grains in the towel. Place an inverted beaker over the towel.

Day 5

Number three petri dishes containing sterile starch agar 1, 2, and 3. Number a dish containing sterile plain agar 4.

Take two corn grains from the second towel. Using a scalpel, cut the grains longitudinally and parallel to the flat surfaces (Figure 13.3-1). Using the forceps, carefully place each half-grain (cut surface downward) on the starch agar in Dish 1. (See Figure 7.2-2 for technique of preserving sterile conditions in dish.) Avoid pressure that might break the surface of the agar. Using the same techniques, cut two of the corn grains that were killed and preserved on Day 3, and place the four halves of these grains on the agar in Dish 2. Nothing is to be added to Dishes 3 and 4. Put all the dishes in a place designated by your teacher.

Cut the two remaining corn grains and test the cut surfaces with iodine solution. Note the result in your data book.

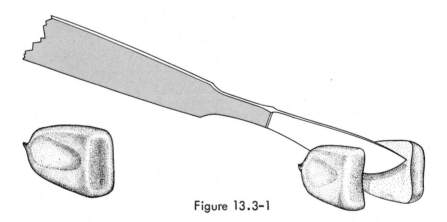

Figure 13.3-1

Day 7 or 8

Remove the lids from all the dishes. Using forceps, carefully remove the half-grains from the surface of the agar. Place small strips of Tes-tape over the places where the grains lay in Dishes 1 and 2. Test the surfaces of the other dishes with Tes-tape. Record the results in your data book.

Using a medicine dropper, add iodine solution to all four dishes until the agar in each is completely covered with the solution; then pour off the excess. In your data book record the appearance of the agar in each dish—either in words or by means of labeled sketches.

STUDYING THE DATA

First, compare the results in Dish 1 with the results in Dish 3. Explain the differences. (1) What kind of substance may have been involved in the action that occurred? (2) What name can be given to it (see Exercise 12.6)? (3) Compare the results in Dish 1 with the results in Dish 2. Explain the differences, if any. (4) What is the purpose of Dish 4? (5)

CONCLUSION

What do the results of this experiment reveal about the physiology of a germinating seed? (6)

FOR FURTHER INVESTIGATION

Is the enzyme detected in Exercise 13.3 present in dormant corn grains, or does it develop as the grain germinates? Plan and carry out a procedure that will provide data to answer this question.

EXERCISE 13.4

CHEMICAL CONTROL OF PLANT GROWTH

INTRODUCTION

The experiments of Darwin, Boysen-Jensen, Went, and others established that chemical substances influence the growth of plants (text pages 444-447). These experiments arose from curiosity concerning the bending of plants toward or away from light.

As frequently happens in science, the results of these experiments have led to much more than satisfaction of the curiosity that started the investigation. Practical uses of the chemical substances discovered have encouraged further experimentation. This has in turn resulted in a large amount of information. As yet, however, attempts to gather the information into a general statement (principle) have not been successful.

PURPOSE

This exercise adds to the text discussion of chemical growth substances by means of experiments dealing with two questions: (1) How does the application of indoleacetic acid to the stem of a plant affect the phototropic response? (2) How does the application of indoleacetic acid affect the growth of a plant that has lost its terminal bud?

MATERIALS AND EQUIPMENT (for each team)

1. Young bean plants, in individual pots, 5
2. Pot labels, wooden, 5
3. Indoleacetic acid in lanolin
4. Swab stick
5. Scissors

PROCEDURE

Experiment A

Choose five plants that have straight stems and that are at approximately the same stage of development. Using wooden labels, mark two of the pots 1 and 2. Put these two plants in a place where they will receive most of their illumination from one side. Do not change their position until the experiment is completed. Apply a thin layer of lanolin containing indoleacetic acid to the illuminated side of the stem of Plant 1. Repeat the application daily for four days. Leave Plant 2 untreated.

Experiment B

Using wooden labels, mark the remaining pots 3, 4, and 5. Place these plants where they will receive illumination from all sides; if this is impossible, turn each plant 90 degrees every day until the experiment is completed. With scissors remove the terminal bud from Plant 3. Leave Plant 4 intact. Remove the terminal bud from Plant 5 and cover the cut end of the stem with a thick coat of lanolin containing indoleacetic acid. Maintain the coating of lanolin throughout the experiment.

OBSERVATIONS

Observe Plants 1 and 2 daily for one week. Record observations in your data book. Observe Plants 3, 4, and 5 weekly for four weeks. Note especially any increase in the number of lateral buds, the development of such buds, the production of flowers, and the general shape of the plants. Be sure to keep separate notes for each plant and identify all observations with the correct plant number. Some students may find sketching the most convenient way to record observations.

STUDYING THE DATA

Experiment A

Did Plant 1 bend as it grew? If so, in what direction (with respect to the light) did it bend? (1) Did Plant 2 bend as it grew? If so, in what direction? (2) Was there a difference between the two plants in the amount of bending? If so, which plant bent more? (3) Taking into account only the facts of this experiment, attempt to explain any difference that occurred in the bending of the two plants. (4)

Experiment B

Compare Plants 3 and 4. How does the presence or absence of a terminal bud seem to affect the growth of the plants? (5) Compare Plant 5 with Plants 3 and 4. Which does it most resemble? (6) What effect does indoleacetic acid seem to have on the growth of the plant? (7)

CONCLUSIONS

Assuming that some substance causes a normal plant to bend to-ward a light source, give as many explanations as you can for the effects of indoleacetic acid in Experiment A. (8)

Considering Plant 4 as the control, how can you explain the re-sults of Experiment B?

FOR FURTHER INVESTIGATION

1. It is not difficult to show the effects of natural auxin by the method illustrated in text Figure 13.30. The oat seedlings are used when the coleoptile (the first shoot) is about 1.5 cm high. About 3 mm of the tip is cut off in making the test.

2. Indolebutyric acid and alpha naphthalene acetic acid are two other substances that have growth-promoting effects on plants. How do these effects compare with those of indoleacetic acid under the conditions of the experiments in this exercise?

3. Are the results of these experiments dependent upon the species of plant used?

EXERCISE 13.5

PHOTOSYNTHETIC RESERVES

INTRODUCTION

Each of us has two eyes, two lungs, two kidneys, intestines sev-eral meters long, thirty-two teeth (when all have been developed), and so on. Yet many persons live comfortably and efficiently after loss of one eye, one lung, one kidney, some of the intestine, or some of the teeth. It seems that there is a "reserve capacity for life," a margin of safety in the normal quantities of organs.

Is there a similar reserve in plants? Leaves are important plant organs that are frequently damaged or destroyed by insects, fungus diseases, and storms. Since leaves provide the plant with food, it might be expected that loss of leaves would affect the growth of the plant. Sometimes simple observations seem to show that extensive loss of leaves does affect a plant; sometimes there seems to be little effect. Here is a matter in which quantitative experimental methods rather than simple observations are required.

PURPOSE

This experiment is designed to provide evidence that can be used in answering the following question: To what extent is the growth of a plant affected by the loss of photosynthetic function in its leaves?

MATERIALS AND EQUIPMENT (for each team)

1. Young plants in individual pots, 5 (each bearing four leaves) or 6 (each bearing five leaves)
2. Pot labels, wooden, 5 or 6
3. Metric ruler
4. Thin aluminum foil (amount depends upon size of leaves)
5. Graph paper, 1 sheet per student
6. Pencils, 5 or 6 colors

PROCEDURE

All the plants used in this experiment by any one team must be of the same species and must have the same number of leaves. If a comparison between species is desired, some teams may work with different kinds of plants.

Using the pot labels, number the plants. Measure the height of each plant to the nearest millimeter, and record the measurements in your data book. Do nothing further with Plant 1. Carefully wrap light aluminum foil around the lowest leaf of Plant 2. Use only enough foil to cover both sides of the leaf, excluding light. To avoid putting pressure on the leaf and to allow for ventilation, wrap the foil loosely. Wrap foil around the two lowest leaves of Plant 3. Wrap foil around the three lowest leaves of Plant 4, and so on, until the last plant has all leaves covered.

Place the plants in a position where all will receive the same amount of light. Water the plants daily.

Every day for ten to fourteen days, measure each plant and record the data. Also note any changes in the size or color of uncovered leaves and the size and number of any new leaves that develop.

STUDYING THE DATA

Using a different color for each plant, plot the height data on one grid (time on the abscissa, height on the ordinate). Which plant is the control in this experiment?(1)   Compare the growth curve of each of the other plants with the curve of the control plant. Is the final height of the control greater than that of the experimentals?   Is there relationship between height and the number of leaves that carried on photosynthesis? If so, what is the relationship?(2) Did the plant with all leaves covered continue to grow?   If so, how can you explain the continued growth?(3) Do you have any evidence that loss of function in some leaves brings about changes in other leaves?   If so, what is the evidence?(4)

CONCLUSIONS

On the basis of your data, write a brief statement answering the question with which this experiment began.(5) If your class experimented with more than one species of plant, did you find differences among species in response to the experimental treatment? If so, were the differences in the kind of response, in the amount of response, or in both?(6)

FOR FURTHER INVESTIGATION

1. Height is a convenient measure of growth—but not the best. In this exercise you were concerned with the amount of new living material produced by the plant. For this, weight is a better measure (see Exercise 3.2). Do the conclusions obtained from weighing plants agree with the conclusions obtained from measuring height?

EXERCISE 13.6

RATE OF GROWTH: LEAVES

INTRODUCTION

Growth is one of the characteristic processes of living things. In Exercises 2.1, 2.2, and 2.3, we studied the rate at which populations grow under various conditions. The growth rates of individual organisms—or even of particular <u>parts</u> of individuals—are also of interest to biologists. From investigation of many kinds of biological growth rates it may be possible to develop some generalizations about growth as a process.

In Exercise 3.5 the growth rates of whole individual plants were studied, but attention was centered on experimental conditions rather than on natural growth. Now we will study natural growth rate in only part of a plant—two leaves.

Within the seed of any spermatophyte an embryo plant exists; in most cases much of the embryo consists of a bud. In the text (page 443) it was pointed out that the multiplication of leaf cells takes place chiefly while the leaf is still in a bud. And the expansion of the leaf from the bud is largely a result of the enlargement of cells. A simple and convenient study of growth can be made by beginning with the leaves in this embryonic bud.

PURPOSE

In this exercise the growth rate of the first pair of leaves of a spermatophyte is measured under natural conditions and compared with other growth rates.

MATERIALS AND EQUIPMENT (for each team)

1. Bean seeds, 18
2. Beaker, 250 ml
3. Fungicide solution
4. Scalpel
5. Hand lens
6. Metric ruler

7. Seed flat or box
8. Sand or vermiculite
9. Graph paper, 1 sheet per student

PROCEDURE

Select eighteen bean seeds of approximately the same size. Place in a beaker. Add fungicide solution to the seeds until the volume of the solution is approximately twice that of the seeds. Allow the seeds to remain in the fungicide twenty minutes. Then pour off the solution and rinse the seeds thoroughly with water. Fill the beaker with water and leave the seeds in it overnight.

After twenty-four hours take three of the seeds from the beaker. Using a scalpel, cut carefully through the seed coat of each of the three beans. Remove the seed coats and open the beans. Using a hand lens, find the embryo plant that lies between the two large cotyledons in each seed. Measure the length of the embryo leaves in each seed. In your data book, record the measurements and calculate the average.

Plant the remaining fifteen seeds about 1.5 cm deep and 5 cm apart in sand or vermiculite. After planting, water thoroughly; provide abundant light and a relatively constant temperature; keep the "soil" damp but not flooded.

On Days 3, 6, 10, 13, 17, and 20 after planting, measure the length of the first two leaves of three plants to the nearest millimeter. On Day 3 (and possibly on Day 6 also) you may find it necessary to dig up three germinated seeds, since the plants may not have grown above the surface. If this is necessary, discard these seeds after you have made your measurements. After the plants appear above the soil, measure the leaves on the <u>same</u> <u>three</u> <u>plants</u> each measurement day. Make the measurement along the center vein (midrib) of each leaf, from the apex to the base; do not include the length of the petiole. Average the measurements each day.

STUDYING THE DATA

Plot the data (time on the abscissa, average length of leaves on the ordinate), and draw a graph. The rate of growth is indicated by the slope of the graph line. Does the slope change? If so, describe the change. (1) When did the most rapid growth occur? (2) Are there fluctuations? If so, try to explain them. (3) Compare this graph with the ones you drew in Exercises 2.1, 2.2, and 2.3. Which does this one most resemble? (4) In which part of the graphs—beginning, middle, or end—is there most resemblance? (5)

SUMMARY

From your study of the graphs, what general statements can you make that apply to all of them? (6)

FOR FURTHER INVESTIGATION

1. Obtaining data on the growth of individual plants through maturity usually requires a considerable amount of time. Figure 13.6-1 shows data on the growth of a bamboo—a plant that grows quite rapidly. Draw a graph from these data. Compare it with the graph of leaf growth.

2. Is the shape of a growth-rate graph influenced by the kind of measurement recorded? Weight rather than a linear measurement has frequently been used in growth studies. The data in Figure 13.6-2 were obtained from a field of corn. Every two weeks after the seedlings appeared above ground, several plants were pulled and weighed. The weights were averaged and recorded. Graph these data, and compare the graph with other growth-rate graphs.

AGE (in weeks)	AVERAGE HEIGHT (in meters)
1	0.7
2	1.5
3	2.5
4	4.0
5	6.2
6	8.3
7	10.2
8	12.0
9	13.2
10	13.8
11	14.1
12	14.2

AGE (in weeks)	AVERAGE WEIGHT (in grams)
2	21
4	28
6	58
8	76
10	170
12	422
14	706
16	853
18	924
20	966

Figure 13.6-1   Figure 13.6-2

EXERCISE 13.7

TRANSPORT OF PHOSPHATES IN PLANTS

INTRODUCTION

Radioactive isotopes of elements important in plant metabolism have many uses in the study of plant physiology. Their use in unraveling the biochemistry of photosynthesis (text pages 418 and 423) involves more apparatus and skill than are usually found in the high school biology laboratories. But radioactive isotopes can be used in studying other plant functions if a few precautions are observed.

PURPOSE

This exercise is designed to show the use of a radioactive isotope in tracing the transport of phosphates through a land plant.

BACKGROUND INFORMATION

Because it is present in ATP, phosphorus is clearly a necessary element for organisms (text pages 391-392). Land plants usually obtain phosphorus from the soil in the form of phosphate ions. Chemists can produce phosphates containing atoms of P^{32}, an isotope of phosphorus that is radioactive. By giving plants solutions of such phosphates and then locating the radioactive areas, the movement of phosphates through a plant can be traced.

The human body cannot detect radioactivity. But such energy can be detected with instruments that indicate its presence by means of clicks in an earphone or flashes of light. However, for locating radioactive substances in the body of a plant, a photographic method is preferable. The small bursts of energy given off by a radioactive substance affect a photographic film in the same way that light does. When such film is developed, dark areas will appear wherever it has been exposed to radioactivity. The greater the concentration of radioactivity, the darker the area. Therefore, photographic film can be used to indicate the location and intensity of a radioactive substance within an organism.

MATERIALS AND EQUIPMENT (for each team)

1. Gauze
2. Metric ruler
3. Adhesive tape
4. Scissors
5. Medicine dropper
6. Sodium phosphate solution containing 10 microcuries of P^{32}
7. Tomato plants growing in vermiculite, 2
8. Beaker, 250 ml
9. Thin stick, about 25 cm high
10. Distilled water
11. Blotting paper (slightly larger than 12.5 X 17.5 cm), 4 pieces
12. Paper towels
13. Waste jar (marked "Radioactive Waste")
14. Forceps
15. Thin plastic sheets (such as Saran), 12.5 X 17.5 cm, 4
16. Darkroom
17. Photographic film, 12.5 X 17.5 cm
18. Film holders, 2 (see Figure 13.7-1)
19. Developing solution
20. Fixing solution

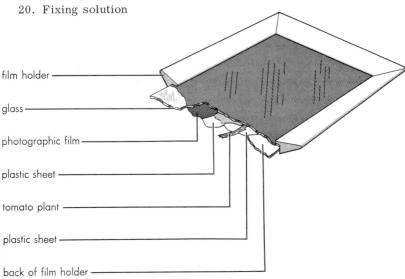

film holder
glass
photographic film
plastic sheet
tomato plant
plastic sheet
back of film holder

Figure 13.7-1

PROCEDURE

Prepare a gauze pad containing four to eight thicknesses and measuring 1.5 cm^2. Cut a strip of adhesive tape 2 X 8 cm and attach the pad to it. Using a medicine dropper, place a few drops of radioactive phosphate solution on the pad. The pad should be saturated but not dripping. (CAUTION: Handle only the adhesive tape; keep your fingers off the pad!) Apply the pad to a leaf of a tomato plant, fastening it in place with the adhesive tape. Pour the remainder of the radioactive phosphate solution into a beaker.

With a pencil, loosen the vermiculite around the base of the second tomato plant. Carefully remove the plant from the vermiculite. Try to avoid damaging the root system. Carefully shake off as much of the vermiculite from the roots as you can. Place the plant in the beaker so that the root system is in the radioactive sodium phosphate solution. Support the plant by taping a stick to the beaker and to the plant. Add enough distilled water to cover the roots. Place both plants in a cool, shaded place for twenty-four hours.

Draw pencil lines on a piece of blotting paper to form a rectangle 12.5 X 17.5 cm. Label this paper A. Remove the first tomato plant from the vermiculite. Carefully peel off the adhesive tape. Place the tape and the gauze pad in the jar marked "Radioactive Waste." Place the plant inside the rectangle drawn on Paper A. Spread the leaves so that they are flat but not lying on top of each other. Spread the roots as much as possible. Bend the stem if necessary—all parts of the plant should be inside the pencil lines. Cover with another piece of blotting paper, then with several layers of paper towel. Finally, place a large book or other weight on top.

Draw a rectangle 12.5 X 17.5 cm on another sheet of blotting paper. Label this paper B. Lift the second tomato plant just enough to raise the roots out of the solution in the beaker. Shake as much solution off the roots as you can. (CAUTION: Shake inside the beaker; do not splatter drops outside!) Spread this plant on the blotting paper as directed for the first plant. (CAUTION: Use forceps to spread the roots!) Cover, and add a weight.

After twenty-four hours, uncover the plants. Place the plant from Paper A on a sheet of thin plastic marked A. Cover with another sheet of thin plastic. Place the plant from Paper B on a sheet of thin plastic marked B. Cover with another sheet of plastic. In a darkroom hold each wrapped plant against a sheet of photographic film and place in a film holder (Figure 13.7-1). Store in the dark for three days.

After three days, develop both films. (Avoid confusing A and B.) Place the plants and the plastic sheets in the jar marked "Radioactive Waste."

CONCLUSIONS

Consider Film B first. Into what parts of the plant was the P^{32} absorbed? (1) In what parts does the radiograph (it isn't a photograph, because no light is involved) indicate the greatest concentration of P^{32} after twenty-four hours? (2)

Now consider Film A. What evidence do you have, if any, that phosphates can be absorbed through the leaf of a plant? (3)

CHAPTER 14

The Functioning Animal

EXERCISE 14.1

ANIMAL STRUCTURE AND FUNCTION: THE FROG

INTRODUCTION

Frogs have long been used for studying animal anatomy and physiology. Of course, we know from Chapter 4 that no one species can be used to fully illustrate animal structure and function. But the use of frogs has some advantages: they are of a convenient size, they are easily obtained, they are easily kept in the laboratory, and they are comparatively cheap. Still more important, they are vertebrates—they are enough like man to throw some light on our own structure and function. Yet, they are sufficiently unlike man to provide some important contrasts.

PURPOSE

This exercise provides an opportunity for direct observation of the structure and function of a vertebrate.

MATERIALS AND EQUIPMENT (for each team)

A. The Live Frog

1. Live frog
2. Cord, 60 cm
3. Ruler
4. Forceps
5. Live mealworms (or small earthworms)
6. Aquariums, at least 60 cm long and containing water to a depth of at least 10 cm, 2 (for the whole class)

B. Dissection of Pithed Frog

1. Pithed frog
2. Dissecting pan
3. Pins, 10
4. Forceps
5. Scissors
6. Scalpel
7. Watch with a second hand
8. Pipette
9. Sodium chloride crystals
10. Petri dish
11. Distilled water
12. Slide
13. Sugar solution
14. Medicine dropper
15. Monocular microscope
16. Paper towel
17. Saline solution (0.7% sodium chloride)
18. Plastic bag
19. Glass-marking crayon
20. Rubber band
21. Refrigerator

C. Dissection of Dead Frog

1. Dead frog (from Part B)
2. Dissecting pan
3. Pins, 10
4. Forceps
5. Hand lens
6. Scissors

PROCEDURE

A. The Live Frog

Each team will be provided with a live frog. Moisten the top of the table where the frog will be placed. To aid in handling the animal, a piece of cord has been tied to one leg. Tie the other end of the cord to a leg of the table or to any other fixed object. Sit quietly by the table and allow time for the frog to become accustomed to its sur- roundings. By avoiding sudden motions, you will increase your op- portunities for making accurate observations.

Compare the general structure of the frog's body with that of your own. Think of your body as consisting of a head, neck, trunk, and four appendages. Which (if any) of these is lacking in the frog?(1) Consider a cat, cow, or lizard. What major division of the body is present in these and many other vertebrates but is lacking in the structure of both frog and man?(2) Place the edge of a ruler along the backbone of the frog. Compare the structure to the left and to the right of the backbone. What kind of symmetry (Exercise 4.1, page 67) does the frog's body have? Your body?(3)

Locate the eyes, the nostrils, and the ears. In what ways do the frog's eyes differ from yours?(4) The ears are located behind and below the eyes. The eardrum is stretched across the ear opening. How do your ears differ from those of the frog?(5)

In the human body each of the upper appendages consists of a series of parts called the upper arm, the forearm, the wrist, the hand, and the fingers; each of the lower appendages consists of the thigh, shank, ankle, foot, and toes. Which (if any) of these parts is lacking in the appendages of the frog?(6) In what ways do the terminal parts (those farthest from the trunk) of the frog's appendages differ from those of man?(7) In what ways does the skin of the frog differ from yours?(8)

You will have to observe very carefully to see the breathing mo- tions of the frog. Ducts lead from the nostrils to the posterior part of the mouth cavity. Without touching the frog, observe the floor of the mouth (upper throat); when it is lowered, the mouth cavity enlarges. From where can air come to fill the enlarged mouth cavity?(9) As the floor of the mouth is raised, where can the air in the mouth cavity go?(10) Observe the motion of the nostrils. How does this motion relate to the motion of the floor of the mouth?(11) When you breathe, where does the principal motion occur?(12) Can you breathe with your mouth open? Can the frog?(13) With forceps, pick up a live worm. Slowly move the worm toward the frog until it is within 10 cm of the frog's head and on about the same level. If the frog takes the worm, describe the action, noting the tongue, the arms, the throat, and the eyes.(14)

Using the eraser end of a pencil, gently prod the frog until it jumps. What is the function of each pair of appendages in the jumping process?(15) You can leap somewhat as the frog does, but the frog cannot stand erect as you do. By examining the structure of the frog's legs and trunk, give evidence to support the preceding statement. (16)

Remove the cord from the frog's leg. Place the frog in the water at one end of a large aquarium. Observe the motions used in swimming. How are the toes used in swimming? (17) What structure is associated with the toes in swimming? (18) Are these structures present on the fingers? (19) Try to get the frog to float. What is the position of the eyes, ears, and nostrils with respect to the surface of the water? (20) Hold the frog under water for two minutes. Do you observe any breathing movements? Try to explain. (21) While the frog is under water, do you see any eye structure that is lacking in man? If so, describe it. (22) Return the live frog to the container designated by your teacher.

B. Dissection of Pithed Frog

Each team will be provided with a frog in which the nervous system has been destroyed—a pithed frog. Although such an animal can have no sense of feeling, its tissues remain active for a considerable period of time, allowing direct observation of several kinds of functions.

Place the frog on the dissecting pan, ventral side up. Fasten the frog to the wax in the pan by inserting pins through the ends of the appendages and into the wax. The skin of the frog is attached quite loosely to the muscles. With forceps, hold the skin free from the muscles of the ventral body wall; use scissors to make a small crosswise cut through the skin at the midline of the abdomen (Figure 14.1-1A). Insert one tip of the scissors into this opening, and cut anteriorly along the midline of the body to the region of the throat. Then cut posteriorly along the midline to the region of the anus (Figure 14.1-1B). Next, cut laterally from the ends of the longitudinal incision (Figure 14.1-1C). There are now two flaps of skin that can be opened to the side. To open them fully and pin them down (Figure 14.1-1D), you must separate the skin from the body wall in a few places; a sharp scalpel is the best instrument for this job.

Now open the muscular body wall, following the same procedure used in opening the skin. The organs of the body cavity lie just inside the body wall; therefore, be sure to hold the body wall up from the organs beneath and to insert only the tip of the scissors when cutting. As you cut anteriorly, you will run into the breastbone; be very careful to avoid cutting the organs that lie beneath it. In opening the body wall laterally, you should remove about 1.5 cm of the breastbone. Some effort will be required to open the body wall at the anterior end.

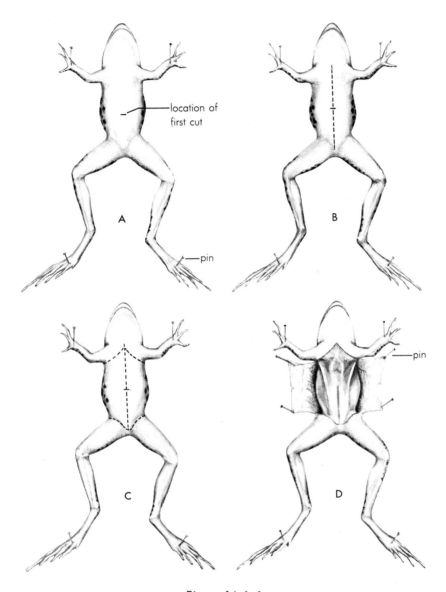

location of
first cut

A

pin

B

C

D

pin

Figure 14.1-1

Observe the beating of the heart. How many times does it contract per minute? (23) Carefully slit the thin, transparent membrane that surrounds the heart. Do the contractions travel from the anterior toward the posterior part of the heart? Vice versa? In neither direction? (24)

Open the mouth and locate the glottis, a slitlike opening in the floor of the mouth. (Do not confuse it with the larger opening into the esophagus.) Insert the end of a pipette into the glottis, and blow gently on the other end of the pipette; if you have located the glottis, the lungs will become inflated as you blow.   Describe their appearance. (25)

Female specimens may contain so many eggs that organs in the posterior part of the body will be difficult to see. If this is true of your specimen, use forceps to remove the eggs and the ovaries (which contain the eggs). Pick the eggs out a few at a time. Avoid disturbing other organs. Attached to the egg masses are white, coiled tubes. These are the oviducts, through which the eggs pass when they are laid. Remove these also, but be careful not to mistake the intestine (Figure 14.1-2) for them.

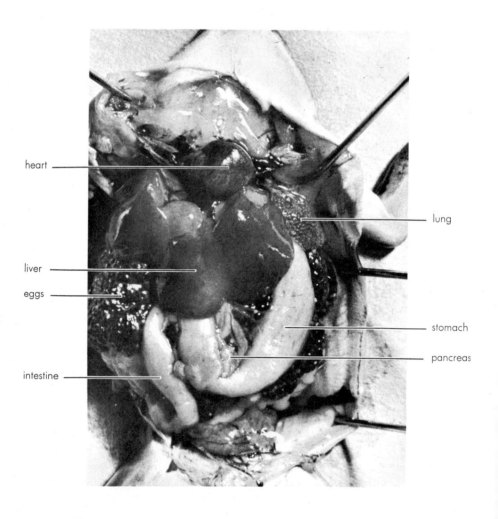

heart

lung

liver

eggs

stomach

pancreas

intestine

Figure 14.1-2.   Ventral view of frog after the body wall has been opened

Sprinkle a few crystals of salt (sodium chloride) along the surface of the intestine. Observe for at least two minutes. Describe any movements of the intestine. (26) Using the scissors, snip the small intestine about 1.5 cm from the stomach and the same distance from the large intestine. Free the small intestine from the mesentery (the membrane that holds it in place) and drop it into a petri dish containing distilled water. Describe any reaction. (27) Now cut a piece about 5 mm long from the intestine in the petri dish. Slit the piece open and spread it out, inner side up, on a slide. Add a drop or two of warm sugar solution and observe (without a cover slip) under low power of a monocular microscope. Note the small projections on the inner wall of the intestine. Describe their activity. (28)

Remove the pins from the frog. Close the body wall and the skin over the body cavity. Wrap the frog in a paper towel that has been dipped in saline solution. Mark a plastic bag with your team symbol. Place the frog in the bag, fasten the bag with a rubber band, and store in a refrigerator.

C. Dissection of Dead Frog

Remove the frog from the plastic bag and paper towel. Pin it to the dissecting pan, as in Procedure B.

Just posterior to the heart is the reddish-brown liver. How many lobes (sections) does it have? (29) On the right side (from the frog's point of view) the liver covers the gall bladder. Using forceps, raise the liver and find the gall bladder. What color is it? (30) Use a hand lens to find the duct leading from the gall bladder, and trace it as far as possible. Where does it seem to lead? (31)

On the left side of the frog, the liver partially covers the stomach. The diameter of the stomach depends upon the amount of food it contains. In what direction (from the frog's viewpoint) does the stomach curve as you follow it from anterior to posterior end? (32) At its posterior end the stomach leads into the small intestine; where these two portions of the alimentary canal join, a narrow constriction, the pylorus, is visible. Between the inner edge of the curving stomach and the first loop of the intestine is the pancreas gland. After you have located the pylorus and the pancreas, remove the stomach. Using the scissors, slit the stomach along its outer curvature and spread it open. Observe the inner surface with a hand lens. Describe it. (33)

You have already removed most of the small intestine and, if your specimen is a female, the ovaries (containing the eggs) and the oviducts. Now push the mesentery and remaining organs aside and look for the kidneys, which are attached to the back. They are reddish-brown in color. Describe their shape. (34) If your frog is a male, you will find a testis, a yellowish, bean-shaped organ, attached to each kidney. Attached to the anterior end of each kidney is a cluster of yellowish, finger-like structures, the fat bodies; they vary in size, depending upon the season of the year. Compare the fat bodies in your frog with those in frogs dissected by other teams. Are the fat bodies usually larger in males or in females? (35)

Using a hand lens, locate the thin tube that leads from the posterior end of each kidney. To what does it lead? (36)

Dispose of your frog as directed by the teacher.

SUMMARY

On the basis of this exercise and your understanding of your own body, write a brief comparison of the structure and function of frog and man. (37)

FOR FURTHER INVESTIGATION

1.   Divide a group of live frogs into two sets, each containing the same number of individuals. Weigh and mark each frog. Leave one set in a container with a small amount of water overnight; then weigh again. Leave the other set in a container without water overnight; then weigh again. Compare the data from the two sets of frogs. Suggest an explanation.

2.   Remove the entire skin of one of the dead frogs used in Exercise 14.1, and investigate the muscular system. Some of the muscles of frog and man are compared on page 428 of Moment's General Zoology (Boston: Houghton Mifflin Company, 1958).

3.   Prepare one of the frogs as a skeleton. First, remove as much flesh as possible, using scalpel and forceps. This is a rather difficult task because many of the bones are small and delicate; be careful not to cut through the small ones in the appendages and the thin ones in the head. Second, gently simmer the roughed-out skeleton for about thirty minutes in a little water to which some soap powder has been added. Third, gently scrape the remaining flesh from the bones, using a scalpel and a stiff-bristled toothbrush. Finally, using thin wire, assemble the bones in their natural relationship to each other and attach them to a piece of stiff cardboard.

EXERCISE 14.2

DIGESTION OF FATS

INTRODUCTION

In chemical digestion large molecules are broken down into smaller molecules. Chemical digestion is, then, the reverse of synthesis. The syntheses described in Chapter 12 of the text involve the formation of substances that make up most of the foods we (and other animals) eat. Therefore, the digestion of such foods must involve chemical processes that are the reverse of those syntheses.

PURPOSE

In Exercises 12.6 and 13.3 you saw how enzymes digest (that is, break down) starches, forming the sugars from which starches are synthesized. In this exercise the digestion of fats is demonstrated.

BACKGROUND INFORMATION

In previous exercises concerned with digestion, enzymes were obtained directly from living organisms—from human saliva in one case, and from a germinating corn seed in the other. Some enzymes, however, can be stored for considerable periods, especially when they are in a dried form. Enzymes in the pancreatic secretion (text Figure 14.5) of cattle and other "meat" animals are preserved in this manner. The product is a powder called pancreatin.

Since digestion is the reverse of synthesis, you can gain some understanding of the chemistry of fat digestion by referring to the discussion of fat synthesis (text pages 396-397). Water is given off when fats are synthesized, so water is required when fats are digested. For this reason, the process is sometimes called a hydrolysis. (You can find the roots of this term among the marginal notes of the textbook.) The kinds of molecules from which fats are synthesized will, of course, be the products of fat digestion. To determine that fats have been digested, it is necessary to show that these products have been formed. It is difficult to show the presence of glycerol, but the presence of fatty acid can be detected easily by means of indicators (see Exercise 9.5). For this purpose we shall use litmus. If you have not worked with litmus before, test its color change with a known acid.

Bile salts are obtained from the bile of slaughtered animals. Because bile normally occurs in the small intestine, where pancreatic juice also occurs (text page 458), it is reasonable to suppose that bile substances may have some influence on the enzymes in pancreatic juice. Therefore, bile salts are used in one of the experimental setups.

MATERIALS AND EQUIPMENT (for each team)

1. Beaker, 600 ml
2. Ring stand
3. Bunsen burner
4. Thermometer (-10°C to 110°C range)
5. Test tubes, 3
6. Glass-marking crayon
7. Fresh cream, 15 ml
8. Graduated cylinder
9. Litmus solution
10. Medicine dropper
11. Distilled water
12. Bile salts
13. Toothpicks (flat)
14. Pancreatin solution

PROCEDURE

One member of the team will prepare a water bath, as follows: Fill a beaker half-full with water. Heat the water over a Bunsen burner, stirring gently from time to time with a thermometer. When the temperature of the water reaches 37°C, reduce the flame or remove the burner until the temperature begins to drop. Then reapply the heat. In this manner keep the temperature as close to 37°C as possible.

The other members of the team will prepare the test tubes, as follows: Using a glass-marking crayon, number three test tubes, placing the numbers close to the rims of the tubes. Into each tube pour 5 ml of fresh cream. Add 2 ml of litmus solution to each tube, and shake. Note in your data book the color of the mixture in each tube.

To Tube 1 add 2 ml of distilled water and 3 mm³ of bile salts— about the quantity that can be held on the flat end of a toothpick. Shake the tube. To Tube 2 add 2 ml of pancreatin solution and about 3 mm³ of bile salts. Shake the tube. To Tube 3 add 2 ml of pancreatin solution. Shake the tube.

Immediately place all three tubes in the water bath. Continue to maintain the temperature of the bath at 37°C. In your data book record the color in each tube at five-minute intervals for twenty minutes.

CONCLUSIONS

After studying the data, write a short statement giving your conclusions and the reasons for your conclusions. Somewhere in your statement include the following points:
  a. the meaning of any color changes that occurred;
  b. the meaning of any differences among the tubes in speed of color change;
  c. the purpose of Tube 1 in the design of the experiment;
  d. the purpose of the water bath.

EXERCISE 14.3

A HEART AT WORK

INTRODUCTION

One of the early milestones in the development of biological science was the discovery of the circulation of the blood. This occurred in the early part of the seventeenth century—the century of Leeuwenhoek—through the research of an English physician, William Harvey (1578-1657). As a physician, of course, Harvey was interested in the physiology of man; but as a scientist his curiosity pushed his investigations in many directions. In his book, On the Motion of the Heart and Blood, he wrote:

"I have also observed, that almost all animals have truly a heart, not the larger creatures only, and those that have red blood but the smaller and seemingly bloodless ones also, such as slugs, snails, scallops, shrimps, crabs, crayfish, and many others; nay even in wasps, hornets and flies. I have with the aid of a magnifying glass, and at the upper part of what is called the tail, both seen the heart pulsating myself, and shown it to many others."

Without any dissection, direct observation of the <u>pulsating</u> (beating) heart is possible in many kinds of small animals that have transparent bodies. Such animals provide an opportunity to study environmental influences on heart activity with a minimum of disturbance to the organism.

PURPOSE

In this exercise the normal heartbeat of a small animal is studied, and the effects of varying environmental temperature are observed.

BACKGROUND INFORMATION

<u>Daphnia</u> is a genus of crustaceans that occurs abundantly in small bodies of fresh water. Individuals are just about large enough to be seen with the naked eye in good light. Even when magnified only twenty times, many of the internal organs—including the heart—can be seen through the body wall. Become familiar with the appearance of the animal before you begin the Procedure (Figure 14.3-1). It is necessary to watch carefully for the beating of the heart, because the legs beat rhythmically and some internal organs other than the heart move.

MATERIALS AND EQUIPMENT (for each team)

1. <u>Daphnia</u>, in a small beaker of aquarium water, 6 to 8
2. Thermometer (-10°C to 110°C range)
3. Medicine dropper
4. Microscope slide with center depression
5. Paper towel
6. Stereomicroscope
7. Watch with second hand
8. Beaker large enough to hold <u>Daphnia</u> beaker
9. Crushed ice
10. Hot water
11. Graph paper, 1 sheet per student

PROCEDURE

The water in which the <u>Daphnia</u> are living should be allowed to come to room temperature before the experiment begins. Check the temperature of the water with a thermometer. With a medicine drop-

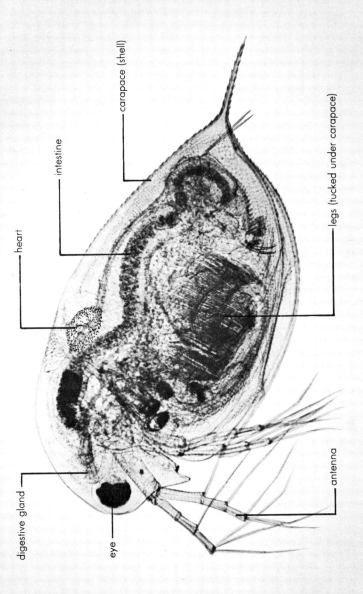

carapace (shell)

intestine

heart

legs (tucked under carapace)

digestive gland

eye

antenna

Figure 14.3-1. Photograph of Daphnia (X 125)

per, transfer one <u>Daphnia</u> to the depression in the slide. Soak up excess water with a piece of paper towel. By keeping the amount of water at a minimum, you increase the likelihood that the animal will lie on its side—the best position for observing heart action.

One member of the team keeps time with a watch while another observes the specimen through the stereomicroscope and counts the heartbeats. It may be difficult to count as rapidly as the heart pulsates. If so, try tapping with a pencil on a piece of paper and then counting the dots. When the counter is ready, the timer says "Go!" At the end of fifteen seconds, he says "Stop!" Multiply the count by 4 to obtain the number of heartbeats per minute. Make at least three timed counts, allowing each member of the team to take a turn as a counter or timer. Return the <u>Daphnia</u> to the beaker.

Place the beaker of <u>Daphnia</u> in a larger beaker containing water and crushed ice. Stir the water in the <u>Daphnia</u> beaker gently with the thermometer. When the water temperature reaches the point assigned to your team by the teacher, <u>quickly</u> transfer a <u>Daphnia</u> to the slide and make at least three counts as quickly as possible.

As soon as the <u>Daphnia</u> is removed from the beaker, members of the team who are not timing or counting should remove the <u>Daphnia</u> beaker from the large beaker, pour out the ice water, and replace it with hot water (50°C to 70°C).

Place the <u>Daphnia</u> beaker in the large beaker again. Stir the water in the <u>Daphnia</u> beaker gently with the thermometer. By the time the water temperature reaches the second point assigned to your team, counting at the lower temperature should be finished. <u>Quickly</u> transfer a <u>Daphnia</u> from the warm water to the slide and make at least three counts as quickly as possible.

STUDYING THE DATA

First, consider the data obtained from <u>Daphnia</u> at room temperature. Why were several counts taken? (1) What factors might account for variability in these data? (2) Assemble on the chalkboard the room-temperature data from all teams. Compare the variability in the data from all teams with the variability in the data from your own team. How can you account for any differences? (3) Calculate the average rate of heartbeat from the assembled class data. (4)

In measuring, reliability is the closeness with which a second measurement approaches a first (see Exercise 7.7, page 137). Which is likely to be more reliable—the average obtained by your team or the average obtained by the entire class? This question can be asked in another way: Which is more likely—that an average obtained by a team in another class would come close to your team's average, or that the average obtained by another class would come close to your class average? Explain. (5)

Now assemble the data on heartbeat at different temperatures. If two or more teams obtained data at the same temperature, calculate a general average for that temperature. Graph the data, plotting rate of heartbeat (abscissae) against temperature (ordinates).

CONCLUSIONS

On the basis of your graph, make a general statement concerning the effects of variation in environmental temperature on the rate of heartbeat in Daphnia. (6) Would you expect similar effects in a cold-blooded vertebrate, such as a frog? (7) In a warm-blooded vertebrate, such as man? (8) Explain your answers to these two questions. (9)

FOR FURTHER INVESTIGATION

1. Young pond snails have thin shells through which the heart can be seen, just as it can in Daphnia. You can use the Procedure in Exercise 14.3 to make a study of snail heartbeat for comparison with that of Daphnia. Try to account for any differences you observe.

2. Rate of heartbeat can be regarded as an indicator of the activity of the nervous system. Thus, the easily observed heart of Daphnia can lead to some understanding of the way in which substances affect the nervous system. Investigate the effects of alcohol (about 5 percent), of tranquilizers (such as chlorpromazine), and of stimulants (such as dexedrine sulfate) on Daphnia heartbeat.

EXERCISE 14.4

CHEMORECEPTORS IN MAN

INTRODUCTION

Chemoreceptors—nerve endings sensitive to chemical substances— are common among animals that have well-defined nervous systems.

Among arthropods they are often found in the antennae. Among vertebrates they are found mostly in the mouth and nasal passages. Students of human physiology think of chemoreceptors as involving the senses of taste and smell.

The study of chemoreceptors among animals other than man is complicated by a lack of communication: How can we find out just what an animal senses? When studying chemoreceptors in man, we can at least obtain descriptions ("sour," "sweet," "bitter," "spicy," etc.) of particular stimuli. But then there are difficulties in interpreting such reports, so that complete understanding of chemoreceptors—even in man—is not easy.

PURPOSE

The purpose of this exercise is to investigate some physiological characteristics of the chemoreceptors associated with taste and smell.

MATERIALS AND EQUIPMENT

A. Location of Taste Receptors (for each pair of students)

1. Syracuse watch glass or other small container
2. Salt solution (10%), 2 ml
3. Applicators (toothpicks with small pledget of cotton wrapped around one end), 4
4. Waste jar (1 for every 6 students)
5. Beakers filled with water, 2
6. Sucrose solution (5%), 2 ml
7. Acetic acid solution (1%), 2 ml
8. Quinine sulfate solution (0.1%), 2 ml

B. Taste Threshold (for each student)

1. Small paper cups, 6
2. Sucrose solutions (0.001%, 0.005%, 0.01%, 0.05%, 0.1%, and 0.5%), 2 to 3 ml of each
3. Salt solutions (0.001%, 0.005%, 0.01%, 0.05%, 0.1%, 0.5%), 2 to 3 ml of each
4. Beaker filled with water
5. Medicine dropper
6. Waste jar (1 for every 6 students)
7. Chalk, 3 colors

C. Relation of Smell to Taste (for teams of 3 students)

1. Handkerchief (for blindfold)
2. Small paper cups, 3 to 6
3. Solutions of orange juice, milk, onion juice, vinegar (2%), sugar, dill-pickle juice (any 3 or all 6)

PROCEDURES

A. Location of Taste Receptors

During Procedure A you will work in pairs. Designate yourself and your partner "A" and "B," and follow directions accordingly.

Student A: Pour about 2 ml of 10-percent salt solution in a watch glass.

Student B: In your data book, make a copy of Figure 14.4-1 and label it Salt.

Student A: Dip an applicator (a small pledget of cotton wrapped around the end of a toothpick) into the solution. Drain excess solution from the applicator. Touch the applicator to the tongue of Student B at the point marked 1 in Figure 14.4-1.

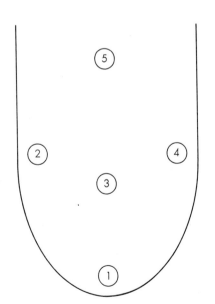

Figure 14.4-1. Diagram of tongue

Student B: At point 1 in your drawing, place a minus sign (-) if you sense no taste of salt, a plus sign (+) if you sense a mild taste of salt, and a double plus (++) if you sense a strong taste of salt.

Student A: As soon as Student B has recorded his sensation, touch the applicator to his tongue at point 2.

Student B: Record your sensation, using the appropriate symbol.

Continue until sensation has been recorded at all five points on the tongue.

Student B: Rinse your mouth with water.

Student A: Break the applicator and discard it. Pour the salt solution from the watch glass into the waste jar. Rinse the watch glass.

Student B: Pour about 2 ml of 10-percent glucose solution into the watch glass.

Student A: In your data book, make a copy of Figure 14.4-1. Label it Sweet.

Student B: Dip an applicator into the glucose solution, drain off excess solution, and touch the applicator to the tongue of Student A at point 1.

Student A: Record your sensation as described on page 253.

Continue until sensation has been recorded at all five points.

Student A: Rinse your mouth with water.

Student B: Break the applicator and discard it. Pour the glucose solution from the watch glass into the waste jar. Rinse the watch glass.

Student A: Pour about 2 ml of 1-percent acetic acid solution into the watch glass.

Student B: Make another copy of Figure 14.4-1 and label it Sour.

Student A: Dip a new applicator into the acid solution and proceed to test Student B, following the procedure described above.

Student B: Record sensation, as above.

Following the same procedure for changing solutions and students, test the effects of a 0.1-percent solution of quinine sulfate. The diagram on which sensation is recorded should be labeled Bitter.

B. Taste Threshold

Stimuli have different degrees of intensity. The intensity of a stimulus may be so low (weak) that it is not detected by the organism. The degree of intensity that an individual can just barely detect is the threshold intensity for that individual. In tests for the taste threshold, intensity is expressed as the percentage of the test substance in a given volume of water.

During Procedure B you will work alone. Using a pencil, mark six paper cups as follows: 0.001%, 0.005%, 0.01%, 0.05%, 0.1%, and 0.5%. From the stock bottles pour into each of the cups 2 to 3 ml of the solutions assigned to you. (Be sure to match the labels on the bottles with the labels on the cups, pouring the 0.001-percent solution into the cup marked 0.001%, and so on.) Arrange the cups in order of increasing concentration. Using a medicine dropper, transfer 2 drops of the 0.001-percent solution to your tongue. In your data book, write the name of the solution and its concentration. Beside this information write a minus sign if you cannot taste the substance in solution; write a plus sign if you can taste it. Rinse the medicine dropper, and follow the same procedure with the solution of next higher concentration. When you reach a concentration you can taste, check by testing the next higher concentration. Then stop testing.

C. Relation of Smell to Taste

During Procedure C you will work in teams of 3 students. Designate the team members "A," "B," and "C." It is important that the subject (the student being tested) be unaware of the identity of the substance.

Student B: Blindfold Student A, the first subject. Obtain a paper cup containing a few milliliters of test solution A.

Student C: In your data book, copy the form shown below. Write the letter A in the first space under the heading "Solution Presented." Record the name of the solution.

SUBJECT	SOLUTION PRESENTED	NOSE CLOSED		NOSE OPEN	
		Taste	Identity	Taste	Identity

Student A: Holding your nose tightly, sip the solution; report its taste, and try to identify the substance in the solution.

Student C: Record these reports on the form.

Student A: Without holding your nose, sip the same solution; again report its taste, and try to identify the substance.

Student C: Record these reports.

Now repeat the procedure, with Student B as the subject. Student C obtains test solution B, and Student A records the reports. When tests with solution B are completed, repeat the procedure, with Student C as the subject. Student A obtains test solution C, and Student B becomes the recorder.

If time permits a second round of testing, use solutions AA, BB, and CC.

STUDYING THE DATA

On the chalkboard make four large diagrams of the tongue (Figure 14.4-1). Label them Salt, Sweet, Sour, and Bitter. Assemble from all students the data obtained in Procedure A. At each test point on the diagrams record the total number of minus, plus, and double-plus responses. What are some of the possible causes for variability in the data? (1) Which kinds of variability are the result of "errors of observation"? Which are the result of physiological variability? (2)

On the chalkboard, assemble the data obtained in Procedure B. Beside each concentration, use two colors of chalk to tally separately the number of male subjects and the number of female subjects for whom that concentration represented the taste threshold. Add the two counts, and write the total in a third color. For each kind of solution, calculate the <u>mean</u> (average) threshold concentration for males, for females, and for the entire class.

On the chalkboard list the solutions (A, B, C, etc.) used in Procedure C. Tally separately the tastes reported with nose closed and with nose open; also tally the identifications of solutions. In general, are the kinds of tastes reported with nose open more varied than those reported with nose closed? Less varied? Neither? (3) In general, are the identifications made with nose open more accurate than those made with nose closed? Less accurate? Neither? (4) What assumption is involved in holding the nose closed? (5)

CONCLUSIONS

Do the data from Procedure A support the hypothesis that receptors of the four kinds of taste are unequally distributed on the surface of the tongue? Explain. (6) If the data support this hypothesis, where on the tongue is each kind of taste receptor most numerous? (7)

Do the data from Procedure B support the hypothesis that the taste threshold for sweetness is lower than that for saltiness? Higher? Neither? (8) Do the data indicate that the sense of taste in one sex is more acute (that is, has a lower threshold) than in the other? If so, which sex has the lower threshold for sweetness? For saltiness? (9)

On the basis of the data from Procedure C, write a brief statement concerning the relationship of the sense of taste to the sense of smell. (10)

FOR FURTHER INVESTIGATION

1. <u>Fatigue of a chemoreceptor</u>. Smell oil of cloves through one nostril, expiring air through the mouth. Hold the bottle containing the oil about 1.5 cm from the nose. How much time passes before the smell of cloves is no longer detected? This is called "olfactory fatigue." Immediately smell oil of peppermint through the same nostril. Is the latter odor detectable?

2. A factor in the process of tasting. Stick your tongue out and keep it out during the following procedure: Wipe your tongue dry with a piece of gauze or paper toweling. Place a few crystals of sugar on the tongue, and note the time. How much time passes before the sugar is tasted? Rinse your mouth with water. Again stick your tongue out, but do not dry it before placing sugar crystals on it. How much time passes before the sugar is tasted? Try the same procedure with salt crystals.

3. The sound threshold. Use the ticking of a watch as the stimulus and the distance of the watch from the ear as the measure of intensity. The subject should be blindfolded, and the test should be made where other sounds are at a minimum.

EXERCISE 14.5

CAPILLARY CIRCULATION

INTRODUCTION

William Harvey (see Exercise 14.3) discovered that the blood of man and other vertebrates circulates. His ingenious experiments showed that blood leaves the heart through one set of vessels and returns through another set. Therefore, by reasoning he concluded that the blood circulates. But he did not know by observation how the blood passes from the arteries to the veins.

Harvey lived in the first part of the seventeenth century, before microscopic studies became widespread. It remained for an Italian microscopist, Marcello Malpighi (text page 376), a contemporary of Leeuwenhoek and Hooke, to discover the capillaries.

PURPOSE

In this exercise you will observe the circulation of blood through capillaries and the effects of several chemical substances on this circulation.

MATERIALS AND EQUIPMENT (for each team)

1. Live frog
2. Wet towel
3. Cord (about 1 m) or rubber bands (4 or 5)
4. Soft pine board, about 10 X 25 X 0.7 cm, with a hole 2 cm in diameter near one end
5. Straight pins, 3 or 4
6. Medicine dropper
7. Ringer's solution
8. Monocular microscope
9. Solutions of nicotine sulfate, lactic acid, histamine acid phosphate, adrenalin chloride, acetylcholine bromide, alcohol, and sodium nitrite
10. Finger bowl

PROCEDURE

Wrap a live frog in a wet towel and tie it to an observation board, as shown in Figure 14.5-1. One leg is to be extended. It does not matter whether the frog is lying on its back or on its belly. Pin the foot so that the thin web between the toes is stretched over the hole in the board. Using a medicine dropper, wet the web with a few drops of Ringer's solution. Keep the web moist throughout this exercise.

Remove the clips from the stage of a monocular microscope. Place the board on the stage so that the hole in the board is over the opening in the stage. Use books or other objects to support the part of the board that projects beyond the stage. Adjust the illumination, and examine under low power.

Your observation should be guided by the following questions: What is the ratio of the diameter of the smallest vessel you can see to that of the largest? How can you distinguish between arterioles (small arteries) and venules (small veins)? (Refer to text page 464 if necessary.) Which of the vessels, if any, can be seen to pulsate? Is the speed of flow the same in all vessels? If not, is it faster in the smaller or in the larger vessels? Red cells average 22μ long, 15μ wide, and 4μ thick. What is the approximate diameter of a capillary?

Many factors are known to affect the diameter of capillaries. Among these are a number of chemical substances known as drugs. The teacher will provide your team with one or more such substances in solution. Using a medicine dropper, apply one of these to the web of the frog's foot. One member of the team applies the solution; another member closely observes (through the microscope) the capillaries before, during, and after the application. Keen observation is necessary to see dilation (widening) or constriction (narrowing) of the capillaries. The dimensions of the red blood cells and the rate of flow are two reference points for determining dilation and constriction.

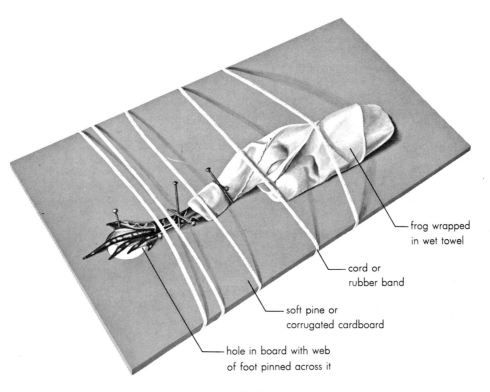

frog wrapped
in wet towel

cord or
rubber band

soft pine or
corrugated cardboard

hole in board with web
of foot pinned across it

Figure 14.5-1

Observation should be continuous for at least three minutes to allow time for the drug to diffuse into the tissues.

Wash the web of the foot thoroughly with Ringer's solution, using a medicine dropper to apply the solution and a finger bowl to catch it. Continue the washing for about five minutes. Then apply the second drug, following the procedure used with the first.

SUMMARY

Write a brief description of normal capillary circulation. (1)

Assemble the data from the drug tests on the chalkboard. To what extent are the results obtained by teams using the same drug in agreement? (2)   What factors may have caused any lack of agreement that exists? (3)   According to the data, which drugs act as <u>vasodilators</u> (vessel dilators) in the frog? (4)   Which act as <u>vasoconstrictors</u>? (5) For which drugs are your data inconclusive? (6)

EXERCISE 14.6

TESTING FOR VITAMIN C

INTRODUCTION

Foods supply the energy required by animals. But animals cannot live on a diet made up entirely of carbohydrate or fat or protein. Nor can they live even on a diet consisting entirely of two or all three of these foods. All animals require additional substances from the environment—additional nutrients (text page 452). Aside from water and oxygen (which are not usually classified as nutrients anyway), they require various inorganic substances—minerals, such as sodium chloride. But animals also require additional organic substances, most of which are used in carrying on biochemical processes in cells.

These organic substances are called vitamins. In the organism they become parts of enzymes. Without them the organism is unable to carry on its metabolism; the organism develops a deficiency disease (text page 193) and eventually dies.

PURPOSE

In this exercise a chemical test is used to detect a vitamin, and comparisons of vitamin content are made among several items of the human diet.

BACKGROUND INFORMATION

In 1498, during his voyage around the Cape of Good Hope, Vasco da Gama lost almost two-thirds of his crew to a disease called scurvy (text page 193). First a sailor's gums began to bleed. Then some of his teeth fell out. Then great blotches appeared on his skin; his wrists and ankles swelled; he developed a bloody diarrhea. Finally he died. In succeeding centuries, as long sea voyages became more common, scurvy was an ever present threat, the curse of seafaring life.

As early as the first part of the seventeenth century, it was claimed that lemon juice would prevent or cure scurvy. But not until 1768, during Captain James Cook's long voyage to the South Pacific, was the theory given experimental support. From that time on, **British ships carried lemons and limes on all voyages.**

In the latter part of the nineteenth century it was believed for a time that all diseases might be "caused" by germs. By the first decade of the twentieth century, however, a number of diseases, such as scurvy, had become associated not with microorganisms but with some lack in the diet. Though the exact chemical nature of the lacking substances was not then known, the word "vitamin" was coined (1912) for them. The substance supplied to the diet by lemons and other citrus fruits—the substance that overcame the effects of scurvy—was called vitamin C. Some years later the substance was extracted from juices and identified chemically as ascorbic acid. More recently, ascorbic acid has been shown to be part of one of the enzymes that catalyze the long series of reactions in aerobic respiration.

Ascorbic acid—vitamin C—is the nutrient you will be testing for in this exercise. (Information about other vitamins can be found in Villee's Biology [Philadelphia: W. B. Saunders Company, 1962] , pages 318-327.)

MATERIALS AND EQUIPMENT
(for each team, if two test solutions are used per team)

1. Test tubes, 13 X 100 mm, 4
2. Test-tube rack
3. Glass-marking crayon
4. Indophenol solution, 8 ml
5. Graduated cylinder or 5-ml pipette
6. Ascorbic acid solution
7. Medicine droppers, 4
8. Distilled water
9. Test solutions made from fresh lemon juice, frozen lemon juice, lemon juice left standing forty-eight hours, fresh orange juice, frozen orange juice, frozen pineapple juice, canned pineapple juice, juice of fresh green pepper, juice of cooked green pepper, juice of fresh cabbage, juice of cooked cabbage, and fresh apple juice

PROCEDURE

Label two test tubes A and B; into each tube pour 2 ml of indophenol solution. To Tube A add ascorbic acid, drop by drop, counting the drops as you add them. Shake the tube gently after each addition. In your data book, record the number of drops required to cause the color of the indophenol to disappear. To Tube B add the same number of drops of distilled water. Shake the tube and record the color in it.

The result of your experiment with Tube A gives you a standard of ascorbic acid strength. Against this standard you can compare the strength of ascorbic acid in other solutions.

Each team will be given several solutions of items included in the human diet—"foods" (in the broad sense). Label with additional letters (C, D, E, etc.) as many tubes as you have solutions to test. Into each tube pour 2 ml of indophenol solution. Use Tube C for the first test solution. Add the test solution, drop by drop, to the indophenol in the tube, following the procedure used with Tube A. (If the color of the indophenol has not disappeared after the addition of 40 drops of the solution, you may assume that no measurable amount of ascorbic acid is present.) Because of the color of the test solution itself, it may be difficult to determine the point at which the color of the indophenol disappears. In your data book write the letter of the tube, the identity of the solution tested, and the number of drops required to cause the color of the indophenol to disappear. (If 40 drops were used without results, write "No ascorbic acid.")

Repeat the procedure, using Tube D and a second test solution. Follow the same procedure with any other test solutions you are given.

STUDYING THE DATA

On the chalkboard assemble the data from all teams. List the names of the solutions tested. Beside each name record the number of drops required to cause the color of the indophenol to disappear (or "No ascorbic acid") as reported by each team testing the substance. Wherever more than one team reports on the same solution, average the data. Rank the test solutions according to the amount of ascorbic acid they contain, beginning with the one containing the most and ending with the one containing the least or none.

CONCLUSIONS

According to the data, which of the foods tested are good sources of vitamin C? (1) What methods of handling or preparing foods reduce the vitamin-C content? (2)

FOR FURTHER INVESTIGATION

1. Cooks sometimes add sodium bicarbonate to vegetables such as peas, spinach, and broccoli to preserve their green color. Does this practice have any effect on the vitamin-C content of the vegetables?

2. Does cooking vegetables in a pressure cooker affect their vitamin-C content?

EXERCISE 14.7

MAINTAINING WATER BALANCE

INTRODUCTION

The physiology, behavior, and habitat of an organism are all closely related. Tolerances (text pages 210-214) are physiological characteristics. As such, they influence the organism's behavior, and they are factors in determining the kinds of habitats in which the organism can survive.

Water balance is one of the most important aspects of an organism's survival (text page 472). Both the physiological ability to retain moisture in the body and the humidity of the environment are factors in maintaining water balance. Therefore, it is convenient to use water balance as a means for investigating the relationship between the physiology of an organism and its choice of environment.

PURPOSE

In this exercise the rates of water loss in different kinds of arthropods are compared and an attempt is made to correlate this information with the animals' environments.

MATERIALS AND EQUIPMENT (for each team)

Day 1

1. Cobalt chloride
2. Beaker, 250-ml
3. Glass stirring rod
4. Filter paper, 2 sheets
5. Wires (12-cm lengths), 4
6. Corks, to fit test tubes, 4
7. Metric ruler
8. Forceps
9. Medicine dropper
10. Test tubes, 18 X 150 mm, 4
11. Pins, 4
12. Drying oven

Day 2

1. Rectangular plastic dish, about 8 X 18 X 4 cm
2. Fine soil
3. Wireworms (Agriotes), 4 or 5
4. Wood lice (Armadillaria), 4 or 5
5. Mealworms (Tenebrio), 4 or 5
6. Forceps

PROCEDURE

Day 1

Dissolve crystals of cobalt chloride in 50 ml of water until a deep wine color appears.

Cut filter paper into strips 6 mm wide. Stack the strips of filter paper together, and trim them all to the same length. Cut the strips into 6-mm squares. It is important that all the squares be the same size.

With a pin or dissecting needle, punch a tiny hole in the center of a stack of five of the paper squares. Insert a piece of wire into the center of the bottom of a cork. Straighten the wire as much as possible. Now run the wire through five of the squares of filter paper. Hold the bottom edge of the cork at the zero mark on a metric ruler; using forceps, space the squares 1 cm apart—the first square 4 cm from the cork, and the last square 8 cm from the cork. The squares should fit tightly on the wire; if any square slips easily, replace it. Prepare three more assemblies of wire, cork, and filter-paper squares.

Using a medicine dropper, wet the filter-paper squares thoroughly with the concentrated cobalt chloride solution. Gently shake off the excess, and place the four assemblies in the four test tubes. Insert a pin in the bottom of each cork, and rest the corks on the edges of the test tubes, as shown in Figure 14.7-1. Place the tubes and assemblies in a drying oven overnight.

Day 2

Cover the bottom of a rectangular dish with a layer of soil about 8 mm deep. Gently add enough water to wet the soil thoroughly. Cover the wet soil with a sloped layer of fine, dry soil—about 30 mm deep at one end of the dish and about 2 mm deep at the other end (Figure 14.7-2). With your hand, press the soil to make the slope firm but not packed. Allow the apparatus to stand for about fifteen minutes. In this time a moisture gradient should form: the bottom end of the slope quite wet, the central part moist, and the upper end dry.

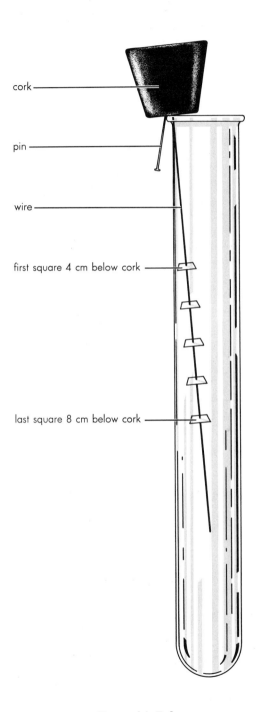

cork

pin

wire

first square 4 cm below cork

last square 8 cm below cork

Figure 14.7-1

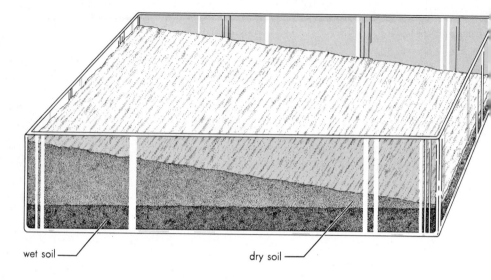

wet soil

dry soil

Figure 14.7-2. Moisture-gradient apparatus

While waiting for the gradient to form, remove the test tubes from the drying oven. <u>Immediately</u> remove the pins and insert the corks tightly into the test tubes. Check to see that the filter-paper squares are equally spaced on the wires. If they are not, quickly adjust them with a <u>dry</u> pair of forceps. In your data book, record the colors of wet and of dry cobalt chloride.

Using dry forceps, place a wireworm in one of the tubes. Open and close the tube <u>quickly</u>; avoid disturbing the position of the filter-paper squares. In the same manner, place a wood louse in a second tube and a mealworm in a third tube. Add nothing to the fourth tube. For the remainder of the laboratory period observe the tubes at ten-minute intervals, recording any changes in the color of the filter-paper squares.

When the moisture gradient has formed in the rectangular dish, place the remaining animals (wireworms, wood lice, and mealworms) together in the center of the slope. Observe the activities of the animals for a few minutes, recording your observations. Then place over the dish a book or other cover that will reduce the light. After ten minutes, remove the cover and record in your data book the position of each of the nine animals on the slope.

At the end of the laboratory period, place the test tubes and the moisture-gradient apparatus in a place designated by your teacher. At least one member of each team should be assigned to observe the tubes after a number of hours have passed. If your class meets in the morning, observation should be made after school; if the class meets in the afternoon, observation should be made the following morning, before school. The observer should record in his data book the number of hours since the animals were placed in the tubes and the color of each filter-paper square in each tube.

Day 3

All team members should record final observations of the filter-paper assemblies and the moisture-gradient apparatus.

STUDYING THE DATA

Consider first the behavior of the animals in the moisture-gradient apparatus. As in all work with living things, individuals of the same species may react differently. Therefore, the behavior of all the individuals of each species must be taken into consideration. Which species (if any) tended to move toward a dry habitat? (1)   Which species (if any) tended to move toward a wet habitat? (2)

Now consider the data from the test tubes. What was the purpose of the tube that contained no animal? (3)   As indicated by the change in color of cobalt chloride, which species lost water most rapidly? (4) Which species lost water most slowly? (5)

CONCLUSIONS

Comparing your data from the two tests, what relationship (if any) can you see between the rate at which an arthropod species loses water and the behavior of that species in choosing a habitat? (6)

EXERCISE 14.8

RATE OF HEARTBEAT IN A MAMMAL

INTRODUCTION

In Exercise 14.3 you studied the rate of heartbeat in a small in-vertebrate animal. The animal was transparent; this allowed direct observation of heart action without dissection. In most large animals such direct observation of the heart is impossible. There are, how-ever, a number of indirect ways by which the rate of heartbeat in a mammal can be determined.

In Exercise 14.3 you also studied the effects of varying environmental temperatures on heartbeat. But in birds and mammals (after hatching or birth) the heart lies in an internal environment where a relatively stable temperature is maintained independently of the external environment. Thus the problems and methods that are suitable for the study of heartbeat in mammals are quite different from those suitable for such study in small invertebrates.

This situation provides an opportunity. You have had several months of experience carrying out experimental procedures and drawing conclusions from data. You should now be able to set up a problem, work out a procedure for gathering data, carry out the procedure, and then draw conclusions.

PURPOSE

This exercise has two aims: (1) to give you an opportunity to formulate a problem and devise a procedure for investigating it; (2) to extend your knowledge of the physiology of mammalian heartbeat.

EQUIPMENT (for each pair of students)

1. Watch with a second hand

PROCEDURE

In carrying out the purpose of this exercise the only requirements are: (1) Your problem and your procedure must deal with the rate of heartbeat in a mammal; (2) your equipment must be limited to a watch with a second hand. The following statements may help you:

1. Man is a mammal.

2. In the text (pages 485–486) it was pointed out that an increase or decrease in the activity of an animal may be reflected in changes of heartbeat rate.

3. Physicians use stethoscopes to listen to the heartbeat. But they are interested in more than the rate of heartbeat. With only a watch, nurses can easily determine the rate.

CHAPTER 15

Reproduction

EXERCISE 15.1

VEGETATIVE REPRODUCTION: REGENERATION (ANIMAL)

INTRODUCTION

Vegetative reproduction is dependent upon the ability of an organism to grow new parts from old. This ability is called <u>regeneration</u>, and in some degree all organisms seem to have it. In man, skin and nails are constantly being regenerated, but man cannot regenerate a finger or an arm. A crab can regenerate a claw, but a claw cannot regenerate a whole crab. Regeneration can result in reproduction only if half or less than half of an organism can regenerate the missing parts.

The freshwater flatworm called "planarian" sometimes separates into two parts, each of which may become a whole new planarian—thus accomplishing vegetative reproduction. We have used planarians frequently as examples in the discussion of animal physiology (Chapter 14), and living planarians were studied in Exercise 4.4. Now we will use them to investigate the process of regeneration.

PURPOSE

In this exercise the process of vegetative reproduction is investigated by experimentally bringing about regeneration in planarians.

MATERIALS AND EQUIPMENT (for each team)

1. Petri dishes, 2 or 3
2. Glass-marking crayon
3. Spring water, pond water, or conditioned tap water
4. Planarians, 3
5. Water-color brush
6. Microscope slide
7. Razor blade
8. Stereomicroscope

PROCEDURES

The teacher will assign one of the following four procedures to each team:

Procedure A

Using a glass-marking crayon, label the bottom half of one petri dish A (anterior) and the bottom half of a second petri dish P (posterior). Into each dish pour spring water, pond water, or conditioned tap water to a depth of 6 to 8 mm. Using a water-color brush, transfer a planarian and a drop of water to a clean glass slide. Allow the animal a few moments to stretch out. Then, using a razor blade, divide the planarian into halves by cutting perpendicularly to the long axis of the body (Figure 15.1-1A). Next, using the brush, place the anterior half in the dish marked A and the posterior half in the dish marked P. Repeat the operation with two other worms.

Place covers on the two dishes and store in a cool (but not refrigerated), dark place. Examine the dishes every other day for about ten days, using a stereomicroscope. Remove any pieces that are obviously dead. The best way to record observations is by sketching. Be sure to date each sketch. Take special care to note any changes in the appearance of the cut edges of the pieces.

Procedure B

Following Procedure A, cut three worms into halves—but cut obliquely, as shown in Figure 15.1-1B. Observe and sketch the pieces as directed in Procedure A.

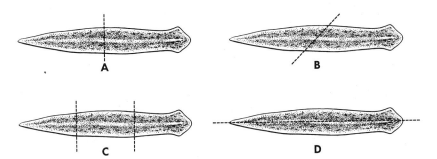

Figure 15.1-1.   Planarians.   Dotted lines indicate cuts to be made.

Procedure C

Follow Procedure A, but label three petri dishes—one A (anterior), one M (middle), and one P (posterior)—and cut three worms into thirds, as shown in Figure 15.1-1C.   Place the pieces of worm in the appropriate dishes.   Observe and sketch the pieces as directed in Procedure A.

Procedure D

Follow Procedure A, but label the petri dishes R and L, and divide three worms into halves by cutting along the midline, as shown in Figure 15.1-1D.   Place the right half of each planarian in Dish R and the left half of each in Dish L.   Observe and sketch.

STUDYING THE DATA

Each team should consider the following questions: Which parts had the greatest survival rate (anterior, middle, posterior, right, left)? (1)   Along which part of the cut edges did regeneration appear first? (2)   How does the appearance of regenerated tissue differ from that of old tissue? (3)   Which pieces, if any, regenerated into whole worms? (4)   If some did, are there any differences in appearance between regenerated worms and the worms with which you began the exercise? (5)

Teams that followed the same procedure should consult together and prepare a report for the whole class.

SUMMARY

From the combined results of all teams, consider the following:

Of the four procedures, Procedure A is most like the natural process of vegetative reproduction in planarians. Therefore we might hypothesize that this procedure would be the one most likely to produce successful regeneration of whole worms. Do the data obtained support this hypothesis? (6)

State a hypothesis that is tested by Procedure B. (7) Do the data support the hypothesis? (8)

From the results of Procedure C, make a general statement concerning the original position of pieces of planarians that can regenerate whole worms. (9)

As far as is known, planarians do not naturally divide longitudinally. Therefore, in Procedure D you are studying an entirely artificial situation. From the results of this procedure, make a general statement concerning the relationship between natural vegetative reproduction and the ability to regenerate. (10)

FOR FURTHER INVESTIGATION

1. What is the effect of temperature on regeneration in planarians? The Temperature Gradient Box, mentioned in Exercise 2.4, is useful for investigating this matter.

2. Salamanders do not reproduce vegetatively, but they can regenerate tails. In these animals regeneration requires more time than it does in planarians, but salamanders are larger and therefore easier to observe. Many hypotheses concerning regeneration may be investigated with salamanders.

3. How rapidly do your fingernails grow? Dip a toothpick in dilute nitric acid; draw the toothpick across a thumbnail (near the base). The nitric acid makes a permanent yellow line. Measure the distance from the line to the base of the nail. Repeat the measurement each week until the yellow line reaches the tip of the nail. Prepare a graph showing your data.

EXERCISE 15.2

MEIOSIS

INTRODUCTION

The events of meiosis are difficult to understand from a written description; they are almost as difficult to understand from diagrams. Description and diagrams are supplied in the text (pages 506-508). An easier way to gain an understanding of meiosis is to watch a motion picture of the process. Perhaps you will have an opportunity to see such a film. But even with that experience, it may still be desirable to look at meiosis in the step-by-step manner provided in this exercise.

PURPOSE

The process of meiosis is illustrated in this exercise by means of a model.

MATERIALS AND EQUIPMENT (for each team)

1. Poppit beads, two colors, 36 of each color
2. Pipe cleaners, 2
3. Scissors
4. Wrapping paper
5. Crayon

PROCEDURE

Make up eight strands of poppit beads as follows:
    2 eight-bead strands, all of the first color
    2 eight-bead strands, all of the second color
    2 ten-bead strands, all of the first color
    2 ten-bead strands, all of the second color
Each strand of beads represents a chromatid. Using short pieces of pipe cleaner to represent kinetochores, fasten the like "chromatids" together, as shown in Figure 15.2-1. The joined chromatids represent chromosomes as they look before separation.

Use a large sheet of wrapping paper to represent the cytoplasm of a cell. On the paper draw a spindle large enough to contain the "chromosomes" you have made.

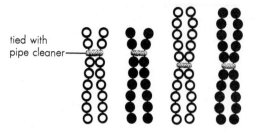

Figure 15.2-1. Strands of poppit beads, joined to represent chromosomes

You now have a model with which you can trace the events of meiosis. Assume that the early events of the first division have already occurred—the formation of the spindle from the division of the centrosome, the disappearance of the nuclear membrane, the appearance of the chromosomes from the nuclear material.

Arrange the four chromosomes along the equator of the spindle, one long chromosome beside the other long chromosome and one short chromosome beside the other short chromosome. In text Figure 15.9 you can see that chromosomes occur in pairs. Since gametes contain only half the number of chromosomes characteristic in a species, we can assume that any individual obtained one chromosome of each pair from its male parent and one of each pair from its female parent. The chromosomes of such a homologous pair cannot be distinguished from each other under the microscope. In this exercise, however, one color has been used to indicate the chromosomes obtained from the male parent, and a second color to indicate those from the female parent.

When the chromosomes of a homologous pair are close beside each other, the chromatids of one chromosome often overlap the chromatids of the other at one or more points. Show this by overlapping the strands of beads representing the chromatids of each homologous pair. Crossing-over (text pages 507-508) can then be shown by breaking the strands at the points where they cross and reassembling, thus exchanging beads from one chromosome with beads from its homolog. The colors will make the exchange visible throughout the rest of the meiotic process.

Now begin to move the chromosomes of each homologous pair toward opposite poles of the spindle. Move the chromosomes by grasping the kinetochores and pulling; the strands of beads will trail behind the advancing kinetochores. At this stage, each chromosome has a distinctive shape resulting from its length and the position of the kinetochore. Therefore, during cell division cytologists can identify particular chromosomes in many well-investigated organisms.

When the chromosomes of each homologous pair have been separated—one at each of the two poles of the spindle—draw two more spindles. These two spindles should be centered on the poles of the

first, and their axes should be perpendicular to the axis of the first
(Figure 15.2-2). You are now ready for the second division of meiosis.

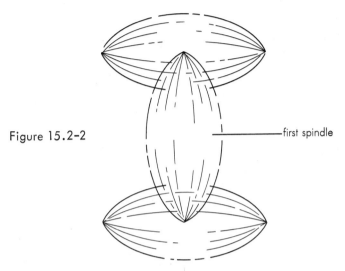

Figure 15.2-2   first spindle

Place the chromosomes, which are now at opposite poles of the
first spindle, along the equators of the two new spindles. Loosen the
kinetochore (pipe cleaner) of each chromosome. Grasping each chromatid of a chromosome at the kinetochore, pull the chromatids to
opposite poles of their spindles. If there are four members of your
team, all the chromatids can be made to move at the same time—which
they do in a living cell. If four pairs of hands are not available, the
chromatids will have to be separated at different times.

Reassemble the chromosomes as they are shown in Figure 15.2-1.
Be sure to rearrange the beads. Place the chromosomes at the equator
of the first spindle. Now try to go through the process of meiosis
without referring to this exercise.

EXERCISE 15.3

DEVELOPMENT OF AN EMBRYO: CHICK

INTRODUCTION

In the method of reproduction called fission (text pages 499-500),
offspring have the appearance of adults as soon as they are formed.

Although some time (less than an hour in a few species of bacteria) must pass before the new individuals are able to reproduce, no visible changes occur during this "growing-up" period. Offspring produced by other methods of reproduction, however, undergo visible changes on the way to adulthood. In some larger organisms such maturing continues for years.

Embryology is the branch of biology that deals with the early stages of the maturing process. But the limits of this science are difficult to define; they vary widely, depending upon the organism studied. In general, we can say that an embryo is an unhatched (or unborn, or ungerminated) organism.

There are, however, further problems of definition: When does hatching occur in eggs that have no shells? When does germination occur—when the sprout appears above ground, when the seed coat bursts, or even earlier? And when is a marsupial born—when it leaves the mother's uterus, or when it leaves the mother's pouch? With a bird, at least, there are no such difficulties; until it emerges from the shell, the organism is an embryo.

PURPOSE

Embryology is best understood by making direct observations—and such is the purpose of this exercise. In it much background information is interwoven with the procedure.

MATERIALS AND EQUIPMENT (for each team)

A. The Unincubated Egg

1. Fertilized chicken egg, unincubated
2. Finger bowl (about 250-ml)
3. Stereomicroscope

B. The Two-Day Embryo

1. Paper towels
2. Finger bowl
3. Egg incubator
4. Chicken egg, incubated 48 to 52 hours
5. Scissors (fine-pointed)
6. Forceps
7. Medicine dropper
8. Stereomicroscope or hand lens
9. Watch with a second hand

10. Filter paper
11. Syracuse watch glass
12. Physiological saline solution
13. Heat source
14. Centigrade thermometer
15. Monocular microscope

C. The Five-Day Embryo

1. Paper towels
2. Finger bowl
3. Egg incubator
4. Chicken egg, incubated 5 to 6 days
5. Scissors (fine-pointed)
6. Forceps
7. Medicine dropper
8. Stereomicroscope or hand lens

D. Later Stages of Development

1. Egg incubator
2. Chicken egg, incubated 10, 14, 18, or 21 days
3. Scissors
4. Forceps
5. Finger bowl
6. Physiological saline solution
7. Heat source
8. Centigrade thermometer
9. Hand lens

PROCEDURE

A. The Unincubated Egg

In animals that lay eggs having shells, an ovum must be fertilized before the shell is formed. Therefore fertilization must occur internally. In birds the ovum consists of the part of the egg commonly called the "yolk," though biologists often use this term to describe only the food supply within the ovum. After fertilization the albumen ("white") of the egg is secreted around the zygote, and a membrane and shell are formed. By the time the egg is laid, the embryo has begun to develop. Then development ceases until incubation begins—that is, until the egg is placed in an environment where a temperature of approximately 38°C is maintained.

Crack a fresh, fertilized chicken egg and carefully place its contents in a finger bowl. Observe the albumen, which is made up largely of protein and water. Where is it most dense? (1) The embryo appears as a white area on the surface of the yolk; at this stage it is called the <u>blastoderm</u> (see marginal notes of the text for roots of this term). Describe its appearance under the stereomicroscope. (2) Examine the inside of the shell. Note the membrane that lines it. At which end of the egg is the membrane not closely attached to the shell? (3) What occupies this space between membrane and shell? (4)

B. The Two-Day Embryo

Figure 15.3-1 shows a chick embryo after 33 hours of incubation. This embryo has developed from the blastoderm, which you saw in the fresh egg. At this stage the embryo is still so thin that the parts shown in the drawing can be observed only after staining. The <u>somites</u> are blocks of tissue from which vertebrae and muscles develop. Notice that only the head and neck regions of the chick have begun to form. (Refer to Figure 15.3-1 for identification of structures and comparison of stages as you observe the 48- to 52-hour embryo.)

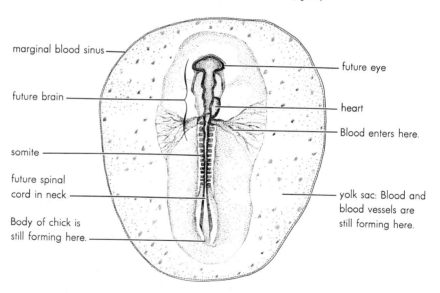

Figure 15.3-1. Chick embryo at 33 hours. At this stage the yolk sac is about 1 cm in diameter and is growing along its entire edge.

Crumple one or two paper towels into a finger bowl and hollow out a space for an egg in the center of the crumpled paper. This will support the egg as you work with it.

Obtain an egg that has been incubated 48 to 52 hours. Before re-moving the egg from the incubator, mark a <u>T</u> on the top of the egg. Then carry the egg to your work space, holding the marked side up. Keeping the marked side up, place the egg in the hollow of the crum-pled paper.

Hold the egg gently but firmly. To expose the embryo, follow the steps shown in Figure 15.3-2. If you have not rotated the egg since taking it from the incubator, the embryo should be on the top of the yolk. If it is not, <u>gentle</u> pushing with the medicine dropper may rotate the yolk until the embryo is on top—but great care must be taken not to break the yolk.

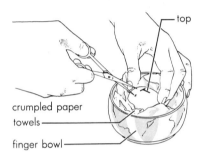

A. Carefully push point of scissors just through egg shell.

B. Slowly clip around shell, as shown.

C. Using forceps, carefully lift loose piece of shell and discard it.

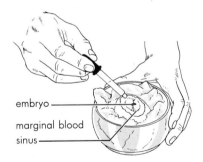

D. Draw off albumen with medicine dropper until none is on top surface of yolk.

Figure 15.3-2. Exposing the chick embryo in early stage of development

When the embryo is exposed, the extent of the <u>yolk sac</u> (Figure 15.3-1) can be observed by noting the blood vessels on the surface of the yolk. Approximately what percentage of the yolk is now covered by the yolk sac? (5) Using a stereomicroscope or hand lens, examine the embryo. Locate the heart by looking for its pulsating movement. How fast is the heart beating (pulsations per minute)? (6)

Further observation will be improved by removing the embryo from the yolk. To do this, follow the steps shown in Figure 15.3-3. Before placing the filter-paper ring on the yolk, make sure that none of the albumen is on the surface of the embryo. If it is, repeat Step D, Figure 15.3-2.

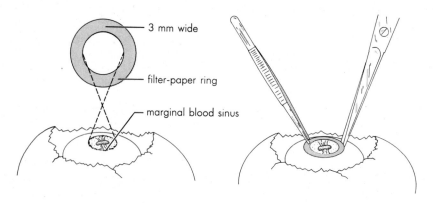

A.   Measure diameter of marginal blood sinus. On filter paper, draw a ring that has inner diameter slightly less than diameter of marginal blood sinus. Cut out ring and place over edges of sinus.

B.   Grasp ring and edge of membrane. Clip membrane all the way around ring. Slowly lift ring, membrane, and embryo away from yolk.

Figure 15.3-3.
Removing the chick embryo from the yolk

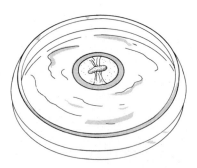

C.   Place ring, membrane, and embryo in Syracuse watch glass containing physiological saline solution (3 mm deep) at 38° C.

After the embryo has been transferred to the watch glass, the solution may become cloudy (due to the presence of yolk on the embryo). If this happens, draw off the saline with a clean medicine dropper and replace it with fresh, warm saline. Place the watch glass on the stage of a monocular microscope and observe under low power. Since you are not using a cover slip, you must be careful to keep the objective <u>above</u> the surface of the liquid. Which of the structures that appear in Figure 15.3-1 can you see? (7) Sketch the embryo. Compare its general shape with that of the 33-hour embryo. (8) Most of the large mass of tissue adjacent to the heart will become the brain. This part of the embryo may appear to have a membrane over it. This membrane is the developing amnion (text page 312). You may be able to see an ear opening; this was not visible in the 33-hour embryo. Examine the heart carefully. Can you trace the pathway of the blood through the heart? If so, describe it. (9) A slowing of the rate of heartbeat indicates that the temperature of the saline solution is falling. If this occurs, draw off the saline with a medicine dropper and replace it with warm saline.

C. The Five-Day Embryo

Using the technique shown in Figure 15.3-2, open an egg that has been incubated 5 days. (CAUTION: Now the yolk has become quite watery, and some of the delicate membranes are close to the shell; therefore, it is important that you insert only the <u>tips</u> of the scissors beneath the shell.)

At this stage the embryo is completely surrounded by the amnion. Gently probe the surface of the amnion with a blunt pencil. What besides the embryo seems to be inside? (10) Next to the amnion and apparently attached to it by a stalk is a bladder-like membrane covered with blood vessels. This is the <u>allantois</u>. Later in development it enlarges and eventually lines the whole inner surface of the egg. Through it the embryo obtains oxygen and excretes carbon dioxide. What structure in the mammalian embryo performs a somewhat similar function (see text)? (11) Observe the extent of the blood vessels on the surface of the yolk. Approximately what percentage of the yolk is now covered by the yolk sac? (12)

Using forceps and scissors, carefully cut away the amnion, exposing the embryo. Compare the size of the eyes with the size of the head. (13) This size relationship is a characteristic of bird embryos in contrast to mammalian embryos. Look for the two pairs of <u>limb buds</u>, the parts that will become the appendages. Is it possible to distinguish wings from legs at this stage? (14) Make a sketch of the embryo, and label as many parts as you can identify.

D. Later Stages of Development

Eggs incubated 10, 14, 18, and 21 days are to be opened by different teams. In these late stages of development, a new technique is needed to open eggs containing embryos. Figure 15.3-4 shows this technique. Try to remove the shell without breaking any of the membranes.

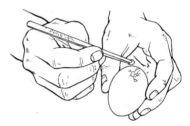

A. Crack the large end of the egg with scissors or forceps handle.

B. Using forceps, carefully pick shell away. If possible, avoid breaking membranes.

Figure 15.3-4.
Exposing the chick embryo in late stage of development

C. After much of shell is removed, place egg in finger bowl containing physiological saline solution (at 38° C). Pick away remaining shell.

Figure 15.3-5 is a cross-sectional diagram showing the relationship of parts in an egg in a late stage of incubation. It will help you to identify what you find as you dissect the egg. As you continue with this exercise, make notes in your data book, to be used in summarizing your observations. Be sure to keep separate notes for each stage.

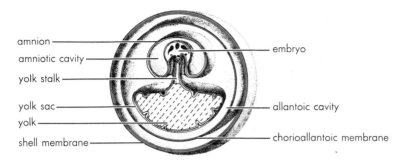

amnion
amniotic cavity
yolk stalk
yolk sac
yolk
shell membrane
embryo
allantoic cavity
chorioallantoic membrane

Figure 15.3-5.   Section (across the body) of a late-stage chick embryo

In the stages you are now observing, the allantois (seen in the five-day egg) has developed into the chorioallantoic membrane, which lines the entire egg. It lies just within the membrane that surrounded the albumen in the unincubated egg.   When the shell is removed, blood vessels can be seen in the chorioallantoic membrane.

Using scissors and forceps, carefully remove the chorioallantoic membrane. Can you find the yolk sac? How is it connected to the embryo? (15)   How is the food in the yolk transported to the embryo? (16)

Remove the amnion.   Note all embryonic features that indicate the organism is a bird.   Look for characteristics that you know occur in a chick (beak, feathers, wings, claws, scales on the feet) and note the stage in which these characteristics first appear. (17)

After each team has studied an embryo, exchange the embryos until all teams have seen each stage of development.

SUMMARY

Review all your notes and sketches.   Use this firsthand information to write a description of the development of a chicken embryo, from the laying of the egg to hatching. (18)

EXERCISE 15.4

VEGETATIVE REPRODUCTION: REGENERATION (PLANT)

INTRODUCTION

Vegetative reproduction is dependent upon the ability of an organism to grow new parts from old. This ability is called <u>regeneration</u>, and in some degree all organisms seem to have it. In man, skin and nails are constantly being regenerated, but man cannot regenerate a finger or an arm. A crab can regenerate a claw, but a claw cannot regenerate a whole crab. Regeneration can result in reproduction only if half or less than half of an organism can regenerate the missing parts.

As the term implies, <u>vegetative</u> reproduction is more widespread among plants than among animals. Plants that (under natural conditions) reproduce by vegetative methods have great powers of regeneration, but plants that do not naturally reproduce by vegetative methods also have much regenerative ability. Therefore, in many plant species it is rather easy to bring about vegetative reproduction experimentally.

PURPOSE

This exercise is concerned with two questions: To what extent does coleus—a plant that does not naturally reproduce vegetatively—have the power of regeneration? Does it have sufficient regenerative ability to reproduce vegetatively under experimental conditions?

MATERIALS AND EQUIPMENT (for each team)

1. Flower pot (shallow form), 15- to 20-cm diameter
2. Stone or piece of broken pot
3. Sand, enough to fill flower pot
4. Saucer or shallow pan
5. Pot labels (wooden), 4
6. Live coleus plant, in a pot
7. Scalpel
8. Plastic bag
9. String

PROCEDURE

Place a large stone or a piece of broken pot over the hole in the bottom of the empty flower pot. Pour sand into the pot until (when leveled) its surface lies within 2 cm of the rim. Place the pot in a saucer or shallow pan, and water the sand thoroughly. Pour excess water from the saucer. With a pencil, divide the surface of the sand into quarter sections. Mark four pot labels A, B, C, and D, and place one along the outer edge of each section (see Figure 15.4-1).

Examine the coleus plant. You are to obtain four cuttings from it. Three of these (A, B, C) must each have three pairs of leaves and a terminal bud; the fourth cutting (D) must be at least 5 cm long and must be taken from between pairs of leaves. (If possible, obtain D and one of the other cuttings from the same branch.) Using a scalpel, make the necessary cuts.

From Cutting A remove the bottom pair of leaves. With a pencil, make a hole in the center of Section A in the pot; the depth of this hole should be about 1 cm less than the distance from the base of Cutting A to the lower pair of remaining leaves. Insert Cutting A (cut end first) into the hole so that the lower pair of leaves is just above the sand. Press the sand together around the cutting.

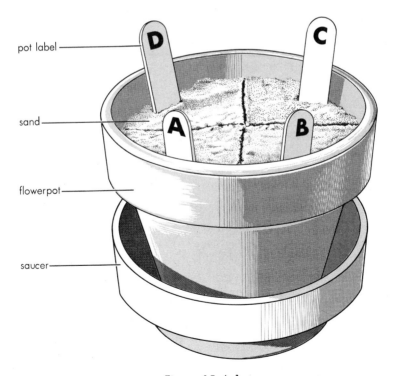

pot label

sand

flowerpot

saucer

Figure 15.4-1

From Cutting B remove the tip of the branch and all but the upper-most pair of leaves. Make a hole in the center of Section B; the depth of this hole should be about 1 cm less than the distance from the base of Cutting B to the remaining pair of leaves. Insert Cutting B so that its leaves are just above the sand. Press the sand together around the cutting.

Prepare Cutting C just as you did B, and plant it in Section C. Then remove its remaining pair of leaves. Press the sand together around the cutting.

Plant Cutting D in a hole about 4 cm deep in Section D. Press the sand together around the cutting. Check Figure 15.4-2 to make sure you have prepared and planted all four cuttings correctly.

Place a plastic bag over the cuttings, and close the open end of the bag around the rim of the pot with a piece of string. Set the pots containing the coleus plant and the cuttings in a place where they will receive abundant light. Add water to the saucers whenever necessary.

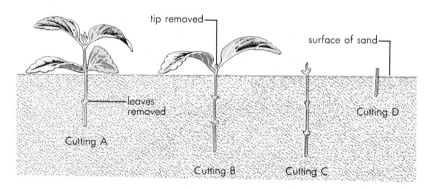

Figure 15.4-2. Coleus cuttings

OBSERVATIONS

After three weeks examine the plant from which the cuttings were taken. What, if anything, has happened at the points where cuttings were removed? (1) Remove the plastic cover from the pot containing the cuttings, and examine them. Which ones seem to be alive? In each case, what is the evidence for your decision? (2)

Loosen the sand and remove Cutting A. Have roots developed? If so, at what points on the cutting have they developed? (3) What, if anything, has happened to the cut surface? (4)

Loosen the sand and remove Cutting B. Have roots developed? If so, at what points? (5) What, if anything, has happened to the end that was under ground? (6) What, if anything, has happened to the end above ground? (7)

Loosen the sand and remove Cutting C. Have roots developed? If so, at what points? (8)   What, if anything, has happened to the end that was under ground? (9)   What, if anything, has happened to the end above ground? (10)

Loosen the sand and remove Cutting D. Have roots developed? If so, at what points? (11)   What, if anything, has happened to the end that was under ground? (12)   What, if anything, has happened to the end above ground? (13)

CONCLUSIONS

First consider only the plant from which the cuttings were taken. What evidence do you have that coleus has the ability to regenerate parts lost by injury? (14)

Now consider the evidence from the cuttings.   To what extent might the accidental breaking up of a coleus plant (by a hailstorm, for example) result in the multiplication of coleus plants? (15)

FOR FURTHER INVESTIGATION

1. Plants vary greatly in their ability to regenerate. Use the procedure given in Exercise 15.4 to investigate the regenerative ability of other plant species—tomato, household geranium, begonia, bean, pepper, marigold, zinnia, for example.

2. Regeneration of roots is likely to proceed more slowly in woody plants than in herbaceous plants. Investigate the effects of various "growth substances" (see text Figure 13.31) on the rate of root regeneration in several species of woody plants.

3. Does the age of the plant (or the age of the plant part) affect the ability to regenerate?

4. Remove the tip and leaves from a branch of coleus, and split the branch lengthwise. Lay one half in a pot containing wet sand, split side down. Place the other half on the wet sand, split side up. Cover the pot with a plastic bag. What happens? Explain the results.

EXERCISE 15.5

DEVELOPMENT OF AN EMBRYO: FROG

INTRODUCTION

If you did not do Exercise 15.3, read the introduction to it now.

In most amphibians the word "embryo" may be applied to any stage of development, from the cleavage of the zygote to the emergence of the organism from the jelly that surrounds it. But neither of these limits is very definite. In studying the embryology of the frog, it will be convenient to begin observation before fertilization and to continue into the early development of the tadpole.

PURPOSE

Embryology is best understood when direct observations can be made; the purpose of this exercise is to enable you to make such observations of the developing embryo. In addition, the exercise includes an experiment on the influence of temperature on the rate of development in frog embryos.

BACKGROUND INFORMATION

In vertebrates the pituitary gland, which is attached to the lower surface of the brain, influences the activity of the gonads by means of hormones called gonadotrophins. In the female frog the seasonal changes of spring stimulate the pituitary to secrete large quantities of gonadotrophins into the bloodstream. Reaching the ovaries, these hormones cause eggs to be released into the oviducts—a process called ovulation. After these eggs are laid, the ovaries build up a new crop of eggs during the summer. When the female frog goes into hibernation in the autumn, the eggs to be laid the following spring need only the stimulus of gonadotrophins to be released from the ovaries. Therefore, if gonadotrophic hormones are injected into the female frog during late fall or winter, eggs can be obtained long before the frog's own gonadotrophic hormones are secreted from its pituitary.

In the male frog, also, the pituitary hormones stimulate the gonads by secreting gonadotrophins. This results in normal mating behavior and the release of sperm cells over the eggs as they are laid by the female. Gonadotrophins may be secreted by the frog's own pituitaries in spring, or they may be injected into the frog. But active sperm cells may be obtained—even in winter—by removing the gonads (testes) from a frog and chopping them up in a little water.

MATERIALS AND EQUIPMENT (for each team)

A. Inducing Ovulation

1. Live female frog, at least 8 cm from snout to anus
2. Hypodermic syringe, 2 ml or larger
3. Hypodermic needle, #25
4. Pituitary suspension
5. Battery jar with weighted-screen cover

B. Fertilizing Frog Eggs

1. Pithed male frog
2. Scissors
3. Scalpel
4. Forceps
5. Petri dish
6. Pond water
7. Graduated cylinder (25 ml or 100 ml)
8. Female frog (from A, above)
9. Syracuse watch glass
10. Medicine dropper
11. Stereomicroscope
12. Finger bowls or plastic dishes, approximately 10 cm in diameter and 4 cm deep, 3 or 4
13. Glass-marking crayon
14. Frog eggs, fertilized several hours before the laboratory period
15. Temperature Gradient Box, 1 per class

C. Observing Frog Embryos

1. Developing frog eggs (from B, above)
2. Stereomicroscope
3. Centigrade thermometer
4. Medicine dropper
5. Forceps
6. Graph paper, 1 sheet per student
7. Pencils, 4 or 5 colors

PROCEDURE

A. Inducing Ovulation

Injection of a female frog with pituitary suspension can best be done by three members of the team (Students "A," "B," and "C"); the other members assist by keeping all materials ready for use as needed.

Student A: Grasp the female frog gently in the left hand. The dorsal surface of the frog should rest against the palm of the hand. The posterior legs should be held firmly between the fingers of the right hand.

Student B: Grasp the skin of the ventral surface between the thumb and forefinger of one hand and lift it away from the body wall.

Student C: Draw into the hypodermic syringe the amount of pituitary suspension recommended by the teacher. Attach the needle and insert it through the frog's skin and into the muscle of the body wall. (CAUTION: Do not insert the point of the needle <u>through</u> the body wall!) Inject the pituitary suspension.

Put the female frog into a battery jar. Add water to a depth of about 2 cm and cover the mouth of the jar with a weighted screen. Place the jar where the frog will not be disturbed and will have an even room temperature (20° to 22°C). In two or three days the frog should be ready to release eggs.

B. Fertilizing Frog Eggs

When the female frog is ready to ovulate, open the abdominal cavity of a pithed <u>male</u> frog quickly, using the technique described in Exercise 14.1. Move the internal organs aside and locate the testes. These are two whitish, oval organs located on each side of the backbone and just ventral to the kidneys. Using scissors and forceps, remove both testes and put them in a petri dish containing about 2 ml of pond water at room temperature. With a scalpel cut the testes into fine pieces; use the flat side of the blade to mash the pieces against the bottom of the dish. Add 20 ml of pond water, and set the dish aside for ten minutes. During this time, sperm cells released from the testes will become active and form a sperm suspension.

While this is happening, place a few milliliters of pond water in a Syracuse watch glass. Grasp the ovulating female frog in one hand, dorsal side against the palm, and extend the hind legs with the other hand. Hold the frog in this position over the watch glass. Then squeeze the abdomen gently, applying pressure gradually from the anterior part of the abdomen toward the posterior part. In this manner strip a few eggs into the watch glass.

When the sperms have had ten minutes to become active, use the squeezing technique to strip 100 to 150 eggs from the female frog into the petri dish containing the sperm suspension. Bathe the eggs with the sperm suspension, using a medicine dropper. Allow the eggs to remain in the sperm suspension for ten minutes.

Meanwhile, observe the eggs in the Syracuse watch glass, using a stereomicroscope. In your data book, note whether the eggs are floating dark side up, light side up, or without regard to color. Note the thickness of the eggs in relation to the thickness of the jelly that surrounds them.

When the eggs have been in the sperm suspension ten minutes, gently pour the sperm suspension out of the petri dish, disturbing the eggs as little as possible. Use a medicine dropper to remove the last few milliliters of the suspension, picking up any remaining pieces of testes as you do so. Replace the sperm suspension with pond water. Again allow the eggs to stand—this time for fifteen minutes.

While you are waiting, number the finger bowls in which the eggs are to develop (the teacher will designate the quantity needed). Label the bowls with the team symbol; pour 100 ml of pond water into each of the bowls.

Place in the watch glass a few of the frog eggs that were fertilized before your laboratory period began. Observe with the stereomicroscope. In your data book, record the time at which these eggs were fertilized (obtain this from the teacher) and the time at which you observe them. Study the stages of development shown in Figure 15.5-1, and record the number of the stage that most resembles the eggs you are observing. Also compare these eggs with the ones just fertilized and with the unfertilized eggs, noting any differences.

When jelly has swelled around the eggs in the petri dish, it is safe to handle them. Use a scalpel to free any eggs that stick to the dish. With scissors, cut the ribbon of eggs into groups of 5 to 10 eggs each. (CAUTION: Be careful to avoid stretching or squeezing the eggs.) Using forceps, gently transfer 25 to 30 eggs into each of the finger bowls. Put the bowls in the Temperature Gradient Box or in other places designated by your teacher.

C. Observing Frog Embryos

On each succeeding day, for as long as the teacher directs, observe the embryos in each bowl. During the first few days watch for eggs that are not developing. Using a medicine dropper and forceps, remove any dead eggs. In your data book, record the day of observation (if the eggs were fertilized on Monday, Tuesday is recorded as "Day 1," and so on). Next to this, record the number of the bowl observed. Next to this, record the temperature of the water in the bowl at the time you begin observation. Finally, record the number designating the stage in Figure 15.5-1 that most closely resembles the majority of the embryos.

In Figure 15.5-1 the eggs and embryos are shown without the surrounding jelly. In your own observations (through Stage 19) the jelly

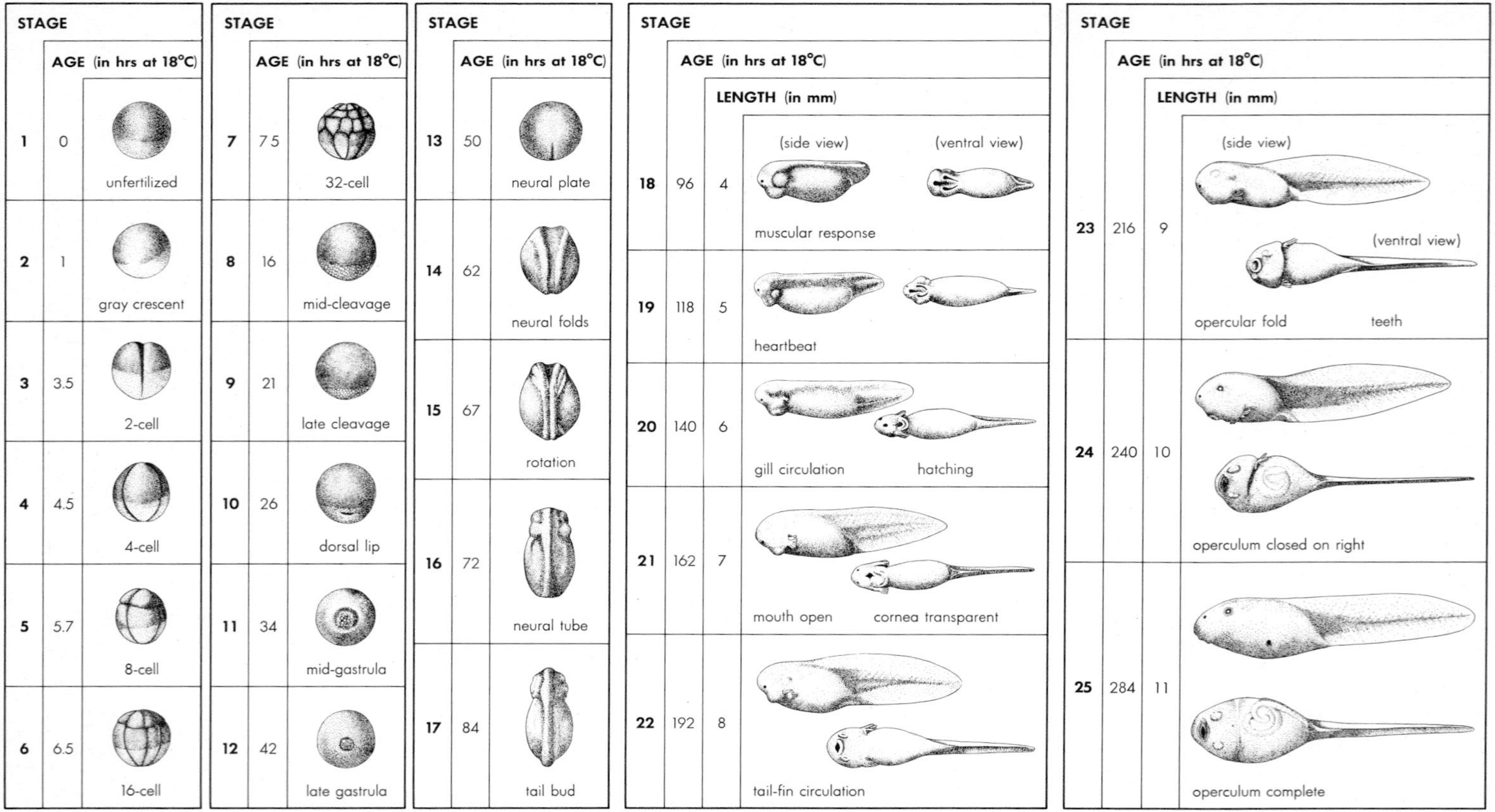

Figure 15.5-1. Shumway's chart showing stages of development of Rana pipiens. (Courtesy The Anatomical Record: Volume 78, No. 2, Oct., 1940)

will look something like a halo. You will probably have particular difficulty seeing the differences among Stages 15, 16, 17, and 18, since at those stages the embryos will be somewhat folded in the jelly covering. As you refer to Figure 15.5-1, keep these points in mind: (a) The drawings and the ages given are those of embryos developing at a <u>constant</u> <u>temperature</u> of 18°C. (b) The notes under the drawings should help you to identify stages in the embryos you are observing. (c) The drawings show stages at which the embryos can be clearly distinguished; the embryos, of course, gradually change from one stage to another. Many of the embryos you observe will be at inter-mediate stages and will not look exactly like any one of the drawings. You may use decimals (6.5, 10.5, etc.) to indicate intermediate stages.

After each day's observation, be sure to return the finger bowls to their places, so that the temperature in each may be kept as stable as possible.

STUDYING THE DATA

Plot the data from your team's bowls on one grid, using a different color for each bowl. Show stages of development on the ordinate and time on the abscissa. Compute the average temperature maintained in the water of each bowl; in the key to the graph, write each average next to the appropriate color. Finally, use another color to plot the data from Figure 15.5-1; write "Constant 18°C" next to this color in the key. Which line shows the most even development? (2) Which line shows the most rapid development? (3) The least rapid development? (4) Explain. (5)

SUMMARY

From the results, what general statement can you make about the influence of temperature on the rate of embryonic development in a frog? (6)

FOR FURTHER INVESTIGATION

1. You may wish to follow the development of the tadpoles after they hatch. If so, you will need to feed them, beginning a few days after hatching. Use spinach prepared as baby food. Place not more than 0.25 ml of the food in each dish, and allow the dish to remain undisturbed for about thirty minutes. Then pour out the water and re-place it with fresh pond water.

2. It is possible to induce frog eggs to develop parthenogenetically. The procedure may be found in Moog's <u>A Laboratory Block on Animal Growth and Development</u> (Boston: D. C. Heath & Co., 1963).

EXERCISE 15.6

EFFECTS OF X-IRRADIATION UPON SEEDS

INTRODUCTION

Radiation from radioactive isotopes that occur naturally in the rocks of the earth has always been a part of the normal environment of organisms. Now, however, much more intense radiation arises from the radioisotopes produced by human activities in the field of atomic energy. Thus the effects of radiation on organisms are of increasing biological importance.

In Exercise 13.7 you found that the radiations given off by some substances are useful in studying the physiological processes of organisms. However, some kinds of radiation also change the biochemistry of cells, thereby affecting the individual's entire metabolism. The changes may be so great that the organism dies. Or if the organism survives, they may visibly affect its structure and growth rate. Often the changes affect not only the organism exposed to the radiations but also its descendants—that is, the changes are hereditary.

If an organism is exposed to such radiations during an early stage of development, the effects are often easily observed in later stages. Therefore, irradiation of embryos is a particularly useful method for studying radiation effects.

PURPOSE

In this exercise you will study the effects of irradiation by X-rays upon the growth and development of embryos in seeds.

MATERIALS AND EQUIPMENT (for each team)

1. Seeds of oats, sunflower, or corn, 80
2. Glass-marking crayon
3. Plastic vials, with lids or stoppers, 4
4. Dissecting needle
5. Bunsen burner
6. Metric ruler
7. X-ray source
8. Cardboard boxes, 12 X 24 X 10 cm or larger, 4
9. Sheets of plastic or aluminum foil, large enough to line boxes, 4
10. Stapler
11. Vermiculite (or sand)
12. Petri dishes, 4
13. Paper towels
14. Scissors
15. Graph paper (1 sheet per student)
16. Pencils, 4 colors

PROCEDURE

Place 20 seeds (of the kind assigned to your team) in one of the four plastic vials. Using a glass-marking crayon, mark the level of the top seeds. Empty the seeds from the vial. Mark three other vials at the same level. The marks indicate the portions of the vials that the seeds will occupy. Heat a dissecting needle in the flame of a Bunsen burner. Use the heated needle to punch holes in each of the four vials; punch holes only in the part of the vial that will be occupied by 20 seeds. Space the holes about 5 mm apart. Using a glass-marking crayon, number the vials 1 to 4. Place 20 seeds in each vial.

The teacher or a student will take the seed vials of all teams to a source of X-rays. Expose the vials numbered 1 for 8 seconds, the vials numbered 2 for 16 seconds, and the vials numbered 3 for 32 seconds; the vials numbered 4 receive no irradiation.

Number four boxes 1 to 4, and mark each with the team symbol. Line each box with a sheet of plastic or aluminum foil. Shape the linings to fit the bottoms and sides of the boxes. Fold the corners as you would in wrapping a package, and staple them to the sides of the boxes. Pour vermiculite (or sand) into the boxes to a depth of about 8 cm. Moisten it thoroughly.

Using a glass-marking crayon, label the lids of four petri dishes with numbers and the team symbol. Line the bottom half of each dish with four disks of paper towel, cut to fit snugly. With a pencil, number the top disk in each dish. Moisten the paper thoroughly. Transfer 5 seeds from each irradiated vial to the dish bearing the corresponding number (from Vial 1 to Dish 1, etc.). Cover the seeds in each dish with two more disks of wet paper towel. Cover each dish with its

numbered lid.   Put the dishes of all teams together in a dark place
where the temperature will remain stable.

Transfer the remaining seeds from each vial to the box bearing
the corresponding number.   In each box plant the seeds in three rows
of five at a depth of about 1 cm.   For recording data, it is necessary
to identify the seedlings by number.   On the side of each box, place a
form like the following:

1	2	3	4	5
6	7	8	9	10
11	12	13	14	15

Water the seeds thoroughly, but do not flood the boxes.   Put the boxes
in a place where direct sunlight does not reach them.

Observe the petri dishes each day.   When no further germination
occurs for three days, record in your data book the number of seeds
that germinated in each dish.

Observe the boxes each day.   When the first seedlings appear,
begin a daily record of the height (in millimeters) of each seedling.
Each day calculate the average height of seedlings in each box.   A
convenient form for recording these data is shown below.   When a
seedling dies, write D under the appropriate day number.   In the last
column on the right, record anything unusual in the appearance of the
plants.

Kind of Seed _____   Box No. _____   Irradiation _____

SEEDLING	DAILY HEIGHT RECORD (in mm)							DESCRIPTIVE DATA
	1	2	3		19	20	21	
1								
2								
3								
15								
Average								

STUDYING THE DATA

Calculate the percentage of seeds that germinated in each petri
dish. (1)   If other teams worked with the same kind of seed, combine
your data with theirs.   On the chalkboard record the combined data
and the percentages derived from them.

Calculate the percentage of seedlings in each box that survived to the end of the experiment. (2)

For each box, plot average daily height on one grid. Using a different color for each box, connect the plotted points. If other teams worked with the same kind of seed, combine the data on <u>final</u> height in each box. On the chalkboard record the averages derived from the combined data.

Among your team's plants, what differences besides those already noted appear to be associated with irradiation? (3)

CONCLUSIONS

From the data on germination, what can you conclude about the effects of radiation on the mortality of embryo plants? (4)   Do the data indicate a difference among species with respect to embryonic resistance to irradiation?   If so, which of the tested species was most resistant? (5)

On the basis of the data obtained from the measurement of seedlings, what effect (if any) does radiation have on the growth rate and size of plants? (6)   Do the data indicate a difference among species with respect to the effect of radiation on size?   If so, which of the tested species was most resistant to this effect? (7)

DISCUSSION

If data obtained by the class indicate that there are differences between irradiated and nonirradiated populations of a species, which (if any) of such differences might increase the death rate? (8)   Which (if any) might decrease the death rate? (9)

If the data indicate that there are differences in radiation effects among plant species, suggest hypotheses to explain the differences. (10)

FOR FURTHER INVESTIGATION

The strictly genetic effects of irradiation can be determined only over a long period of time.   Your class can contribute to a long-term study of such effects.   Care for the plants until they have produced seed.   When you harvest the seeds, be sure to store in separate packets the seeds from plants that received different amounts of irradiation.   If such work was done by other classes in previous years, the teacher may be able to supply you with seeds from plants that were irradiated several generations ago.

CHAPTER 16

Heredity

EXERCISE 16.1

HEREDITY AND ENVIRONMENT

INTRODUCTION

The small boy asked, "How come Bill Dorsey has a wooden leg?"

"Must be hereditary," answered his older brother. "His father had a wooden leg."

Few of us would reason in this way. But the question so inadequately answered above echoes a basic biological problem: To what extent are the characteristics of an organism the result of the organism's parentage—its heredity—and to what extent are they the result of the environment in which the organism has developed?

PURPOSE

This exercise is an experiment designed to produce data for studying the relative effects of heredity and environment on a characteristic of tobacco seedlings.

MATERIALS AND EQUIPMENT (for each team)

1. Paper towels
2. Scissors
3. Petri dishes, 2
4. Beaker filled with water
5. Tobacco seeds, 60
6. Forceps
7. Box (large enough to cover half the dishes used by the class)
8. Medicine dropper
9. Hand lens

PROCEDURE

Cut eight disks of paper towel to a size that fits snugly into the bottom half of a petri dish. On two of the disks draw diameters at right angles to each other, so that the disks are divided into quarters. Write a large <u>A</u> on one of these disks; write a large <u>B</u> on the other. Place four disks (with <u>A</u> on top) in one petri dish and four (with <u>B</u> on top) in another. Pour water into each dish; when the paper is thoroughly soaked, pour off the excess water.

Sprinkle 30 tobacco seeds into each dish. Using forceps, arrange the seeds so that none lie on the lines you have marked on the papers. No seed should be closer than twice its own length to another seed.

Place covers on the dishes and label with the team symbol. Put both dishes in a warm place that receives strong light—but not direct sunlight. Cover the <u>B</u> dishes of all teams with a box or other device that will keep them in darkness. Check the dishes each day to make sure the paper does not dry out. If it begins to do so, add water with a medicine dropper.

When at least half of all the seeds have germinated, examine them with a hand lens. Each young tobacco plant consists of a white or colorless root and two tiny leaves, the cotyledons (Figure 16.1-1). Usually the root appears first, but in this experiment you are concerned only with the cotyledons. Some of the seedlings will have green cotyledons, and some will have creamy or yellowish ("albino") cotyledons. Count the number of green and the number of albino seedlings

Figure 16.1-1

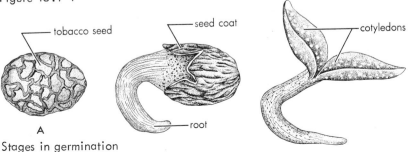

Stages in germination
of a tobacco seed

A

B

C

in each dish; do not count seedlings in which the cotyledons have not yet appeared. The division of the paper into quarters will help you to count accurately. At least two members of the team should take counts; recount if the two disagree. Copy the form shown below in your data book, and record the counts opposite "Day 1." Replace the lids on the dishes; return the dishes to the assigned location, covering the B dishes as before.

DAY	DISH A			DISH B		
	Green	Albino	% Albino	Green	Albino	% Albino
1						
2						
3						
4						

On the following day (Day 2) take another count. The number of germinated seedlings may have increased; but if the number of seed-lings of either kind is less, then an error in counting must have been made on one of the days. Record the counts. To calculate percentages of albino seedlings, divide the number of seedlings having albino cotyledons by the total number of seedlings that have cotyledons. Make this calculation for each dish. Return the dishes to the assigned loca-tion, but do not cover the B dishes with the box; allow all dishes to remain exposed to light.

On Day 3 count the seedlings again. Record the counts and return the dishes to their assigned place, allowing all dishes to remain exposed to the light.

On Day 4 make final counts and calculate the percentage of albinos in each dish.

STUDYING THE DATA

From the data obtained on Day 2, compare the percentages of albinos in Dish A and Dish B. In what way are they different? (1) What experimental variable may be associated with this difference? (2) Can this variable be considered the cause of albinism in tobacco seed-lings? Why or why not? (3)

Compare the percentage of albinos in Dish B on Day 4 with the percentage on Day 2. What striking change has occurred? (4) What experimental variable may be associated with this change? (5) Can this variable be considered the cause of green coloration in tobacco seedlings? Why or why not? (6) Is the experimental variable a hered-itary factor, or is it an environmental factor? (7) How can you account for the difference among seedlings in Dish A? (8)

CONCLUSIONS

Which data support the statement "Albinism in tobacco seedlings is caused by environment"? (9) Which data support the statement "Albinism in tobacco seedlings is caused by heredity"? (10) Try to formulate a statement that accounts for all the data. (11)

EXERCISE 16.2

PROBABILITY

INTRODUCTION

In forming his theory of heredity, Mendel made use of the mathematics of probability. This branch of mathematics was originally developed by persons interested in gambling—in games of chance. "Chance" is a term used to describe any situation in which the factors affecting the outcome are so numerous and (taken individually) so weak that we can never hope to determine a "cause." "Random" is another term that applies to such situations. "Choosing at random" is a common expression; it means choosing entirely by chance—which results in a completely impartial choice.

To understand genetics, we need to know something about the mathematics of probability. Furthermore, we need to know something about probability to understand the nature of modern science. For science deals largely (some scientists would say entirely) with probabilities—not with certainties. For example, the principles of probability are at work in the disintegration of radioactive atoms and in the collision of molecules in gases—as well as in the distribution of genes from one generation to the next.

PURPOSE

This exercise provides an opportunity to work out experimentally two principles of probability that are important in genetics.

BACKGROUND INFORMATION

The basic question in probability is: How often should we <u>expect</u> a particular event to occur in a given number of events? Notice that we do not say, "How often <u>will</u> it occur?" Of course, the gamblers who first worked out the mathematics of probability would have liked to know exactly when, for example, the ace of spades would appear in a given deal of cards. But the best that the mathematics of probability can ever do for gamblers or for scientists is to tell what expectation will <u>least</u> <u>often</u> be disappointed. In the language of gamblers, it gives us the "odds."

The simplest way to express probability mathematically is by means of fractions. A coin has two sides, distinguished as "heads" and "tails"; when tossed into the air, it may land on either of the sides. The number of possibilities is the denominator of the fraction. What is the probability that "heads" will come up when you toss the coin? In this question you are looking for <u>one</u> specific event; this is the numerator of the fraction. Thus, the probability of a coin's landing "heads" up is 1/2. Of course we can write this as 0.5 or 50 percent, but the common fraction is the starting point.

Let us use this mathematical notation in some further examples: There are 52 cards in a deck (not counting the joker), 13 of each suit. What is the probability that you will draw a spade from a shuffled deck? There are 52 possibilities in the deck, of which 13 meet the conditions of the question. Therefore the probability is 13/52, or 1/4, or .25, or 25 percent. What is the probability that you will draw the ace of diamonds? Again there are 52 possibilities, but this time only one meets the conditions of the question; the probability is 1/52. A die (singular of "dice") has six sides. What is the probability that a <u>5</u> will come up on one throw of the die? The probability is 1/6. What is the probability that an even number will come up on one throw of the die? Since there are 3 even numbers on the die—2, 4, and 6—there are 3 ways in which the conditions of the question may be met; therefore the probability is 3/6, or 1/2—the same probability as that of obtaining "heads" on one toss of a coin.

EQUIPMENT (per pair of students)

1. Coins, 2 (preferably two pennies—one shiny, one dull)
2. Cardboard box

PROCEDURE

In this exercise you will work in pairs—Student A and Student B.

A. Tossing a Single Penny

Student A: Prepare a score sheet containing two columns. Label one column H ("Heads"); label the other T ("Tails").

Student B: Toss a penny ten times. Toss into a cardboard box to prevent rolling.

Student A: Tally the result of each toss on the above sheet. After the tenth toss, draw a line across the columns of the score sheet. Take the penny and make ten tosses.

Student B: Tally the results of Student A's tosses. Draw a line across the score sheet.

Continue reversing roles until the results of one hundred tosses have been tallied.

B. Tossing Two Pennies Together

Student A: Prepare a score sheet containing four columns: Both H, Dull H/Shiny T, Dull T/Shiny H, and Both T.

Student B: Choose two pennies that can be easily distinguished—one dull and one shiny. Toss both pennies together twenty times.

Student A: Tally the results.

Reverse roles once. Then total the results from the entire class on the chalkboard.

STUDYING THE DATA

A. Tossing a Single Penny

What does the mathematics of probability (see "Background Information") lead you to expect in a series of ten tosses of the coin? (1) In any set of ten throws, did you ever obtain the expected results? If not, how close did you come? (2)

Deviation is a measure of the difference between expected results and actual (observed) results. To calculate deviation, first determine the difference between the number of "heads" you expected and the number of "heads" you observed. Then determine the difference between the number of "tails" you expected and the number of "tails" you observed. Add the two differences together, and divide the sum by the total number of tosses.

Calculate the deviation for each set of ten throws. Then add the results from one hundred tosses and calculate the team deviation. Finally, add the results from all the teams and calculate the class deviation. How does increasing the number of tosses affect the size of the deviation? (3) You have just worked out an important principle of probability.

B. Tossing Two Pennies Together

First consider "heads" on the dull penny; in how many columns does this appear? (4) In what fraction of the total number of tosses did "heads" appear on the dull penny? (5) In how many columns does "heads" on the shiny penny appear? (6) In what fraction of the total number of tosses did "heads" appear on the shiny penny? (7) In how many columns does "heads" on both pennies appear? (8) In what fraction of the total number of tosses did "heads" appear on both pennies? (9) Is this fraction closest to the sum, the difference, or the product of the two fractions for "heads" on one penny? (10) You have just worked out a second important principle: the relationship between the probabilities of separate events and the probability of a combination of events.

APPLICATION

Now assume that the shiny penny represents an egg cell. If it falls "heads" up, it represents an egg cell containing a dominant gene; if it falls "tails" up, it represents an egg cell containing a recessive gene. Likewise assume (as did Mendel) that the combination of egg cells and sperms is a chance, or random, process. On the basis of these assumptions, what is the probability that a zygote will contain at least one dominant gene? (11) What is the probability that it will contain two recessive genes? (12)

EXERCISE 16.3

MENDELIAN MONOHYBRID CROSS IN DROSOPHILA

INTRODUCTION

Mendel's basic experiments—monohybrid crosses of two pure-breeding individuals—have been repeated many times with many organisms. Most species (like Mendel's peas) require long periods of time to produce the necessary F_1 and F_2 generations. But by using fruit flies, you can see the results of a Mendelian monohybrid cross in less than one month.

There are many species of fruit (or vinegar) flies in the genus
Drosophila. The most abundant and widespread species is Drosophila
melanogaster, and, unless otherwise stated, this species is implied
where geneticists speak of Drosophila. It occurs in almost every part
of the world during the warmer seasons. It is found on overripe and
rotting fruit such as bananas, grapes, and plums. It is particularly
common around fruit markets and warehouses.

For many reasons, Drosophila is an excellent organism for genetic studies: (a) It is easy to raise in the laboratory because it has
simple food requirements, takes up little space, and is fairly hardy.
(b) It can complete its life cycle in about twelve days at room temperature. (c) It produces large numbers of offspring. (d) It may be
anesthetized readily for examination and sorting. (e) It has many kinds
of hereditary variations that can be recognized with low-power magnification. (f) It has only four pairs of chromosomes, and these are
easily distinguishable. (g) Extensive study of Drosophila genetics over
the last fifty years has resulted in a wealth of reference literature and
a knowledge of hundreds of genetic loci.

PURPOSE

In this exercise you will use techniques that have been fundamental
in the development of genetics in the twentieth century; at the same
time, you will be able to observe the experimental basis for some of
Mendel's principles.

BACKGROUND INFORMATION

The Fruit Fly

Before using the fruit fly in genetics experiments, you must understand its life cycle, practice techniques for handling the organism,
and learn to distinguish males from females.

As you read the following description of the Drosophila life cycle,
remember that the duration of each stage is affected by several environmental factors. Of these, temperature is the most important: at
$20^{\circ}C$ the complete cycle takes about twelve days; at $25^{\circ}C$ it takes about
ten days.

The eggs are small, ellipsoidal objects, each bearing two filaments on one end; with practice, you can see eggs with the naked eye.
Usually they are laid on the surface of food. The eggs hatch into larvae in about twenty-four hours. The larvae molt twice as they increase
in length. They eat almost continuously; in laboratory culture their
black mouth parts can easily be seen moving back and forth in the

medium.   Larvae channel through the medium while eating; these channels, showing that the food has been "worked," are a good indication of the successful growth of a culture.   The larva stage is followed by an inactive stage, the pupa.   When ready to pupate, the mature larvae (in laboratory culture) usually climb up the side of the bottle containing the culture or onto a paper strip provided in the bottle.   They pupate within their last larval covering, which then becomes harder and darker.   Through the pupal cases the change to adult flies can be observed.   The eyes, wings, and legs are particularly easy to see. When the adult flies emerge from the pupal cases, they are fragile, light in color, and do not have fully expanded wings.   In a few hours the body color darkens and the wings expand.   Adults may live a month or more.   Females do not mate for about ten hours after emerging from the pupae.   During mating they store considerable quantities of sperms; fertilization occurs later, at the time the eggs are laid.

Male fruit flies are usually smaller than females, but there are a number of more reliable characteristics by which the sexes may be distinguished.   Figure 16.3-1 shows these (see also text Figure 16.12); the figures should be studied carefully before work is begun with the flies.   It is not necessary to know the names of the structures to recognize the differences.   The symbols ♂ (for "male") and ♀ (for "female") are widely used by biologists.

Note: The following section may be skipped until you have completed the Procedure.

Use of the Chi-Square Test

In testing a hypothesis that involves numerical data, a scientist is constantly facing the question: Are the numbers obtained in my experiment close enough to the numbers expected from my hypothesis to allow a reasonable degree of confidence that only chance caused the difference—not some defect in the hypothesis or the procedure?   In other words, is the difference between the numbers actually observed and the expected numbers a chance difference—the same kind of difference that occurs when we toss a penny ten times and get 4 "heads" and 6 "tails" instead of the expected 5 and 5 (see Exercise 16.2)?

Consider an example: A geneticist studying a cross between two kinds of tomato plants expected (on the basis of hypothesis) that half the offspring would have green leaves and half would have yellow.   In certain crosses this is a reasonable expectation.   In one experiment the geneticist obtained 1240 seedlings, 671 with green leaves and 569 with yellow leaves; the expected numbers from a total of 1240 are, of course, 620 of each kind.   Is this a minor difference, a matter of chance?   Or is it so large that the geneticist ought to suspect that something is wrong with the hypothesis?   In this case, 620 green-

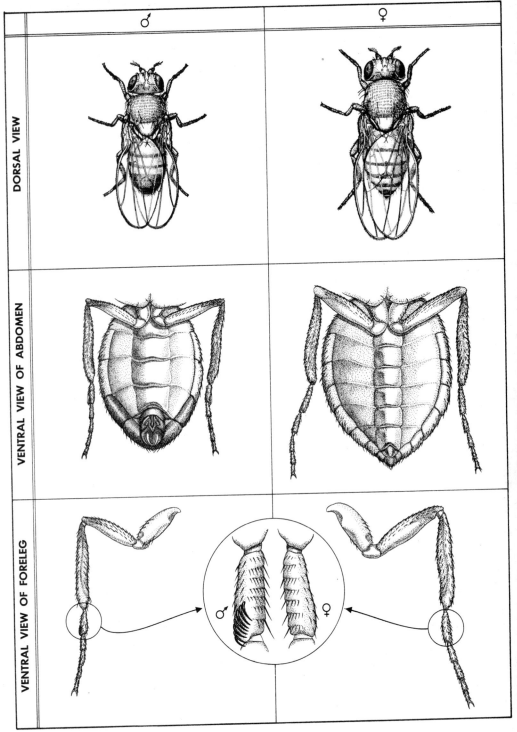

Figure 16.3-1. Comparison of male and female fruit flies. The
further enlargement of forelegs shows the sex comb, a characteristic of male flies.

leaved plants were expected and 671 were counted—a difference of 51. Similarly, 620 yellow-leaved plants were expected and 569 were counted—another difference of 51.

The deviation, or amount of difference (see Exercise 16.2), can be expressed in several ways. One way is to express it as a percentage of the total: $51/1240 = 4.1$ percent. A better way to indicate the deviation was invented in 1900 by Karl Pearson (1857-1936), an English mathematician. He called this measure chi-square (pronounced "kī square"). It is symbolized by the Greek letter chi and the square sign, thus: X^2. Chi-square is found as follows: For each class of objects, obtain the difference between the number expected and the number observed; square this difference; divide by the expected number; finally, add all the quotients together. The sum is the value of X^2. In the example, the difference for the first class of objects, green-leaved plants, is 51; squaring this we get 2601; dividing by the expected number, 620, we get the quotient 4.2. The difference for the other class of objects, the yellow-leaved plants, is 51; squaring this we get 2601; dividing by 620 we get 4.2. Added together, the two quotients come to 8.4, the value of X^2.

But what does this value mean? By solving an elaborate equation, mathematicians have provided the information needed to judge whether any X^2 value represents the sort of difference that occurs very probably by chance alone or very improbably by chance alone, or at probabilities between these extremes. A table prepared from the equation allows us to see how often (in 100 cases) a given value of X^2 could have been produced by chance alone:

X^2 value	.0002	.004	.016	.455	1.074	2.706	3.841	6.635
Times in 100 that chance alone could have been responsible for the difference	99	95	90	50	30	10	5	1

The X^2 value of 8.4 goes beyond the table, which means that there is less than 1 chance in 100 that the deviation between the observed and expected numbers could have been caused by chance alone. When the probability that a difference occurs by chance alone is less than 5 in 100, then the difference is said to be significant—in other words, we may reasonably suspect that the difference did not occur by chance alone and that factors in the hypothesis or in the procedure were affecting the outcome.

Now for the next important question: How consistently will repetitions of the experiment produce differences (from the expected numbers) of approximately the same magnitude? If such repetitions produce about the same results, it is time to search for a cause. (Further crosses of the tomato plants did show about the same results. The investigator found that the difference was caused by a loss of yellow-leaved plants. They were less sturdy than the green-leaved plants; fewer of their seeds germinated and lived.)

Consider another example: A geneticist investigated the inheritance of red flesh and yellow flesh in tomatoes. He predicted that the F_2 generation would show a ratio of 3 red to 1 yellow. This expectation was based on Mendel's principles, plus the assumptions that one pair of genes determines the difference between red- and yellow-fruited tomatoes and that one allele is dominant over the other. From his crossings he obtained a total of 4805 tomatoes. The 3:1 ratio of the theory led him to expect 3604 red-fleshed and 1201 yellow-fleshed tomatoes. But he observed 3629 red-fleshed tomatoes and 1176 yellow-fleshed tomatoes in the F_2 generation. Was the difference between observed and expected results significant and, therefore, suggestive of search for a cause? Or was the difference so small that chance alone could account for it—thus confirming the assumptions? Let us calculate the X^2 value:

$$3629 - 3604 = 25; \quad 25^2 = 625; \quad 625/3604 = .17$$

$$1201 - 1176 = 25; \quad 25^2 = 625; \quad 625/1201 = .52$$

$$X^2 = .17 + .52 = .69$$

Consulting the table, we find that the X^2 value .69 falls between .455 and 1.074, which show (respectively) probabilities of 50 times and 30 times in 100 that chance alone could have been responsible for the difference. From this the geneticist concluded that the difference was not significant and that the data did not justify further experimentation or a search for some other hypothesis. To be sure, the fact that results agree with a hypothesis does not prove that the hypothesis is correct. Some other hypothesis might lead to expectations that would agree with the results just as closely or more closely.

When more than two classes occur among the results of an experiment, it is necessary to use an expanded table. Such a table is needed to test the significance of results where three or four classes occur in a ratio—1:2:1 or 9:3:3:1, for example.

X^2 for four classes	.115	.352	.584	2.366	3.665	6.251	7.815	11.341
X^2 for three classes	.020	.103	.211	1.386	2.408	4.605	5.991	9.210
X^2 for two classes	.0002	.004	.016	.455	1.074	2.706	3.841	6.635
Times in 100 that chance alone could have been responsible for the difference	99	95	90	50	30	10	5	1

When pink-flowered four-o'clocks are crossed, the theory of non-dominance indicates that the offspring will turn out to be red-, pink-, and white-flowered in a 1:2:1 ratio. An experimenter made the cross and obtained 66 red-flowered plants, 115 pink-flowered plants, and 55 white-flowered plants. The X^2 value calculated from these data is 1.18. Consulting the table, we see that more than half the time (between 50 and 95 times in 100) chance alone could have accounted for the difference between observed and expected numbers in the three classes. This, therefore, was not a significant difference, and the experimenter concluded that his results agreed with the 1:2:1 ratio.

MATERIALS AND EQUIPMENT (for each team)

For All Parts of the Procedure

1. Etherizer (funnel and shot glass: see Figure 16.3-2)
2. Ethyl ether, in dropping bottle
3. Examination plate (square of white plastic bathroom tile)
4. Water-color brush, small
5. Stereomicroscope
6. Morgue (jar and motor oil: see Figure 16.3-3)
7. Glass-marking crayon

Part A: Examining Fruit Flies

1. Culture of wild-type flies, in glass vial
2. Culture of mutant flies, in glass vial
3. Culture bottles containing fresh food supply (optional), 2

Part B: The P_1 Mating

1. Culture of wild-type flies from which all adults have been removed eight hours previously (Item 1 from Part A)
2. Culture of mutant flies from which all adults have been removed eight hours previously (Item 2 from Part A)
3. Culture bottle containing fresh food supply

Part C: The F_1 Generation

1. Culture bottle containing offspring of P_1 cross (Item 3 from Part B)

Part D: The F_1 Mating

1. Culture bottle containing flies of F_1 generation (Item 1 from Part C)
2. Culture bottle containing fresh food supply

PROCEDURE

Part A: Examining Fruit Flies

Your team will be given two cotton-plugged vials containing Dro-sophila cultures. Label both vials with the team symbol. The flies in one culture differ in some conspicuous trait from the flies in the other. One culture (marked W) contains wild-type flies bearing the form of the trait that is normal in wild populations. The other culture (marked M) contains mutant flies bearing the trait in a form that has appeared by mutation in laboratory populations. To determine the difference, you must examine and compare the flies in both cultures.

Comparison of the flies can be accomplished only when they are immobile. They must be anesthetized, placed on an examination plate, and observed under a stereomicroscope. Refer to Figure 16.3-2 as you watch the teacher demonstrate the use of the etherizer:

1. Place a finger beneath the neck of the funnel. Put several drops of ethyl ether in the funnel, close to the upper end of the neck. Avoid using too much ether. You need ether vapor in the etherizer; liquid ether will kill the flies. When the ether trickles down the neck and reaches your finger, place the funnel in the glass.

2. Gently but rapidly tap the bottom of the glass vial containing the wild-type flies against your knee; this temporarily forces the flies to the bottom of the vial. Quickly remove the cotton plug, invert the vial, and place it firmly in the funnel.

3. Holding vial, funnel, and glass firmly together, tap the bottom of the glass sharply against your hand or knee. This dislodges the flies into the glass.

4. In the etherizer the flies will be overcome within a few seconds and will fall to the bottom. Watch them through the neck of the funnel or through the side of the glass. As soon as the last fly stops moving, remove the funnel and empty the flies onto the examination plate. (CAUTION: The flies should not remain in the etherizer more than a minute; over-etherized flies will die.)

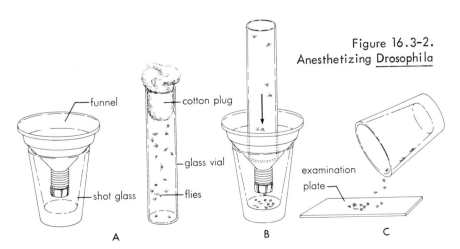

Figure 16.3-2.
Anesthetizing Drosophila

funnel — cotton plug — glass vial — shot glass — flies — examination plate

A   B   C

The flies are easily injured. Use a small brush when moving them about on the examination plate. Etherized flies recover in about five minutes. They may be re-etherized if necessary. Flies that are accidentally killed should be placed in the morgue (Figure 16.3-3).

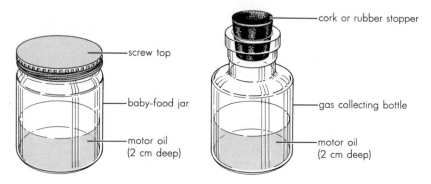

Figure 16.3-3. Drosophila morgues

Examine the flies in the W culture, noting differences between males and females (Figure 16.3-1). When you have finished, either return the flies to the original vial or discard them in the morgue or use them to start a new culture—whichever the teacher directs. If a new culture is to be started, write W and the date on a culture bottle containing a fresh food supply. Place the flies in it, holding the bottle on its side until all the flies have recovered.

Examine all the flies in the M culture. When you have finished, return the flies to the original vial or discard them or transfer them to another (M) bottle—whichever you did with the wild-type flies. In your data book, note the trait in which all the mutant flies differ from all the wild-type flies. The teacher will give you the name Drosophila geneticists use for the trait.

Note: If the class meets in the morning, it is recommended that the flies not be returned to the original vials and that Part B be done not more than eight hours later by a special team.

If the class meets in the afternoon, it is recommended that the flies be returned to the original vials. The flies should then be removed from the original vials not more than eight hours before the next class period, when Part B is to be done.

Part B: The P_1 Mating

In the original cultures new adults have emerged from the pupal stage since the old adults were removed. Using the technique described in Part A, etherize the flies in the culture (either $\underline{W}$ or $\underline{M}$) designated by the teacher. Pick out two or three females. Since mating does not occur until about ten hours after emergence from the pupal stage, these females will not be carrying sperms—they will be virgin females. Do not select flies having a very pale color or incompletely expanded wings; these flies have recently emerged and are easily injured. Place the selected females in a bottle containing a fresh food supply. Return the other flies to the original vial.

Now etherize the flies in the other original vial (the $\underline{W}$ culture if you selected females from the $\underline{M}$ culture; the $\underline{M}$ culture if you selected females from the $\underline{W}$ culture). Select two or three male flies, place them in the new culture containing the female flies, and return the remaining flies to the original vial.

On the bottle containing the mated flies mark the date, the cross (sex and trait of each parent), and the team symbol. Put the bottle where the other culture bottles are kept.

Seven or eight days after the mating, remove the parent flies and place them in the morgue.

Part C: The F_1 Generation

About ten or twelve days after the mating, the adult flies of the F_1 generation should begin to emerge. Etherize them, examine each for the trait you are studying, and place them in the morgue. In your data book tally the counts on a chart similar to the one below:

Date of Mating _____ Date Parents Removed _____
P_1: ♂ _____ X ♀ _____ Generation: _____

DATE	WILD-TYPE	MUTANT
Total		

Each day examine the adult flies that have appeared during the previous twenty-four hours; discard them, and tally the counts. Do not count beyond the ninth day after the emergence of the first F_1 flies; you might then run into some individuals of the F_2 generation.

Part D: The F₁ Mating

On the fifth or sixth day of counting, place five or six males and five or six females from the F_1 generation in a bottle containing a fresh food supply. Mark the bottle with the date, team symbol, and parentage of the flies (with respect to the trait you are studying). After seven or eight days remove the adult flies and place them in the morgue.

After ten or twelve days adults of the F_2 generation should begin to emerge. Make daily counts and record the results on a chart like the one shown in Part C.

DISCUSSION

With respect to the trait studied in this exercise, how many phenotypes occur among the P_1 flies?(1) How many phenotypes occur among the F_1 flies?(2) Compare results obtained by teams that crossed wild-type males and mutant females with results obtained by teams that crossed wild-type females and mutant males. Is the number of F_1 phenotypes the same in both cases? If not, try to explain the difference.(3)

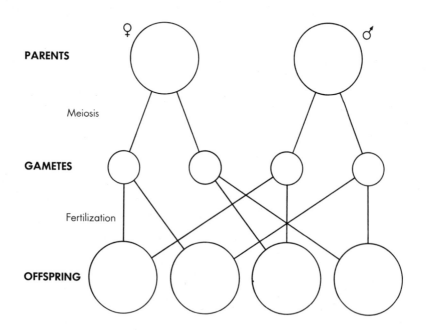

Figure 16.3-4

Make a copy of Figure 16.3-4 and label it P₁ Mating. Fill in the circles with the appropriate gene symbols. (4) If the mutant trait is dominant, symbolize it with the capital form of the first letter in its name. If the mutant trait is recessive, use the same letter but in the lower-case form.   The wild-type allele can then be symbolized by using "+" as a superscript to the gene symbol: A^+, for example.

In making the F_1 mating, why was it unnecessary to follow the precautions of the P_1 mating to insure that only previously unmated females became the parents? (5) With respect to the trait you are studying, how many phenotypes occur among the F_2 flies? (6) Make another copy of Figure 16.3-4. Label it F_1 Mating. Fill in the circles with the appropriate gene symbols. (7)

On the basis of your team's data, calculate the frequency of each phenotype in the F_2 generation. (8)   Now combine the data of all teams and calculate the frequencies. (9)   Are the observed frequencies close enough to those expected by theory (expressed in the chart drawn for Item 7) to give you confidence that only chance has produced the difference?   This question can be answered by calculating chi-square (X^2).   Review the discussion of chi-square under "Background Information" (pages 306-310).   Your calculations of X^2 will be aided by the use of a form like the following:

	CLASS 1	CLASS 2	TOTAL (X^2)
Number observed			
Number expected			
Difference			
Difference squared			
Difference squared divided by number expected			

On the basis of X^2, is the difference between the number of phenotypes observed and the expected number of phenotypes significant? (10) How do you interpret the meaning of the terms "significant" and "not significant" as they are applied to the results of this experiment? (11)

EXERCISE 16.4

HUMAN INHERITANCE

PURPOSE

Difficulties involved in a study of heredity in man have been discussed in the text (pages 562-565). In this exercise some methods of
reasoning used by human geneticists are illustrated.

PROCEDURE

This exercise requires no equipment other than a pencil, paper,
and your mind. You will be given a number of facts and asked to answer questions based on the facts. The answers to one set of questions
lead to the next set of facts, so you must move step by step through
the procedure—a reasoning rather than an experimental process.

Twenty-three pairs of chromosomes occur in each human body
cell. Twenty-two pairs in females can be matched with twenty-two
pairs in males; but the twenty-third pair in females differs from the
twenty-third "pair" in males. The unlike pairs are made up of the
so-called sex chromosomes. In females the two sex chromosomes are
similar; they are called X chromosomes (see text Figure 15.9). In
males the sex chromosomes are different from each other; one is an
X chromosome, and the other is called a Y chromosome (text Figure
16.24). Thus, with respect to the sex chromosomes, females can be
designated XX, males XY. Considering only the sex chromosomes,
how many kinds of gametes can females produce?(1) How many kinds
of gametes can males produce?(2)

The frequency of any particular characteristic within a group is
expressed as a fraction. Thus, in a group of 100 marbles containing
20 red and 80 blue marbles, the frequency of red marbles is $20/100 =
1/5 = 20\% = 0.2$. The frequency of the blue marbles is $80/100 = 4/5 =
80\% = 0.8$. Regardless of the way the fractions are written, their sum
(whether expressing two frequencies, as in this case, or more) must
always be equal to 1:

$$20/100 + 80/100 = 100/100 = 1$$

$$1/5 + 4/5 = 5/5 = 1$$

$$20\% + 80\% = 100\% = 1$$

$$0.2 + 0.8 = 1.0$$

It is customary to represent two frequencies with the letters p and q. The frequencies of the two kinds of marbles may be written as "pR + qB" (R representing red marbles and B representing blue marbles).

Any population of sperms, then, may be represented by the mathematical expression pX + qY. Using your knowledge of meiosis, calculate the values of p and q. (3) The same kind of mathematical expression may be used to represent the population of eggs produced by a female. What are the values of p and q when the egg population is represented? (4)

The percentages of males and females among human offspring may be predicted in the same way you predicted the percentages of "heads" and "tails" when tossing coins (Exercise 16.2). But in predicting, you must make two important assumptions. First, you assume that the X-carrying sperm and the Y-carrying sperm have exactly equal chances of reaching and fertilizing an egg. This is equivalent to assuming that eggs and sperms combine at random. We may therefore use algebraic multiplication (text page 542) to calculate the expected frequencies of the zygotes:

sperms	eggs	zygotes

$$(pX + qY) \quad \times \quad (pX + qX) \quad = \quad ?$$

What percentage of zygotes do you expect to be male? (5) What percentage do you expect to be female? (6)

But a long time intervenes between the formation of the zygote and the birth of the human infant. So you make a second assumption: that XX and XY zygotes have exactly equal chances of developing and being born.

The two assumptions seem natural, and they are commonly made. But the data on human births do not support them. First, data on deaths of embryos and on deaths during birth show that males have a much poorer chance of developing and of surviving birth than do females. Second, data on live births show that for every 100 females born, between 105 and 106 males are born. What do these data suggest about the assumption that the X-carrying sperm and the Y-carrying sperm have equal chances of reaching and fertilizing eggs? (7)

Understanding the inheritance of human traits depends almost entirely on finding and studying pedigrees (text pages 563-564). Two pedigree charts are shown in Figure 16.4-1. Study the two charts. On the basis of the occurrence of red-green color blindness (a visual defect in which a person is unable to distinguish red from green), is the gene for this trait dominant or recessive? Explain your reasoning. (8)

In mammals sex-linkage follows the same pattern that it does in insects. Therefore, you can apply your understanding of sex-linkage in Drosophila (text pages 548-549 and Figure 16.12) to the study of red-green color blindness in the two human pedigrees. Is the trait sex-linked? What evidence supports your answer? (9)

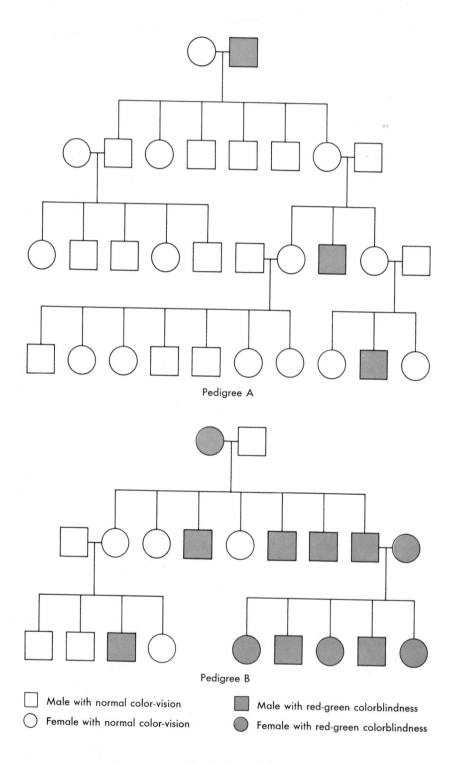

Pedigree A

Pedigree B

☐ Male with normal color-vision   ■ Male with red-green colorblindness
○ Female with normal color-vision   ● Female with red-green colorblindness

Figure 16.4-1

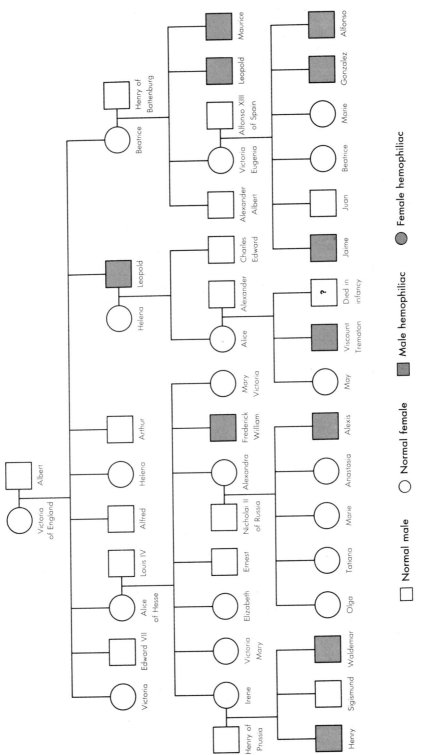

Figure 16.4-2

Hemophilia is a condition in which the blood platelets have great stability, so that normal clotting of the blood does not occur. It is a sex-linked trait, the recessive gene occurring only on X chromosomes. If a female has the gene on both X chromosomes (homozygous), she will show the trait; if she has the gene on one chromosome only (heterozygous), she will not show the trait but will be able to pass the gene along to her offspring—that is, she will be a carrier.

Figure 16.4-2 shows, in part, the occurrence of hemophilia among the royal families of Europe during the nineteenth and twentieth centuries. Study the chart. Then list the mothers that must have been carriers. (10)

The chart shows the actual occurrence of hemophilia in a pedigree. Now consider the frequencies (expressed as percentages) of hemophiliacs—persons afflicted with hemophilia—that we may expect among the offspring of certain marriages.

First, consider the marriage of a hemophiliac man and a woman homozygous for normal blood-clotting. What percentage of the male offspring do you expect to be hemophiliacs? (11) What percentage of the female offspring do you expect to be hemophiliacs? (12) What percentage do you expect to be carriers? (13)

Second, consider the marriage of a man whose blood clots normally and a woman who is a carrier of hemophilia. What percentage of their male offspring do you expect to be hemophiliacs? (14) What percentage of the female offspring do you expect to be hemophiliacs? (15) Carriers? (16)

Some genes are known to act as lethals (text page 559) only when they are homozygous. What information in Figure 16.4-2 suggests that this is true of the hemophilia gene? (17) What additional data are needed to confirm or disprove this point? (18)

EXERCISE 16.5

GENETIC DIFFERENCES IN PEAS

INTRODUCTION

Conspicuous genetic traits are easy to study—which is obviously an advantage from the experimental viewpoint. As long as the geneticist is interested primarily in establishing general principles of heredity, the effect of a particular trait in the life of an organism is of no concern. When, however, the geneticist turns to the heredity of a specific organism—man, for example—the way in which a trait affects the survival of the organism rather than the trait's conspicuousness becomes the primary concern.

Of course, it is difficult to determine just how important the effect of a trait may be. For example, it might be supposed that the excretion of phenylpyruvic acid in the urine is a trait of minor importance. But all persons who have this trait are idiots. From a large mass of evidence it seems certain that the same gene that causes excretion of phenylpyruvic acid also causes the idiocy (text page 565). What we call a "trait" is, in most cases, only one of the effects of a gene. The pleiotropic (multiple) effects of genes have long been known. In fact, Mendel himself noted that the determiner (whatever it was) of seed-coat color in peas also seemed to determine flower color and the presence or absence of red spots at the juncture of stem and leaves. Today it is clear that such visible differences must arise from invisible biochemical differences.

PURPOSE

You can investigate pleiotropic effects in another of the traits that Mendel studied—the shape of pea seeds. In this experiment you will investigate three characteristics associated with seed shape: a macroscopically visible characteristic, a microscopically visible one, and a biochemical one.

BACKGROUND INFORMATION

The biochemical characteristic you will study in this exercise involves an enzyme. The enzyme is extracted from the peas with water. Like most enzymes, it is rather unstable chemically, so the extract must be kept at a low temperature if it is not used immediately.

The enzyme catalyzes the formation of starch from glucose. Therefore you can observe its activity by placing it in contact with glucose and then testing for the presence of starch. For convenience, the glucose is dissolved in an agar medium. From Exercise 12.2 you know how to test for starch.

MATERIALS AND EQUIPMENT (for each team)

Day 1

1. Small bottles, 2
2. Glass-marking crayon
3. Balance (0.1-g sensitivity)
4. Peas of the genetic strains "round" and "wrinkled," 25 of each

Day 2

1. Bottles of soaked peas (from Day 1), 2
2. Paper towels, 2
3. Balance (0.1-g sensitivity)
4. Glass-marking crayon
5. Microscope slide
6. Medicine dropper
7. Scalpel
8. Soaked peas, round and wrinkled, 1 of each
9. Monocular microscope
10. Dry peas, round and wrinkled, 10 g of each
11. Mortar and pestle
12. Graduated cylinder
13. Cheesecloth
14. Beakers (250-ml), 2

Day 3

1. Glass-marking crayon
2. Petri dish, containing glucose agar
3. Extracts of round and wrinkled peas (from Day 2)
4. Medicine droppers, 3
5. Watch
6. Paper towel
7. Forceps
8. Iodine—potassium-iodide solution ($I_2 KI$)

PROCEDURE

Day 1

An apple or a potato wrinkles as it dries out. Therefore, when you first observe round and wrinkled peas together, it may occur to you that some have simply been dried more than others. But if the peas are the F_2 generation descended from a cross between pure-breeding round and pure-breeding wrinkled, both round and wrinkled seeds will occur together in the same ripening pod. In other words, roundness and wrinkledness occur in the same group of seeds even when environmental conditions are identical for all.

Nevertheless, it may be that wrinkling in some of the peas is the result of water loss. There may be an invisible characteristic in seeds that causes some to lose more water than others do, even when conditions are the same for all. You can investigate this matter "in reverse" by determining whether the two kinds of peas take up the same amount of water when they are soaked.

Select two bottles, each of such a size that 25 peas will occupy no more than half of it. Label one bottle R (round) and the other W (wrinkled). Label both bottles with the team symbol. Rinse the bottles and shake out the larger drops of water. Weigh each bottle separately and record the weights in your data book. Place 25 round peas in Bottle R and 25 wrinkled peas in Bottle W. Again weigh each bottle (with its contents) and record the weights in your data book. Fill the bottles with water and allow them to stand overnight.

Day 2

After the peas have soaked twenty-four hours, pour the water from each bottle. Place the round peas on one paper towel; place the wrinkled peas on another. Shake the larger drops of water from each bottle. Return each group of peas to its bottle. Weigh each bottle with the peas it contains. Record the weights.

Using a glass-marking crayon, label one end of a microscope slide R and the other end W. Place a drop of water at each end of the slide. Using a sharp scalpel, cut through a soaked round pea. Scrape the cut surface, and mix the scrapings into the drop of water at the R end of the slide. Clean the scalpel in running water. Cut through a soaked wrinkled pea. Scrape the cut surface, and mix the scrapings into the drop of water at the W end of the slide.

Using low power of a monocular microscope, examine the scrapings from both peas. Look for starch grains in each. Carefully compare the starch grains from the two kinds of peas, moving the slide back and forth, from one drop to the other. In your data book, note the appearance of the starch grains from each kind of pea. The following are some terms you may find useful: "compound," "simple," "divided," "whole," "oval," "spherical." Make sketches of a few grains in each sample.

Weigh out 10 g of dried round peas. Using mortar and pestle, grind the peas in 10 ml of water. Filter the mixture of water and ground peas through two layers of cheesecloth into a beaker. Mark the beaker R and add the team symbol.

Weigh out 10 g of dried wrinkled peas. Grind and filter as directed for the round peas. Mark this beaker W and add the team symbol. Store both beakers in the refrigerator overnight.

Day 3

Using a glass-marking crayon, divide into halves the bottom of a petri dish containing glucose agar. Mark one half R and the other half W. The marks should be visible through the agar when you turn the dish right side up. Remove the cover of the dish. Using a medicine dropper, place four small drops of the extract from round peas on the R half of the agar surface. Space the drops as widely as possible. Note the time. Using a different medicine dropper, place four small drops of the extract from wrinkled peas on the W half of the agar surface. Note the time.

At the end of ten minutes, use a small piece of paper towel held in forceps to blot up one drop of the round-pea extract. (CAUTION: Do not disturb the other drops!) Using a third medicine dropper, place a drop of I_2KI solution on the spot from which the extract has been removed. Immediately carry out the same steps with one drop of the wrinkled-pea extract.

Three minutes later, use a piece of paper towel and forceps to blot up both drops of I_2KI solution. Remove any remaining starch grains from the agar. Look beneath the surface of the agar for evidence of a positive starch test. In your data book, record the time; make a sketch for each drop, accurately showing the size and shape of any area having blue color.

Continuing at ten-minute intervals (twenty, thirty, and forty minutes after the drops of extract were first placed on the agar), blot another drop of extract on each half of the petri dish and repeat the starch test.

STUDYING THE DATA

To draw a conclusion from the soaking experiment, you need to make some calculations from your data. The form at the top of the next page will aid you.

Do round pea seeds differ from wrinkled pea seeds in ability to absorb water? If so, which kind absorbs more water in proportion to dry weight? (1) Assuming that the protoplasm in all developing pea seeds has approximately the same water content, which peas—round or wrinkled—lose the greater amount of water as they mature? Or do they lose equal amounts? (2)

Compare the data of all teams on the shape of starch grains in round and wrinkled peas. Is there a consistent difference? If so, would it enable you to predict seed shape from starch-grain shape, and vice versa? (3)

Compare the data of all teams on the production of starch from glucose. Is there a consistent difference between the enzyme extracts of round and wrinkled peas in speed of starch production? (4) In amount of starch produced? (5)

a. Weight of dried round peas + bottle. . . . . ——— g

b. Weight of bottle . . . . ——— g

c. Weight of dried round peas (a-b) . . . . ——— g

d. Weight of soaked round peas + bottle. . . . . ——— g

e. Weight of soaked round peas (d-b) . . . . ——— g

f. Water absorbed by round peas (e-c). . . . . ——— g

g. Weight of dried wrinkled peas + bottle . . . . ——— g

h. Weight of bottle . . . . ——— g

i. Weight of dried wrinkled peas (g-h) . . . . ——— g

j. Weight of soaked peas + bottle. . . . . ——— g

k. Weight of soaked wrinkled peas (j-h). . . . . ——— g

l. Water absorbed by wrinkled peas (k-i) . . . . ——— g

m. % increase in round peas (f ÷ c x 100). . . . . ——— %

n. % increase in wrinkled peas (l ÷ i x 100) . . . . ——— %

SUMMARY

You have investigated the differences between round and wrinkled pea seeds at three levels of observation. Which characteristics, if any, were always associated with roundness? (6) Which characteristics, if any, were always associated with wrinkledness? (7) Is association between characteristics conclusive evidence that they are pleiotropic effects of one gene? Why or why not? (8) If your answer to the last question is no, what additional evidence might cause you to change your answer? (9)

EXERCISE 16.6

INHERITANCE OF TWO TRAITS

INTRODUCTION

Experimentation with hereditary traits in the fruit fly provided much of the data from which the principles and theories of genetics were developed during the first half of the twentieth century. But geneticists have not worked with fruit flies only. Experiments with many other animals and with plants and protists have provided important data—sometimes confirming ideas developed from fruit-fly experiments, sometimes (as in the case of <u>Neurospora</u>) opening up new lines of investigation.

Besides <u>Drosophila</u>, few organisms have been so extensively and intensively studied by geneticists as has <u>Zea mays</u>, known in much of the world as maize but in the United States and Canada simply called corn. Many genetic traits have been investigated in corn, and dozens of loci have been identified on its ten pairs of chromosomes.

Many of the genetic traits in corn are conspicuous. Unlike the traits of the fruit fly, they can be seen without magnification. And corn does not need to be etherized before it is observed. However, to obtain a single generation of corn offspring, an entire growing season is required. Obviously, then, it is not practical to make the experimental crosses in class; much can be learned, however, from a study of the results of experimental crosses made by others.

PURPOSE

In this exercise the results of an experimental cross involving two genetic traits are studied.

BACKGROUND INFORMATION

The corn grain is a stage in the life history of the corn plant. It is somewhat comparable to the tadpole in the life history of the frog— or more comparable, perhaps, to the chick before hatching. In the fruit fly the characteristics of the early stages—the larva and the pupa —are not usually studied by geneticists. In corn, however, the characteristics of the grain are of considerable genetic interest.

The material to be studied in this exercise is an ear of corn. Each ear contains many grains, but each grain developed from a separate fertilization of an egg cell—from a separate zygote. Therefore, each grain is an individual, an offspring of the parent plant. The grains on the ear you will examine are individuals of an F_2 generation; they are descended from the P_1 crossing of a male and a female that were pure-breeding for the traits to be studied.

MATERIALS AND EQUIPMENT (for each pair of students)

1. Ear of corn representing the F_2 generation of a dihybrid cross
2. Straight pin

PROCEDURE

Examine the ear of corn. The grains may differ in many ways, but you are concerned only with <u>color</u> and <u>texture</u>. Each grain shows one or the other of two colors and one or the other of two textures. Give names to each of the colors and each of the textures. Each grain, of course, has a color and a texture, so there are four possible combinations of these traits.

Student A: Prepare a chart with four columns. At the top of each column write a different one of the four trait combinations.

Student B: Place a pin at the end of one of the rows of grains. (CAUTION: Handle the ear with care so that the grains do not become loose. Do not pick the grains from the ear!) In the row marked with the pin, count all the grains that have the combination of traits given at the top of the first column in Student A's chart.

Student A: Record the count reported by Student B.

Student B: In the same row count all the grains that have the combination of traits given at the top of the second column in the chart.

Student A: Record the count reported by Student B.

Continue until a count has been recorded for each of the four combinations. Then, without moving the pin, make counts of the grains in the next row on the ear. Continue counting and recording, row by row, until you reach the pin again. When you have finished, each column in the chart should have a number for each row of grains, though some numbers may be zeros.

STUDYING THE DATA

Total the numbers in each column of the chart. Which combination of traits occurred most often? (1) Least often? (2) Remembering that these grains are the F_2 generation descended from a cross between individuals that were pure-breeding for the two traits, determine which color is dominant. (3) Determine which texture is dominant. (4) Choose a suitable letter symbol for each of the two traits. Using the capital form of each letter to indicate a dominant gene and the lower-case ("small") form to indicate a recessive gene, write the genotypes (both traits together) of the individuals in the P_1 generation. (5)

Using the same symbols, show all the kinds of gametes that one parent of the P_1 generation could produce. (6) Show all the kinds of gametes that the other parent of the P_1 generation could produce. (7) Show all the genotypes that could occur in the F_1 generation. (8) What are the possible phenotypes in the F_1 generation? (9)

If the loci of the genes determining two different traits are on different pairs of chromosomes, then the genes should separate independently of each other (as the chromosomes do) in meiosis. Therefore the association between the genes at the two loci should be entirely random—just as the association of "heads" and "tails" on two coins that are tossed together is random (Exercise 16.2). Proceeding on the hypothesis that color and texture in corn grains are determined by genes that occur on different chromosomes, show all the gametes that could be produced by individuals of the F_1 generation. (10) According to the hypothesis, all the kinds of gametes will occur in equal frequencies. What is the expected frequency of each kind of gamete? (11) These frequencies must be the same for male and for female gametes. Keeping this in mind, what are all the possible combinations of these gametes? (12) Combining like genotypes, what are the possible kinds of genotypes in the F_2 generation? (13) What is the expected frequency (expressed as a decimal fraction) of each genotype? (14) Combining genotypes that produce the same phenotype, what are the possible kinds of phenotypes in the F_2 generation? (15) What is the expected frequency (expressed as a decimal fraction) of each phenotype? (16)

What was the total number of grains on your ear of corn? (17) According to the fractions obtained in Item 16 above, how many grains of corn should show each combination of traits? (18) How can you explain the difference between the expected fractions and the fractions actually observed? (19)

SUMMARY

Combine the data obtained from all the ears of corn examined by the class. Apply the chi-square test to the combined data. What does the result of the test tell you about the data? (20)

EXERCISE 16.7

A TEST CROSS

INTRODUCTION

When a hereditary trait is determined by a pair of genes at a single locus, an individual that is phenotypically dominant may be genotypically either homozygous dominant or heterozygous dominant. Can we distinguish between the two kinds of dominant individuals? By looking at them, no. But if enough offspring are produced, we can deduce from breeding experiments the unknown genotype. The technique is called a test cross.

PURPOSE

In this exercise you will perform a test cross to determine whether a phenotypically dominant organism carries the recessive gene.

MATERIALS AND EQUIPMENT (for each team)

1. Culture containing fruit flies phenotypically dominant for a particular hereditary trait
2. Etherizer (see Figure 16.3-2)
3. Ether in dropping bottle
4. Examination plate
5. Water-color brush, small
6. Stereomicroscope
7. Culture bottles containing fresh food supply, 2
8. Glass-marking crayon
9. Culture containing fruit flies recessive for the trait shown by the flies in Item 1
10. Morgue (see Figure 16.3-3)

PROCEDURE

Throughout this exercise use the techniques given in Exercise 16.3 for handling and counting fruit flies.

From among the flies phenotypically dominant for the trait you are studying, select—as directed by the teacher—two males or two virgin females. (The technique for obtaining virgin female flies is given in Exercise 16.3.) Place each fly in a separate culture bottle containing a fresh food supply. Label each bottle with the team symbol; also label one bottle A and the other B. From the culture of recessive flies, select individuals of the sex (if female, virgin) opposite to that of the phenotypically dominant flies. Introduce several of these into each bottle.

After a week remove the parent flies. When offspring flies begin to appear, count them and record in your data book the number of flies that are phenotypically dominant and the number that are phenotypically recessive for the trait you are studying. Take counts on eight successive days (or until you have tallied 100 flies).

STUDYING THE DATA

What proportion of the offspring flies are phenotypically dominant? Express the result as a decimal fraction. (1)   What proportion of the offspring flies are recessive? (2)

Using letter symbols for the alleles of the trait you are studying (either those customarily used by geneticists or those agreed upon by your class), write the genotype of a recessive fly. (3)   Using the same symbols, write the genotype of a homozygous-dominant fly. (4)   Calculate the phenotype ratio expected among the offspring produced by a cross of recessive and homozygous-dominant flies. (5)   Write the genotype of a heterozygous-dominant fly. (6)   Calculate the phenotype ratio expected among the offspring produced by a cross of recessive and heterozygous-dominant flies. (7)

CONCLUSIONS

On the basis of the expected phenotype ratios, was the phenotypically dominant parent in bottle A homozygous or heterozygous? (8) Was the phenotypically dominant parent in bottle B homozygous or heterozygous? (9)   Using decimal fractions for the expected and observed (actual) proportions, apply the chi-square test (Exercise 16.3) wherever your results seem doubtful. (10)

ADAPTATION

CHAPTER 17

Genetic Adaptation: Evolution

EXERCISE 17.1

POPULATION GENETICS AND EVOLUTION

INTRODUCTION

Genetics has helped to explain many aspects of evolution. The way in which characteristics are passed from generation to generation, the frequencies with which characteristics occur in populations, the origin of new hereditary characteristics—all these were matters of mystery to biologists of the nineteenth century. Though not all aspects of evolutionary processes are yet understood, the application of genetics to problems of evolution has (during the past forty years) opened new avenues of investigation.

PURPOSE

Building on your knowledge of genetics, this exercise leads to two ideas that are important in understanding genetic mechanisms in evolution.

PROCEDURE

A. Gene Frequencies in Populations

Consider a hypothetical species of beetle. Assume that it lives in a stable environment. Assume that among the variations in this hypothetical species are two hereditary color types—one black, the other white speckled with black. Assume that the difference in color is determined by a single pair of allelic genes and that black (B) is dominant over speckled white (b). Finally, assume that the species population consists of 1000 beetles, with equal numbers of males and females. Among the beetles of each sex, 250 are homozygous black (BB) and 250 are homozygous speckled white (bb).

Diagram all the possible matings in this hypothetical population. Use the symbol ♂ for male and the symbol ♀ for female. (1)   Now list all the possible kinds of matings in terms of genotypes—for example, BB X bb. (2)   Beside each kind of mating write all the kinds of genotypes that can occur among the offspring. (3)   Does any cross produce more than one kind of offspring? (4)

Assume that the offspring generation also consists of 1000 beetles and that each kind of mating listed in Item 2 contributes equally to this population. What will be the ratio of black beetles to white beetles in the offspring? (5)   Is this phenotype ratio the same as that in the first generation? (6)

Now consider the two genes, B and b. What were their frequencies (expressed as decimal fractions) in the original population? (7) What are their frequencies in the offspring population? (8)   Are the gene frequencies the same in the two generations? (9)

Now make the same calculations for a third generation. You can do this by mating every genotype with every other genotype in proportion to their frequencies. But this becomes complicated and tedious. You can obtain the same result by using the "gene-pool" method: First, set down the frequencies of all the kinds of gametes in the second generation. (In this case, they are equivalent to the frequencies of genes in Item 8.) Then assume random combination of these gametes. The frequency of B plus the frequency of b will represent the total sperm population. Likewise, the frequency of B plus the frequency of b will represent the total egg population. By algebraic multiplication (text page 542) the third-generation genotypes and their frequencies will be obtained.

Use the gene-pool method to answer the following questions: What are the frequencies of the genotypes in the third generation? (10)   What are the frequencies of B and b in the third generation? (11)   Is the phenotype ratio the same as that in the second generation? (12)   Are the gene frequencies the same as those in the second generation? (13)

Will similar results follow regardless of what the original frequencies of B and b might be? Letting all other assumptions remain unchanged, assume that the original population contains 400 homozy-

gous black beetles and 600 homozygous white beetles, each group containing males and females in equal numbers. What are the frequencies
of the two allelic genes among males in the population?(14) Among
females?(15) By multiplication determine the frequencies of the three
genotypes among the offspring.(16) What are the frequencies of the
two genes in the offspring population?(17) Calculate the frequencies of
the genes in a third generation.(18) In a single sentence try to state a
conclusion concerning gene frequencies in populations.(19) If you have
been successful in formulating your sentence, you have stated the basic
idea of the Hardy-Weinberg principle.

B. Populations in Changing Environments

In Part A it was assumed that the environment remained stable.
But suppose the environment changes. The same hypothetical species
of beetle is involved.

In Figure 17.1-1, what changes occurred in the environment?(20)
Where the number of birch trees in the environment declined, what
happened to the ratio of black to white beetles?(21) Where the number
of pine trees in the environment declined, what happened to the ratio
of black to white beetles?(22) What evidence indicates that the pines
and birches do not themselves affect the coloration of beetles?(23)
What evidence provides an explanation for the difference between the
two later beetle populations?(24) How would you expect the gene frequencies in the pine-woods population to differ from the gene frequencies in the ancestral population of the mixed woods?(25) How would
you expect the gene frequencies in the birch-woods population to differ
from the gene frequencies in the ancestral population of the mixed
woods?(26) Would you say that evolution has occurred in the beetle
population? Explain.(27) Which factors in this hypothetical situation
would have been known to Darwin?(28) Which would not have been
known to him?(29)

EXERCISE 17.2

A STUDY OF POPULATION GENETICS

INTRODUCTION AND PURPOSE

Evolution results from a change in the frequencies of inherited
traits in a population. Therefore the mechanism of evolution depends

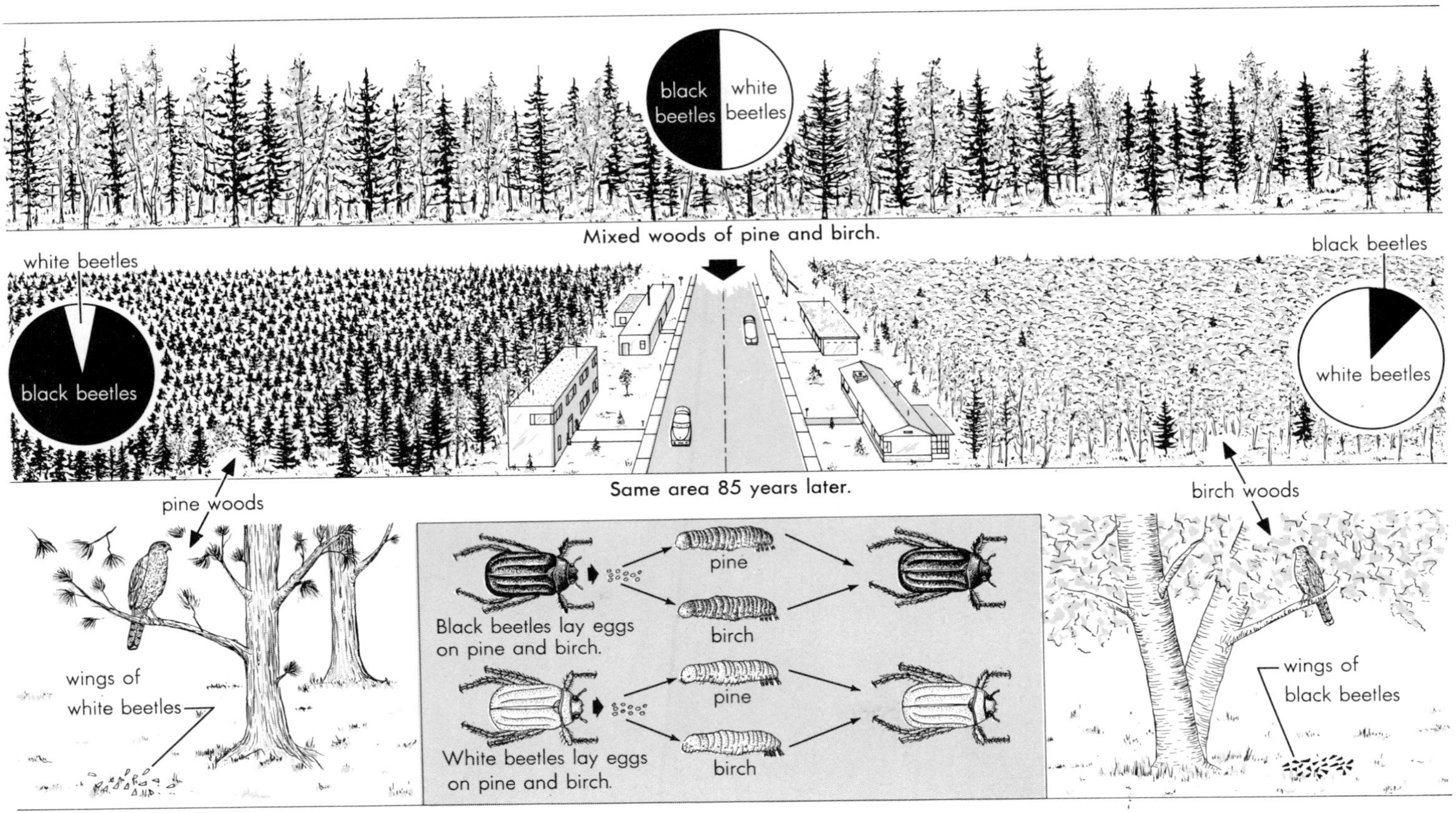

Mixed woods of pine and birch.

white beetles

black beetles

black beetles

white beetles

Same area 85 years later.

Black beetles lay eggs on pine and birch.

White beetles lay eggs on pine and birch.

pine   birch   pine   birch

birch woods

wings of black beetles

pine woods

wings of white beetles

white beetles

black beetles

Figure 17.1-1

upon genes, and the ways in which gene frequencies are studied become of primary importance.   But genes cannot be examined and counted directly, so the frequencies of genes in a population must be calculated from the frequencies of the phenotypes.   Because it is seldom possible to examine all individuals in a population, a sample of the population is taken.   If the sampling is properly done, conclusions from the sample can be extended to the whole population.

PURPOSE

In this exercise the frequency of an inherited trait in the human population is determined by sampling, and from this the frequencies of the genes controlling the trait are calculated.

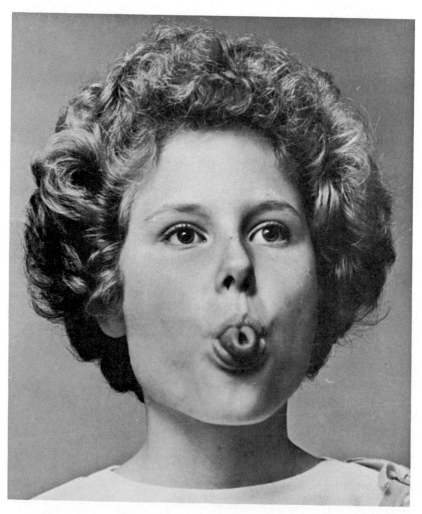

Figure 17.2-1. Tongue-rolling

BACKGROUND INFORMATION

The ability to roll the tongue longitudinally (Figure 17.2-1) is an inherited trait. Most persons find that either they can do this very easily or they cannot do it at all—even after much practice. Because the ability to roll the tongue is an easily observed genetic trait, it is used in this exercise.

You have repeatedly seen that the larger the amount of data, the more likely it is that slight, chance differences will be "smoothed out." Likewise in sampling: A large sample is usually more representative than a small one. However, regardless of size, to be representative a sample must be chosen (with respect to the trait being studied) as randomly as possible. Since tongue-rolling is not affected by age, and since it is not likely that tongue-rolling is a factor in determining whether a person is in school or not, the classes in your school probably give you a population that is random with respect to tongue-rolling.

PROCEDURE

Work in pairs. Each student is to determine whether his partner can roll his tongue. Gather the data for the class and record it on the chalkboard; your teacher will supply data from other classes. Use a form like the following:

CLASS	ROLLERS	NONROLLERS	TOTAL	% ROLLERS
1				
2				
3				
All				

Now determine the tongue-rollers and nonrollers in your immediate family (parents, brothers, sisters, and yourself). Families in which adoptions or remarriages are known to have occurred should not be included. On the chalkboard tally the data from the class. Only one mark is needed to represent each family if you use a form like the following:

	ALL CHILDREN ROLLERS	ALL CHILDREN NONROLLERS	CHILDREN OF BOTH KINDS
BOTH PARENTS ROLLERS			
BOTH PARENTS NONROLLERS			
1 PARENT OF EACH KIND			

Allowing for observational errors, does the tongue-rolling trait seem to be dominant or recessive? Clues: When a trait is dominant, a marriage of two persons showing the trait may produce children not showing the trait. When a trait is recessive, a marriage of two persons showing the trait produces only children showing the trait. (1)

The Hardy-Weinberg principle applies to situations in which neither natural selection nor mutation is occurring. It seems reasonable to suppose that the ability or lack of ability to roll the tongue has little effect upon the ability of a person to survive and produce offspring. The mutation rate of tongue-rolling is not known, but for the purposes of this discussion you may assume that it is not important.

With these assumptions you can use the Hardy-Weinberg principle to calculate the frequencies of the gene for tongue-rolling and its allele for nonrolling. Expressed mathematically, the Hardy-Weinberg principle states that for a trait involving two alleles the ratio of genotypes is $p^2 : 2pq : q^2$ (p representing the frequency of the dominant gene and q representing the frequency of the recessive gene). You have already calculated the percentage of rollers in the sample population. By subtracting from 100 percent, you can obtain the percentage of nonrollers. And from a study of families, you have decided whether rolling is dominant or recessive. The expression q^2 represents all the individuals showing the recessive trait, because such persons must have two recessive genes. You can calculate the frequencies of the allelic genes from the percentage of recessive individuals. First change the percentage of persons showing the recessive trait to a decimal fraction—for example, 36 percent = .36. (2) Then find the square root of the decimal fraction. (3) This gives you the value of q, which is the frequency of the recessive gene in the sample of the population. Is the frequency of the recessive gene larger or smaller than the frequency of individuals showing the recessive trait? (4) Having determined the value of q, you can now find the value of p, since $p + q = 1$ (see Exercise 16.4). What is the value of p—the frequency of the dominant gene—in the sample of the population? (5)

The phenotype data show directly the number of homozygous recessive individuals. But they do not show directly the number of homozygous dominants or the number of heterozygous dominants, because both kinds of dominants have the same phenotype. The Hardy-Weinberg expression $p^2 : 2pq : q^2$ provides this information: The square of the value of p gives the expected frequency of homozygous dominants. What is it? (6) The expression $2pq$ gives the expected frequency of heterozygotes. What is the value of the expression in this case? (7)

According to Mendelian principles, if both parents are heterozygous, the children are expected to include three dominant phenotypes for every recessive. In the sample is there a 3:1 ratio between individuals of the dominant type ($p^2 + 2pq$) and individuals of the recessive type (q^2)? Explain. (8)

SUMMARY

List the steps by which the ratio of genotypes in a population can be calculated from the phenotypes when the trait is one controlled by a single pair of allelic genes. (9)

FOR FURTHER INVESTIGATION

By means of the Hardy-Weinberg expression $p^2 : 2pq : q^2$, the probabilities of marriages between persons of each of the three genotypes can be calculated, provided that the trait studied does not affect the choice of mates. Since it seems unlikely that tongue-rolling is of any importance when a person is choosing a wife or husband, this trait can be used to illustrate these calculations. Remember that the probability of two events occurring together is the product of their separate probabilities (Exercise 16.2). The frequencies of rollers and nonrollers may be considered equivalent to the probabilities of their occurrence in a given population. Then the probability of a male roller's meeting (and marrying) a female nonroller is q^2 $(p^2 + 2pq)$ or $(p^2 + 2pq)q^2$, depending on whether rolling or nonrolling was found to be recessive. But the same combination of traits in a marriage would occur if a male nonroller met a female roller, so the total probability of such a marriage combination is $2 \left[q^2 (p^2 + 2pq)\right]$. From the values of p and q obtained by sampling in Exercise 17.2, calculate the probability that (a) a roller will marry a nonroller, (b) a homozygous roller will marry a homozygous nonroller, (c) two persons heterozygous for the trait will marry, (d) a homozygous roller will marry a person heterozygous for the trait, and (e) a homozygous nonroller will marry a person heterozygous for the trait.

EXERCISE 17.3

EFFECT OF POPULATION SIZE—A STUDY IN HUMAN EVOLUTION

INTRODUCTION

Has the development of rapid and easy transportation brought about a reduction in the number of undesirable hereditary characteristics? Some people think so.

Before travel became easy, people tended to intermarry within small groups. Only occasionally did people in distant communities meet and marry. Now, however, there is much intermarriage between persons in widely separated communities.

To explore the reasoning involved in the question, we shall take an extreme case. Suppose that two small, village populations ("A" and "B") of equal size are separated from each other by about 20 km. Suppose that for many generations little or no intermarriage occurs between Populations A and B or between these and other populations. Finally, suppose that Population A contains some albino individuals and that the gene for albinism is lacking in Population B. In man, albinism—the lack of all pigment in skin and hair—is a recessive trait. Under present environmental conditions albinism can be considered undesirable. Albino individuals have no protection against sunburning. More important, because an albino has no pigment in the iris of the eye, the amount of light that enters the eye cannot be regulated—hence an albino sees well only in dim light.

Suddenly, with the invention of the automobile, easy transportation is made available. An automobile salesman sets up his business in the village of Population A. Population B has its enterprising businessmen, too—a movie theater and recreation center are started in the second village. Under these conditions, within a few years the two communities become a single, large, intermarrying population.

PURPOSE

This exercise makes use of a model to produce data bearing on the question, How may the formation of a large, interbreeding population by the merging of separate smaller ones affect the number of recessive phenotypes?

MATERIALS AND EQUIPMENT (for every four students)

1. Beans, 160 brown and 40 white
2. Containers for the beans, 2

PROCEDURE

In your model each of the two containers represents a village. Into one container place 60 brown and 40 white beans. The beans represent gametes in Population A. Each brown bean is a gamete bearing a gene for normal pigment; each white bean is a gamete bearing a gene for albinism.   What is the frequency of the gene for albinism in this population?(1)   Since Population B is the same size as Population A and contains no genes for albinism, place 100 brown beans in the second container.

Now determine the frequency of albino individuals that could be expected to occur by random intermarriage (random with respect to albinism, not necessarily with respect to height or intelligence or other traits) in Population A.   Designate the four team members "A," "B," "C," and "D."

Student A: Stir the "gametes" (beans) in Population A.

Student B: Without looking into the container, draw out one bean.

Student C: Do likewise.

Student D: Prepare a score sheet, and tally the combination (representing a zygote—a new individual) under one of the three possible headings: Brown-Brown, Brown-White, White-White.

Students B and C: Return the beans to the container.

Repeat this procedure 25 times, stirring the "gametes" just before each drawing.   Then rotate the assignments among team members. Change assignments after every 25 drawings until 100 drawings have been made.

Because Population B contains no genes for albinism, drawing from it is unnecessary. But further drawings are needed to determine the frequency of albino individuals when the two populations become one intermarrying population.   Pour all the beans into one container, mix thoroughly, and repeat the entire procedure outlined above.

STUDYING THE DATA

On the chalkboard tabulate the data from all teams.   Which pairs of beans represent normally pigmented individuals?(2)   Which pairs represent albinos?(3)   What frequency of albinos (expressed as a percentage) is expected in Population A?(4)   What frequency of albinos is expected in Population B?(5)   What frequency of albinos is expected in the large (A + B) population?(6)

DISCUSSION

Many "undesirable" human traits are inherited in the same way that albinism is—through recessive genes.   Probably no human population is completely isolated; some migration and mixture occur in each generation.   Thus, the model, in which complete isolation of two populations and then complete mixture are assumed, is an oversimplification.   But it does illustrate that increasing intermarriage between populations may change the frequencies of phenotypes.

CONCLUSION

Use the data to answer the question posed in the "Purpose,"
page 340.(7)

EXERCISE 17.4

SICKLE CELLS AND EVOLUTION

INTRODUCTION

What difference does it make if a person's red blood cells are
oddly shaped? What causes the red blood cells of certain individuals to
take on peculiar shapes? These questions must surely have occurred
to a Chicago physician, James B. Herrick, when, in 1910, he examined
the blood of a Negro boy ill with a mysterious disease. The red blood
cells of the boy were shaped like crescents—"sickle-shaped" (Figure
17.4-1). Soon after Dr. Herrick wrote an account of his discovery,
other physicians uncovered cases of the same illness.

Today not only physicians but biochemists, physiologists, and
geneticists are working on various aspects of the questions stated
above. In the course of their work, they have discovered facts that
make the "case of the sickle cells" one of the best examples of a genetic mechanism in human evolution.

Figure 17.4-1.
Human red blood cells
(greatly magnified)

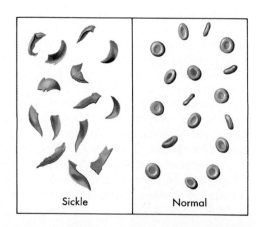

Sickle   Normal

PURPOSE

This exercise provides an opportunity to explore a real situation in human genetics, to reason from data, and to draw some important conclusions about evolution.

BACKGROUND INFORMATION

In the disease called <u>sickle-cell anemia</u>, newly formed red blood cells are normal in shape; but when the oxygen in their hemoglobin is released to the body tissues, most of them change to the abnormal sickle shape. The sickle cells are destroyed in the spleen. This reduction in the number of red blood cells cuts down the amount of oxygen available for the body cells. Also, because the sickle cells are much less flexible than normal red blood cells, they do not pass through capillaries as easily. By clogging the capillaries, sickle cells further reduce the efficiency of the circulation. Persons with sickle-cell anemia usually die in childhood.

Individuals with less severe cases of sickling may produce sickled red blood cells when the supply of oxygen is low (as at high altitudes) or when their need for oxygen increases (as during strenuous exercise). Such persons are said to have the "sickle-cell trait."

It has been demonstrated that sickling is a characteristic not of the red blood cells themselves but of the hemoglobin in the cells. In cells that sickle, the hemoglobin molecule differs from a normal hemoglobin molecule in just one of the 557 amino acids that make up the protein part of the molecule.

PROCEDURE

Figure 17.4-2 is a pedigree of a family in which sickling occurs. How many phenotypes are there in the family? (1) If the trait is determined by a single pair of allelic genes—one for normal hemoglobin and one for the hemoglobin of sickling—what kind of inheritance must be involved? (2) The gene for normal hemoglobin may be symbolized as $\underline{H}^n$ and the gene for the hemoglobin of sickling as $\underline{H}^s$. What, then, is the genotype for Individual 1 in the pedigree? (3) Recall that the sickle-cell trait is a mild form of sickling. What, then, is the genotype of Individual 2? (4) Of Individual 3? (5) If Individual 4 marries a man with a genotype like her own, what percentage of her children may be expected to have sickle-cell anemia? (6)

The gene that brings about the formation of the hemoglobin associated with sickling is rare in most human populations. In some parts of Africa, however, the sickle-cell trait is found in as much as 40

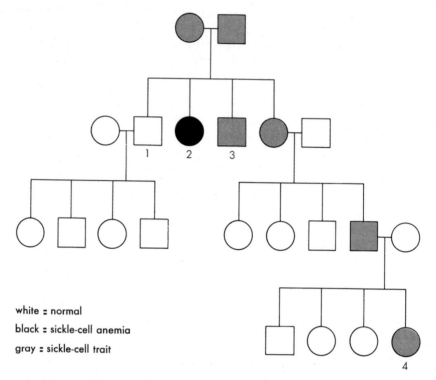

white = normal
black = sickle-cell anemia
gray = sickle-cell trait

Figure 17.4-2

percent (0.4) of the population. In such a population, what is the probability that any one heterozygous individual will marry another heterozygous individual? (7)   What percentage of their offspring may be
expected to be homozygous for the sickle-cell gene? (8)   On the average, then, which would you expect to leave more offspring—individuals
with the sickle-cell trait (heterozygous individuals) or individuals with
normal red blood cells? (9) How many sickling genes are lost from the
gene pool when a child with sickle-cell anemia dies? (10)   What effect
would you expect the death of children with sickle-cell anemia to have
on the frequency of the gene for sickling in any population? (11)   You
have described an evolutionary change in the terms of modern genetics.
How would Darwin have described this situation? (12)

Actually, there is no evidence that the frequency of the gene for
sickling is becoming less in African populations.   Therefore, a biological problem arises: How can the frequency of the gene for sickling
be maintained at such a high level when selection works so strongly
against the gene?   Now, after several months in this course, you know
that the scientist begins his attack upon such a problem by devising
hypotheses—explanations that may be tested by making suitable observations or by carrying out suitable experiments.

Biologists have developed at least three hypotheses to account for the high frequency of the sickling gene in African populations. One involves mutation rates; a second involves fertility; a third involves resistance to disease. Using these clues, devise three hypotheses to explain the persistently high frequency of the sickling gene in African populations.(13) (14) (15) WRITE THESE DOWN BEFORE READING FURTHER.

Through genetic reasoning and mathematical techniques, it is possible to calculate the rate at which genes are lost from the population gene pool by natural selection. This rate has been found to be about 100 times the average rate of mutation at any one locus in human chromosomes. Geographically, mutation rates vary only slightly. Does this information support or weaken your first hypothesis? Explain.(16)

At present there is no evidence that individuals with the sickle-cell trait (heterozygotes) produce more children than do individuals with normal red blood cells. Does this information support or weaken your second hypothesis? Explain.(17)

As data on sickling were collected, the frequencies of the sickle-cell trait in various populations were plotted on maps; it became clear that the gene is most common in a belt extending across central Africa. In the same region malaria and hookworm are common diseases. From your knowledge of these two diseases and from your knowledge of the part of the body affected by sickling, which of the two diseases would be more likely to be associated with sickling?(18) The foregoing question—and its answer—provides a new hypothesis. How would you word it?(19)

To test this hypothesis, one investigator examined the blood of 290 children in an East African tribe where both malaria and sickling were common. The results are given in Figure 17.4-3.

	WITH MALARIA	WITHOUT MALARIA	TOTAL
SICKLERS	12	31	43
NONSICKLERS	113	134	247

Figure 17.4-3

Calculate the percentage of "sicklers" (heterozygotes plus recessive homozygotes) with malaria and then the percentage of "nonsicklers" with malaria.(20) Apply the chi-square test (Exercise 16.3) to determine whether the difference between "sicklers" and normal children with respect to malaria is significant.(21) Do these data tend to support or to weaken the hypothesis?(22) To test the hypothesis further, 30 volunteers were inoculated with malaria parasites. The volunteers were men of approximately the same age and physical condition. A blood examination at the beginning of the experiment showed that none of the 30 had malarial parasites; 15 had the sickle-cell trait and 15 had normal red blood cells. Two of the "sicklers" and 14 of the "non-sicklers" developed malaria. Apply the chi-square test to see whether the difference between the "sicklers" and the normal individuals with respect to malaria infection is significant. (23) Does the result tend to support the hypothesis developed in Item 19? (24)

The present frequency of the sickle-cell trait in parts of Africa from which the ancestors of American Negroes came indicates that the early American-Negro population contained about 22 percent "sicklers." Would mixture with the European population and the American-Indian population have caused this frequency to increase, to decrease, or to remain the same? (25) In the United States, man has almost completely eliminated the vector of malaria, the <u>Anopheles</u> mosquito. Do the heterozygotes still have a survival advantage over the homozygotes in this country? (26) Recalling that an individual homozygous for sickling usually dies before reaching reproductive age, and considering your answer to Item 25, what would you expect to happen to the frequency of the gene for sickling in the United States? (27)

CONCLUSIONS

How are the factors in the evolutionary process (text pages 583-585) illustrated in the case of the sickle cells? (28) How does this exercise show that evolution involves interaction between the genetic makeup of an organism and its environment? (29)

Hereditary traits (and the genes that determine them) are sometimes described as "beneficial," "good," "harmful," or "bad." Keeping in mind all the ideas developed in this exercise, comment on such use of these terms. (30)

CHAPTER 18

Individual Adaptation: Behavior

EXERCISE 18.1

SOCIAL BEHAVIOR IN FISHES

INTRODUCTION

In man, much behavior is social—that is, it involves reactions between different individuals of the same species. Human social behavior is difficult to study not only because it is complex but also because much of it is expressed in words rather than in actions. In addition, the student of human social behavior, being human himself, may easily confuse his own reactions with the reactions of the group he is studying; or he may unconsciously allow his emotions and attitudes to influence his observations.

Much can be learned about social behavior—some of it perhaps meaningful for human society—through observation of, and experimentation with, other species. Of course, there are difficulties in observing, describing, and interpreting the behavior of other species, too. The dangers of anthropomorphism (text page 614) are great, but they may be less with some organisms than with others. Perhaps such dangers are easier to guard against when fishes rather than mammals or birds are studied.

PURPOSE

In this exercise a number of simple experiments with two species of fishes should enable you to draw some conclusions about simple social behavior.

MATERIALS AND EQUIPMENT (for each team)

 1. Glass jars, about 1-liter capacity, 5
 2. Glass jar, about 4-liter capacity
 3. Glass-marking crayon
 4. Cardboard pieces, about 30 X 30 cm, 5
 5. Aquarium water, about 5 liters
 6. Corydoras, males, 4
 7. Betta, males, 2
 8. Mirror
 9. Cardboard, smooth sheet about 10 X 20 cm
10. Scissors
11. Tempera paints, several colors
12. Paintbrushes

PROCEDURE

Arrange the six jars in a row on a table that does not receive direct sunlight. Place the large jar at one end of the row. Number the jars 1 to 6, beginning with the large jar; the numbers should be small and near the tops of the jars. Place pieces of cardboard between the jars so that fish in adjacent jars will not be able to see each other.

Pour aquarium water into the jars until each is about half full. Into each of the first four jars place a male Corydoras. Into each of the last two jars place a male Betta.

Allow a day or two for the fish to become accustomed to their jars. Then try the following experiments:

Experiment A

Remove the cardboard from between Jars 5 and 6 (containing the two Betta), thus allowing the two fish to see each other. In your data book, record the behavior of each fish; note especially the use of fins, tail, mouth, and gill covers. After observing the behavior—called a display—replace the cardboard between the jars.

Experiment B

Remove the cardboard from between Jars 2 and 3 (two Corydoras). In your data book, record the behavior of each fish as accurately and in as much detail as possible. Replace the cardboard between the jars.

Experiment C

Fifteen minutes after Experiment A is completed, press a mirror against the side of Jar 6 (Betta). In your data book, record the behavior of the fish.

Experiment D

Fifteen minutes after Experiment B is completed, press a mirror against the side of Jar 3 (Corydoras). In your data book, record the behavior of the fish.

Experiment E

Remove the cardboard from between Jars 4 and 5 (Corydoras and Betta). Using your notes from Experiments A and B as a basis for comparison, record in your data book the behavior of each fish.

Experiment F

Allow a day or two to pass. From a sheet of smooth cardboard, cut three fish models in the shape of Betta and two in the shape of Corydoras. Paint one of the Betta models to resemble the Betta; paint the second Betta model to resemble the coloration of Corydoras; paint the third Betta model some other colors. Paint one of the Corydoras models to resemble the coloration of Betta; paint the other Corydoras model some other colors.

Using both Betta, and allowing about six minutes between trials, place each of the models, one at a time, against Jars 5 and 6. Record the reaction of the fish during each trial.

Experiment G

When the fish have been in the jars for one week, remove the Corydoras from Jar 4 and place it in Jar 1. Note the behavior of both fish—the original occupant and the "newcomer." Now remove the Corydoras from Jar 3 and place it also in Jar 1. Note the behavior of the three fish.

Allow the three fish to live together for one week. Observe them occasionally during this time. Note whether they tend to band together or to go separate ways. Note also any reactions to accidental collisions.

Experiment H

When the three Corydoras have been together for one week, remove a fish from Jar 1 and place it in one of the empty jars. Next day return it to Jar 1. Note the behavior of the two fish that remained in Jar 1; note also the behavior of the "returnee." Now remove the fish from Jar 2 and place it with the three in Jar 1. Note the behavior of the fish already in Jar 1, comparing their reactions to this "stranger" with their reactions to the "returnee."

SUMMARY AND CONCLUSIONS

The experiments in this exercise are designed to bring out reactions that provide data for understanding the behavioral relationships between individual fish. To accomplish this, each separate observation must be linked with the others. Study your notes and attempt to write a summary ending with one or more conclusions concerning social behavior among fishes. Your conclusions, of course, must be consistent with your observations. The following questions are intended to guide your thinking; they need not all be answered specifically: Why was the exercise performed with male fish only? Do males of all fish species react in the same way to other males of their species? Do males react to males of other species in the same way that they react to males of their own species? By what means—shape, color, movement, other means—does a male Betta recognize another male? Is Corydoras individualistic, or do the individuals tend to associate in groups? Do Corydoras recognize other Corydoras as individuals?

FOR FURTHER INVESTIGATION

Techniques similar to those described in Exercise 18.1 can be used with other kinds of aquarium fishes. With some modifications, these techniques can also be used to investigate some aspects of the behavior of cage birds.

EXERCISE 18.2

PHOTOPERIODIC CONTROL OF PLANT BEHAVIOR

INTRODUCTION

Except in cave, soil, and deep-sea habitats, light plays an important part in the lives of organisms. Many living things respond to
changes in the color and intensity of light. In addition, many organisms respond to <u>photoperiod</u>, the duration of the periods of light that
everywhere on earth alternate with periods of darkness. At the equator the daily period of light is always equal to the daily period of darkness; elsewhere the periods are almost always of unequal length, and
the difference varies with latitude and season.

"Photoperiodism" is a name for the responses of organisms to the
alternating light and dark periods. Such responses are primarily
internal; but they usually have some visible effects, which can then be
termed behavior. Thus, in many birds, changes in photoperiod bring
about the secretion of hormones that results in migratory and reproductive behavior. Whether the photoperiodic responses of plants may
be defined as "behavior" is debatable (text pages 610-611). But plant
responses are rather easier to study than those of other organisms;
plants, therefore, are often used for demonstrating photoperiodism.

PURPOSE

In this exercise the effects of two different photoperiods on three
kinds of plants are investigated.

MATERIALS AND EQUIPMENT (for each team)

1. Flowerpots, shallow form, about 15-cm diameter, 6
2. Small stones or pieces of broken pot, 6
3. Coarse sand
4. Potting soil
5. Morning-glory seeds (Scarlett O'Hara variety), 10
6. Triangular file
7. Radish seeds, 10
8. Seeds of a species to be chosen by the team, 10

9. Pot labels, wooden, 6
10. Pot saucers, 6
11. Lamp with 40-watt or 60-watt bulb

PROCEDURE

Prepare each of the six pots as follows: Place a small stone or piece of broken pot loosely over the hole in the bottom of the pot. Pour coarse sand into the pot to a depth of 4 to 6 cm. Add potting soil. After it has been pressed down firmly (not packed hard), the soil should come to within 2 cm of the rim of the pot.

Using a triangular file, make a deep notch in the coat of each morning-glory seed. In each of two pots plant five of the seeds about 1.5 cm deep. Space the seeds at least 2 cm apart. Using wooden pot labels, mark one pot MG: 10 hr and the other MG: 24 hr.

In each of two pots plant five radish seeds about 0.5 cm deep. It is not necessary to notch these seeds. Space the seeds at least 2 cm apart. Using wooden pot labels, mark one pot R: 10 hr and the other R: 24 hr.

In each of the remaining pots plant five seeds of a species of your own choosing. The teacher will suggest some suitable kinds. Space the seeds about 2 cm apart and plant at the depth recommended on the seed package. Using wooden pot labels and an appropriate seed symbol, mark one pot ---: 10 hr and the other ---: 24 hr.

Place each pot in a saucer, and fill the saucer with water. Throughout the experiment keep the soil in the pots moist by adding water to the saucers as needed. After the seedlings appear, thin them out (if necessary) so that not more than three well-spaced plants are growing in each pot.

The pots marked 10 hr are to receive ten hours of light per day. The pots marked 24 hr are to receive twenty-four hours of light per day. Place all pots in bright sunlight for ten hours each day. At the end of each ten-hour light period, set the pots marked 10 hr in a dark place, such as a cupboard or closet. Be sure that these pots receive no light until the beginning of the ten-hour period next day. At the end of each ten-hour period, set the pots marked 24 hr about a meter from a 40- or 60-watt lamp, and leave them there until the next ten-hour period. Continue this schedule of lighting until flower buds appear on some plants of each species. (If you have difficulty recognizing flower buds, continue the experiment until the flowers open.)

Examine each pot daily. In your data book keep a record of the development of the seedlings in each pot. This record should be in the form of a log. For example:

April 14 — MG: 10 hr   A third leaf developing on one seedling.
          R: 24 hr   Stems average 6 cm tall.
                 *   *   *   *   *
April 24 — ---: 24 hr   One plant seems to have flower bud.

Although the age of the plant at the time of flowering is the basic information you are seeking, the elongation of the stem, the number of leaves, the general form of the plant, the size of the root, and other characteristics are all involved in photoperiodic behavior.

DISCUSSION

Does a difference in photoperiod affect the time of flowering in any of the three species? If so, in which ones? (1) If only one species was affected, in which of the pots containing that species was the flowering time earlier? If more than one species was affected, in which species was the flowering time earlier in the 10 hr pot, and in which was it earlier in the 24 hr pot? (2)

Present the evidence (if any) that difference in photoperiod affects length of stem (3), size of leaves (4), rate of growth (5), storage of food (6).

EXERCISE 18.3

TROPISMS

PURPOSE

This exercise demonstrates tropic responses of plants to two kinds of stimuli.

MATERIALS AND EQUIPMENT (for each team)

Part A

1. Soaked corn grains, 4
2. Petri dish
3. Cotton
4. Scissors
5. Heavy gray blotting paper
6. Scotch tape
7. Glass-marking crayon

Part B

1. Cardboard boxes, to cover flowerpots, 4
2. Scissors
3. Red cellophane
4. Paste
5. Blue cellophane
6. Flowerpots, about 8 cm in diameter, 4
7. Soil
8. Radish seeds, 40

Part C

1. Test tubes, 25 X 200 mm, 4
2. One-hole stoppers, to fit test tubes, 4
3. Shoots of Zebrina, about 20 cm long, 4
4. Melted paraffin in a beaker
5. Small brush
6. Glass-marking crayon
7. Ring stand
8. Burette clamps, 4

PROCEDURE

Part A

Place four soaked corn grains in the bottom half of a petri dish. Arrange them cotyledon-side down, as shown in Figure 18.3-1. Fill the spaces between the corn grains with wads of cotton to a depth slightly greater than the thickness of the grains. Cut a piece of heavy gray blotting paper slightly larger than the bottom of the petri dish. Fit it snugly over the grains and cotton. Hold the dish on its edge and observe the grains through the bottom. If they do not stay in place, repack with more cotton. When the corn grains are secure in the dish, wet the blotting paper thoroughly. Seal the two halves of the petri dish together with strips of scotch tape.

Place the dish on edge in a location that receives dim light. Rotate the dish until one of the corn grains is at the top. Using a glass-marking crayon, write an A on the dish beside the topmost grain; then, proceeding clockwise, label the other grains B, C, and D (see Figure 18.3-1). Fasten the dish to the table or bench with a long strip of tape, as shown. If further support is needed, stack books on top of the tape and against the edges of the dish. Do not change the position of the dish until the experiment is completed.

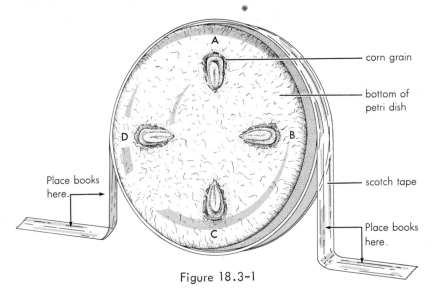

Figure 18.3-1

When the grains begin to germinate, make daily sketches in your data book, showing the directions in which the root and the shoot grow from each grain. Continue your observations for five days (unless otherwise directed by the teacher).

Part B

Obtain four cardboard boxes, each large enough to cover a flower-pot and deep enough to allow a space of at least 5 cm between the top of the pot and the box. Number the boxes 1 to 4 and label each with your team symbol. Turn the boxes bottom side up. Cut a rectangular hole in one side of each of three boxes: the hole should be as wide as the diameter of a pot and about 3 cm high, the lower edge level with the top of a pot (Figure 18.3-2). Paste a strip of red cellophane over the hole in Box 1. Paste a strip of blue cellophane over the hole in Box 2. Leave the hole in Box 3 uncovered. Do not cut a hole in Box 4.

Using a pencil, number four flowerpots 1 to 4 and label each pot with your team symbol. Fill the pots with soil. In each pot plant ten radish seeds about 0.5 cm deep and 2 cm apart. Press the soil down firmly over the seeds, and water the pots. Place the pots in a location that receives strong light—but not direct sunlight. Cover each pot with

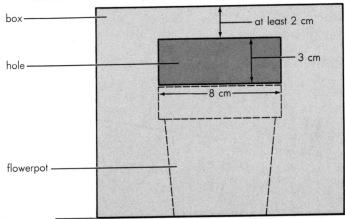

Figure 18.3-2.
Diagram for preparation of Boxes 1, 2, and 3

the box bearing its number. Once each day remove the boxes and water the pots. (CAUTION: Do not move the pots; be sure to place the boxes back in the same position after each watering!)

Observe the radish seedlings each day. When most have been above the ground for two or three days, record in your data book the direction of stem growth in each pot—whether upright, curved slightly, or curved greatly, and, if curved, in what direction with respect to the hole in the box.

Part C

Fill four test tubes with water and insert a one-hole stopper firmly into each tube. Remove all leaves within 8 cm of the cut ends of four Zebrina shoots. Push the cut end of each shoot through a stopper until about 5 cm of the shoot is in water. Seal tubes, stoppers, and shoots by applying melted paraffin with a brush. (CAUTION: The paraffin should be no warmer than is necessary to keep it liquid.) Using a glass-marking crayon, label the tubes A, B, C, and D. Attach a burette clamp to each tube; fasten the tubes to a ring stand, in the positions shown in Figure 18.3-3. Place the entire assembly in a location that receives bright light from one side. Observe the shoots daily for about a week.

STUDYING THE DATA

Consider first the data from Part A. From which end of the grains did the roots grow?(1) Did the root of any grain grow without changing direction? If so, of which grain?(2) Describe the direction of root growth from Grain C.(3) Did the roots of all four grains eventually turn in one direction? If so, what was the direction?(4) From which end of the grains did the shoots grow?(5) Did the shoot of any grain grow without changing direction? If so, of which grain?(6) Did the shoots of all four grains eventually turn in one direction?(7)

Now consider the data from Part B. In which pot were the stems nearest to perpendicular?(8) In which pot were the stems most curved?(9) In which pot (where any curvature occurred) were the stems least curved?(10) In the pots where curvature occurred, were all the stems curved in one direction?(11) If so, in what direction? If not, in what direction did most of the stems curve?(12)

Finally, consider the data from Part C. Did any shoots continue to grow without bending? If so, which ones?(13) Did any shoots bend as they grew? If so, which ones?(14) If you noticed any bending, in what direction did it occur in each case?(15)

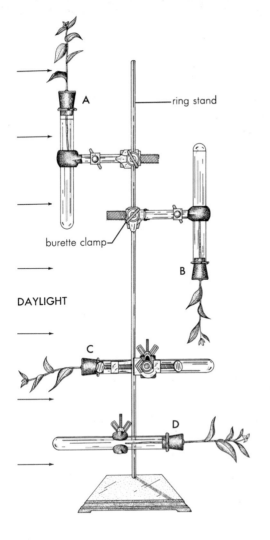

A

ring stand

burette clamp—

B

Figure 18.3-3

DAYLIGHT

C

D

CONCLUSIONS

To what stimulus did the corn roots seem to be responding? Was the response positive or negative? (16) To what stimulus did the corn shoots seem to be responding? Was the response positive or negative? (17)

On the basis of your observations in Part B, make a general statement concerning the response of radish seedlings to direction and color of light. (18)

From your observations in Part C, make a general statement concerning the relative effects of light and gravity as stimuli of tropic responses in shoots. (19)

FOR FURTHER INVESTIGATION

Will centrifugal force overcome the response of plant parts to gravity? To test this idea, the setup used in Exercise 18.3, Part A, may be mounted on an old phonograph turntable.

EXERCISE 18.4

PERCEPTUAL WORLDS

INTRODUCTION AND PURPOSE

In studying animal behavior, biologists often use complicated and expensive apparatus. But much can be learned about animal behavior by merely watching—noting what an animal does and under what circumstances it does it. And some kinds of experimentation can be done with very simple apparatus (text Figure 18.8).

Whether well equipped or not, the student of animal behavior needs first to know something about the perceptual world of the animal under study. In Exercises 4.4 and 9.3, and elsewhere, you investigated some aspects of the perceptual worlds of a few animals. Now you will try to find out all you can—within the limits of available time—about the perceptual world of one particular kind of animal.

PROCEDURE

Each team will choose an animal species for study. The species must be one of which a number of living specimens can be obtained. The teacher will provide a list of suitable species.

Plans for studying the perceptual world of any animal will, of course, depend upon the nature of the species. Size, natural habitat, and the obvious sense organs should be considered. Therefore, each team must become generally familiar with its animal before laying plans for studying behavior. Preliminary observations may lead you to suspect senses that were not at first obvious. Consider such matters as reaction to light (intensity and color), sound, gravity, touch, chemical substances (odor and taste); ability to see and the kinds of things seen; awareness of the biotic environment (organisms of its own species and of others). Consider how you will determine whether or not an observed behavior is brought about by a particular factor in the environment. In planning experiments, remember that the best understanding of normal behavior can be gained when the animal is disturbed as little as possible.

When the team has laid its plans, it must draw up a list of materials and equipment. Keep the list as short and simple as possible. The list will be reviewed by the teacher. The listed items should be assembled and made ready for use before the laboratory periods in which the experimenting is to be done.

SUMMARY

Prepare a team report on the perceptual world of the animal studied. The report should clearly indicate how each bit of information in it was obtained.

MAN AND THE BIOSPHERE

CHAPTER 19

The Human Animal

EXERCISE 19.1

THE SKELETAL BASIS OF UPRIGHT POSTURE

INTRODUCTION

Among mammals, man's outstanding physical peculiarity is his ability to stand, walk, and run upright on his hind legs. This posture leaves his arms ("forelegs") free at all times for carrying and handling things. His hands and most of his other physical peculiarities are simply further developments of characteristics that occur in varying degrees among primates.

It has been argued that man's big brain is an evolutionary result of the support offered by his upright posture. But whether his brain enlarged before or after his unique posture developed is the anthropological equivalent of the old question: "Which came first—the chicken or the egg?"

In a vertebrate, posture is a visible expression of skeletal structure. Therefore, a first understanding of the upright posture of man can be obtained from a study of the human skeleton. Comparison with the skeleton of a quadruped (four-footed) mammal should help to emphasize characteristics of bipedal locomotion.

PURPOSE

In this exercise comparative observations of characteristics in the skeletons of man and cat are directed toward understanding some structural peculiarities of man, especially his upright posture.

MATERIALS AND EQUIPMENT

1. Human skeleton, mounted
2. Cat skeleton, mounted
3. Rulers, 2

PROCEDURE

Throughout this Procedure observations are to be made on both cat and human skeletons. Thus, when you are directed to "Examine the skull," examine the skulls of both animals.

Osteologists (anatomists who specialize in the study of bones) think of the vertebrate skeleton as composed of two major divisions—the axial skeleton and the appendicular skeleton. The axial skeleton consists of the skull and the column of vertebrae (including the ribs that are attached to some of the vertebrae), arranged along the longitudinal axis of the body. The appendicular skeleton consists of the shoulder girdle, the hip girdle, and the bones in the appendages, which are attached to the girdles.

Begin with the axial skeleton. Examine the general outline of the skull. Which occupies the greater volume—the brain case or the bones of the face? In cat? In man?(1) With respect to the rest of the skull, are the eye sockets directed forward, downward, backward, sideward, or upward? In cat? In man?(2) What change in the facial bones of the cat would bring its eye sockets into the human position?(3)

Viewing the skeleton from the side, hold a ruler along the axis of the vertebrae in the upper part of the neck. In which animal is the axis of the vertebrae closer to the vertical midline of the skull?(4) Holding the first ruler in position, place another ruler along the base of the teeth. In which animal is the angle formed by the rulers closer to a right angle?(5) The articulation (jointing) of the skull with the first vertebra occurs around the foramen magnum ("big opening"). Through the foramen magnum the spinal cord connects with the brain. In which animal is the foramen magnum closer to the posterior end of the skull?(6) If you look closely, you will notice roughened areas and ridges on the bones. These mark places where muscles were attached. Examine the back of the skull. In which animal is there a greater area (in proportion to skull size) for muscle attachment?(7)

Examine the vertebral column. Which animal has the greater number of vertebrae? (8) Where are most of the "extra" vertebrae? (9) In general, which animal (in proportion to its size) has the thicker vertebrae? (10) How do the vertebrae in the region of the hip girdle differ in man and cat? (11) Observe the vertebral column from the side. Ignoring the vertebrae of the neck and tail, in which animal does the vertebral column form a single arch? (12)

Now consider the appendicular skeleton. The hind legs are attached to the hip, or <u>pelvic</u>, girdle—a set of bones fused together. In proportion to its size, which animal has the heavier pelvis? (13) Is the pelvis articulated with the vertebral column, or are the two structures fused together? In cat? In man? (14)

The forelegs (arms, in man) are attached to the shoulder, or <u>pectoral</u>, girdle—which is made up of two broad, flat <u>scapulas</u>, two <u>clavicles</u> (collarbones), and a <u>sternum</u> (breastbone). With respect to their attachment to each other, how do the bones of the pectoral girdle differ from the bones of the pelvic girdle? (15) In which animal are the bones of the pectoral girdle more closely associated? (16) How is the pectoral girdle attached to the vertebral column? In cat? In man? (17)

Compare the bones of the human hand with the bones of one of the cat's front feet. In which animal are the bones of the <u>digits</u> (fingers or toes) longer in proportion to the total length of the appendage? (18) In which animal is the inside digit (thumb, in man) articulated in such a way that it is opposable (Exercise 4.2, page 71) to the outside digit? (19)

Compare the cat's posterior appendages with the legs of man. In which animal is the knee joint closer to a $180°$ angle in normal standing position? (20) Consider each leg to be made up of upper leg (<u>femur</u> bone), lower leg, and foot (including toes). What fraction of the length of the femur is equal to the length of the foot? In cat? In man? (21) Which animal normally stands on its toes, with heel raised from the ground? (22)

DISCUSSION

The following questions may help you to interpret your observations and to organize your thoughts. What nonskeletal human characteristic is implied by your answer to Item 1? (23) Items 2 and 3 relate to a visual characteristic found in many primates. What is the characteristic? (24) Observations reported in Items 4 to 7 are concerned with structural adaptations that make possible the support of a relatively heavy head in an upright position. Assume that the structure of man's distant ancestors was somewhat like that of the cat. What mutations in the catlike structure would have brought about changes favorable to the development of both a large brain and an upright posture? (25)

In a quadruped, where is most of the weight of the anterior part of the body supported? (26)   Where is the anterior weight supported in a biped? (27)   How do Items 10 to 13 relate to Items 26 and 27? (28)

From the structure of its pectoral girdle, do you think a cat could easily support its weight on its forelegs? (29)   Can a man? (30)   Of course, a man moving in an upright position does not need to support his weight on his arms.   But he has the same kind of strong pectoral girdle that many primates use in moving about through trees.   How is this structural characteristic an advantage to man, who walks upright on the ground? (31)

How is the position of the legs in a man poised to start a race similar to the normal position of the posterior appendages in a cat? (32)   What advantage does this position have for athlete and cat? (33)   Try to stand in this position.   What disadvantage does it have for man? (34)

SUMMARY

Summarize, in a paragraph, characteristics of the human skeletal system that are related to man's upright posture. (35)

FOR FURTHER INVESTIGATION

Aristotle described man as a "featherless biped."   The adjective was necessary because birds are also entirely bipedal.   (Aristotle, of course, knew nothing of the dinosaurs, some of which were also bipeds.)   Among mammals, kangaroos (also unknown to Aristotle) rest on their hind legs and use their forelegs very little for locomotion— but they do not really stand upright.   So, in the modern world, only birds and man share the characteristic of bipedality.   Using a mounted skeleton of a pigeon or chicken, make a comparison similar to the one in Exercise 19.1.

EXERCISE 19.2

HUMAN BLOOD GROUPS

INTRODUCTION

Blood transfusion—the transfer of blood from one individual to another—was tried as early as the seventeenth century. In some of the first attempts, the blood of domestic animals was transferred to human patients who had lost large amounts of blood. The patients died. Later, when blood was obtained from human donors (givers), some of the patients lived and some died. As a medical treatment blood transfusion was a last resort, used when the patient was likely to die anyway. Then, in 1900, Karl Landsteiner discovered why transfusions were sometimes successful, sometimes not; from that time on, transfusion became a standard, relatively safe medical practice.

Landsteiner's work led to the formulation of the ABO blood groups, briefly discussed in Chapter 16 (text page 554). Other blood groups have been discovered more recently; except for the "Rh groups" (discovered by Landsteiner nearly forty years later, near the end of his career), none of these have any importance in transfusions. But all have importance in biological theory. They are useful in unraveling the intricacies of human genetics. They are useful to the anthropologist in tracing the past history of human racial groups (see Exercise 19.3). And they are biochemical links between man and other primates: for example, the ABO types have been shown to occur in some pongids, and the presence of blood factors called "M" and "N" (not important in transfusions) has been demonstrated in several primates.

PURPOSE

In this exercise you will determine your own ABO blood type and calculate the percentages of the types found in your class.

BACKGROUND INFORMATION

The major difficulty in blood transfusion comes from a clumping of the red blood cells. The clumps of red cells cannot pass through the capillaries; therefore the capillaries become clogged. If many capillaries are clogged, the circulatory system is blocked, and death may result.

Landsteiner demonstrated that the clumping of the red blood cells is brought about by a reaction between substances on the red-cell membranes and substances in the liquid part of blood, the plasma. The reacting substances do not occur together in the blood of any one individual. But since different individuals have different sets of the substances, blood from one individual may contain the plasma substance that reacts with the red-cell substance of another individual. This is an example of the general intolerance of organisms for foreign substances—especially proteins—that may be introduced into their body fluids (text page 199).

In the ABO system of blood types, there are two red-cell substances, "A" and "B," and two plasma substances, "anti-a" and "anti-b." Following are the possible combinations: Individuals with A on their red cells have anti-b in their plasma. Individuals with B on their red cells have anti-a in their plasma. Individuals with both A and B on their red cells have neither anti-a nor anti-b in their plasma. Individuals with neither A nor B on their red cells have both anti-a and anti-b in their plasma.

MATERIALS AND EQUIPMENT (for every four students)

1. Glass-marking crayon
2. Microscope slide, 1 per student
3. Sheet of white, unlined paper, 1 per student
4. Cotton pledgets, several per student
5. Alcohol, isopropyl, 70%
6. Forceps, 2
7. Sterile, disposable lancet, 1 per student
8. Anti-a serum
9. Anti-b serum
10. Toothpicks, 2 per student
11. Monocular microscope

PROCEDURE

Using a glass-marking crayon, draw a line along the short axis of a microscope slide, dividing it into halves. In the upper left-hand corner of the left half, write A; in the upper right-hand corner of the right half, write B. Place the slide on a sheet of white, unlined paper.

Wash your hands thoroughly. Using a pledget of cotton dipped in alcohol and held in forceps, scrub the tip of a finger (on the left hand if you are right-handed, on the right hand if you are left-handed). Allow the alcohol to dry. Using a sterile, disposable lancet, make a small puncture in the tip of the finger. Wipe off the first drop of blood with a pledget of cotton. Place a small drop of blood in the middle of each half of the slide. This may be done by touching the slide to the finger. Cover the puncture in the finger with a pledget of cotton soaked in alcohol, and continue the procedure. (Hold the cotton in place with the thumb of the same hand for about five minutes.)

Immediately place a drop of anti-a <u>serum</u> on a drop of blood that lies on the <u>A</u> half of the slide. (Serum is plasma from which fibrinogen has been removed.) Use a toothpick to mix the blood and serum; be careful to mix them within as small an area as possible. Break the toothpick and discard it. Place a drop of anti-b serum on the drop of blood that lies on the <u>B</u> half of the slide. Use a second toothpick to mix the blood and serum. Break the toothpick and discard it.

Compare the material on each side of the slide with Figure 19.2-1, which shows both clumping and nonclumping reactions. You may check your naked-eye observations by examining the material under the low power of a microscope. Compare your slide with the slides of neighboring students.

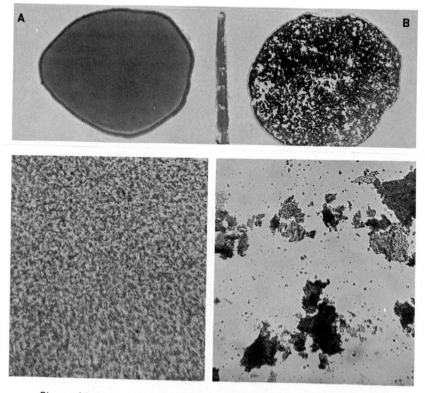

Figure 19.2-1. <u>Above</u>: Blood-typing slide. The blood is Type B. Note the clumping on the right. <u>Below</u>: Appearance of the same samples under low power of the microscope (X 650).

STUDYING THE DATA

If cells are clumped on Side <u>A</u>, your blood type is A.
If cells are clumped on Side <u>B</u>, your blood type is B.
If cells are clumped on both sides, your blood type is AB.
If cells are clumped on neither side, your blood type is O.
What is your blood type? (1)   (CAUTION: There are a number of factors that may produce errors in this test. Your own determination of blood type must not be used for any medical purpose. For this, only the results obtained by an experienced technician are satisfactory.)

Individual errors in determining blood type may occur, but such errors are not likely to greatly affect the percentages of blood types when data are reported by a large number of individuals. On the chalkboard tally the blood types of all individuals in your class. Other classes will do the same. Total the tallies and calculate the percentage of each type. Which type occurs most frequently? (2)   Which type occurs least frequently? (3)

SUMMARY

Assuming that your determination is correct, name the red-cell and plasma substances in your blood—see "Background Information."(4) Relatively few "foreign" red blood cells are introduced in most blood transfusions; the introduced plasma is quickly carried by the circulation to all parts of the bloodstream. Keeping these facts in mind, describe what would happen to your circulation if you were given a transfusion of Type A (5), Type B (6), Type AB (7), Type O (8). Describe what would happen to the circulation of individuals of each type if you were the donor. (9)   (10)   (11)   (12)

Refer to Exercise 17.2—"Background Information." With respect to blood types, can the biology classes be considered a random sample of the population of your community? Explain. (13) Regardless of your answer to Item 13, assume that the percentages derived from the pooled class data represent the percentage in your community. Compare them with the percentages in the following samples:

	A	B	AB	O
London, England	43	8	1	48
Paris, France	42	12	6	40
Berlin, Germany	43	14	6	37
American Indian (Montana)	76	0	0	24
The Congo	30	29	10	31
Peking, China	25	34	10	31
Tokyo, Japan	38	22	10	30

Explain similarities and differences. (14)

EXERCISE 19.3

BIOLOGICAL DISTANCE

INTRODUCTION

Anthropologists have devised many schemes for dividing the people of the world into races. In the past, skin color, hair form, facial features, head shape, body build, and a host of other physical traits have been used in human racial classifications. On such bases, the number of races has been said to be anywhere from four or five to more than sixty. There has been no lack of authorities to support one scheme or another.

In recent years anthropologists have begun to use the gene frequencies of populations (see Chapter 17) as a basis for classification. In this scheme they sometimes speak of "biological distance," which is simply a way of expressing the degree of similarity in the gene frequencies of two or more populations. In other words, the more similar the gene frequencies of populations, the less the biological distance between them; conversely, the less similar the gene frequencies, the greater the biological distance. Two populations having a high degree of genetic similarity are (biologically) "close" to each other; two populations having a low degree of genetic similarity are (biologically) "distant." Of course, it is still a matter of anthropological judgment to decide just how biologically distant two populations must be before they can be considered different races.

William C. Boyd has proposed a human racial classification based on the frequencies of the genes determining blood types. There are several advantages to using blood types as a basis for racial classification: First, the ways in which the blood-type genes are inherited are well known. Second, the blood type of an individual does not change with age or with changes in the environment. Third, natural selection does not seem to cause any rapid changes in the frequencies of blood-type genes; therefore, present frequencies indicate to some extent how human populations have mixed with one another in the past. Fourth, blood types are rather easy to determine from blood samples taken for various medical purposes; therefore, data for a large number of individuals representing many human populations are readily available for study.

PURPOSE

In this exercise the following questions are considered: To what extent are the Eskimos of Point Barrow, Alaska, the Indians of British Columbia, and the Navahos of New Mexico genetically related to each other? How do the migrations of human populations affect gene frequencies? How can the mixing rate of two different populations be calculated?

PROCEDURE

Recall that the four blood types, A, B, AB, and O, are determined by three allelic genes, I^a, I^b, and i (text page 554). Figure 19.3-1 shows the frequencies of these three genes in the Eskimo population of Point Barrow, Alaska, in the Indian population of British Columbia, Canada, and in the Navaho population of New Mexico. These gene frequencies have been calculated from the blood-type frequencies found in samples of the populations (by a method similar to the one you used in Exercise 17.2).

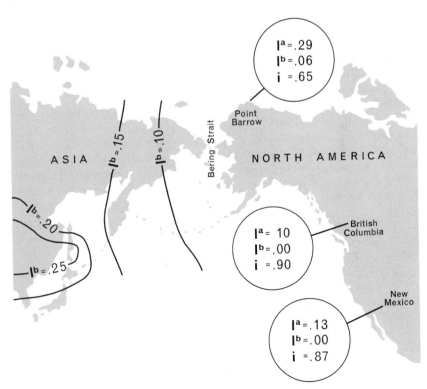

Figure 19.3-1

On the basis of the I^a gene frequencies, which two populations are most alike? (1)   On the basis of the I^b frequencies, which two populations are most alike? (2)   On the basis of the i frequencies, which two populations are most alike? (3)

For the next two questions there are no "correct" answers, only matters of opinion.   Before beginning this exercise, would you have classified Eskimos, British Columbian Indians, and Navahos together in one race?   Why or why not? (4)   Would you classify them in one race now?   Why or why not? (5)   Does the genetic evidence change your idea of "race"?   If so, how? (6)

Now look again at Figure 19.3-1.   Notice that it shows the frequency of gene I^b in five regions of Asia.   As you move westward and southward into Asia from the Bering Strait, what happens to the frequency of the I^b gene? (7)   As you move eastward and southward in North America from the Bering Strait, what happens to the frequency of the I^b gene? (8)   What is the frequency of the gene in the Navaho population? (9)

Over much of Central Asia the frequency of I^b is .25-.30.   Westward from Central Asia into Europe, the frequency declines (text Figure 17.14).   There are several hypotheses to account for this situation, but we shall consider only one.   Briefly, the hypothesis states that the primitive population of Asia had all three allelic genes, that Europe and America were populated from Central Asia, and that the first emigrant populations from the Asian homeland either lacked the I^b gene or lost it along the way—by random genetic drift (see text pages 591-593).   Thus the first populations of Homo sapiens to reach Europe and America had genes I^a and i only.   What blood types could they have had? (10)   Later, according to the hypothesis, other emigrating populations carried the I^b gene outward from Central Asia and, by interbreeding, reintroduced the gene into American and European populations.   Considering the difficulties of primitive travel, where would you expect these later emigrant populations to be most numerous? Least numerous? (11)   On the basis of the frequencies of the I^b gene, which of the North American populations shown in Figure 19.3-1 has probably had the more recent genetic contact with populations of Asia? (12)   The frequency of the I^b gene is .00 in the Basque population of southwestern France.   On the basis of the I^b gene, what can you say about the biological distance between the Basques, the natives of Central Asia, and the Navahos? (13)   Does this mean that the Basques and the Navahos belong to one race?   Why or why not? (14)

You have been proceeding on the assumption that genetic mixing between human populations does occur, but you have been given no data on rate of mixing.   For a study of the rate of gene flow from one population to another, two populations with the following characteristics are needed: Both populations must be large; they must differ markedly in the frequencies of allelic genes at one or more loci; the traits determined by these genes must be easily and precisely identifiable; and, of course, the populations must be mixing.   All of these characteristics are found in the Caucasoid and Negroid populations that have come into North America during recent centuries.

The genetic trait best suited for this study involves another blood characteristic. In 1940 Landsteiner (see Exercise 19.2) discovered that material from the blood of rabbits that have been injected with the blood of rhesus monkeys causes the red blood cells of some persons to clump. Such persons are said to be "Rh positive" (Rh for rhesus monkey); persons whose red blood cells do not clump are "Rh negative." Further study showed that the Rh blood types are, genetically, more complex than the ABO types. Among the genes involved is one that has been symbolized $\underline{Rh}^o$. This gene can be rather easily identified, and its frequency differs markedly in the two populations you are considering.

In Negroid populations of Africa, the frequency of the $\underline{Rh}^o$ gene is about .60; in Caucasoid populations of Europe, the frequency of the $\underline{Rh}^o$ gene is about .03; in the American Negroid population, the frequency of the $\underline{Rh}^o$ gene is about .44. From these figures the rate of mixing between African and European populations in North America can be computed.

What is the difference between the frequencies of the $\underline{Rh}^o$ gene in the African and European populations? (15) What is the difference between the frequencies of the $\underline{Rh}^o$ gene in the African and American Negroid populations? (16) The amount of mixing between the Caucasoid and Negroid populations in North America may be expressed as a percentage: Divide your answer to Item 16 by your answer to Item 15 and multiply by 100. (17)

The year 1625 may be taken as the beginning of genetic mixing between Caucasoid and Negroid in America; the frequency of the $\underline{Rh}^o$ gene in the American Negroid population was obtained from data gathered about 1950. Assuming an average generation length of 25 years, how many generations of mixing could have occurred? (18) On the basis of this number of generations, what was the average amount of mixing per generation? (19)

From such calculations—crude though they may be—anthropologists can estimate the biological distance between populations, the routes of human migration, and the rates at which genetic differences among populations change. And from these studies the biological history of man, as reflected in present racial groupings, can be deduced.

Appendix

ON MEASUREMENTS

In 1790 the French government adopted a new system of measurement to replace the many systems that were then being used in France. This system, called the _metric_ system, had a decimal basis—that is, it was based on multiples of ten—just as did the money system that had recently been adopted by the young government of the United States. As years went by, almost all nations followed the United States in adopting a decimal monetary system, and almost all adopted the French decimal system of measurement. Today among the nations of the world, only Great Britain, Canada, Australia, and the United States use other systems of measurement. And even in those countries the metric system is used by scientists.

The basic unit in the metric system is the _meter_. From this unit all others are derived. The meter is the distance between two scratches on a platinum-iridium bar that is kept in the vaults of the International Bureau of Measures near Paris. The United States Bureau of Standards has copies of this bar. Fractions and multiples of the meter are designated by prefixes: _milli-_ (X 0.001), _centi-_ (X 0.01), _deci-_ (X 0.1), _deka-_ (X 10), _hecto-_ (X 100), and _kilo-_ (X 1000).

The metric unit of volume is the _liter_, which is defined as the volume of a cube having an edge 10 centimeters long. The metric unit of weight is the _gram_, which is defined as the weight of a milliliter of pure water at 4 degrees centigrade (4°C). The metric unit of surface is the _are_, which is defined as an area of 100 square meters. Areas and volumes may also be indicated by the squares and cubes of linear units.

The following units are not properly a part of the metric system but are derived from it:

calorie: the quantity of heat needed to raise the temperature of 1 g of water $1^\circ C$

Calorie: equal to a kilocalorie

curie: the amount of any radioactive substance that emits the same number of alpha rays per unit of time as does 1 g of radium

micron (μ):   a unit of length equal to one millionth of a meter; $1000\mu = 1$ mm

Familiarity with units of the metric system is best acquired through repeated use of them. Memorizing many equivalents in the British system is a waste of time. At the start, however, a few equivalents may be helpful for reference:

1 centimeter =	.3937 inches		1 inch =	2.54 cm
1 meter =	39.37 inches		1 yard =	.914 m
1 kilometer =	.62 miles		1 mile =	1.6 km
1 liter =	1.057 liquid quarts		1 quart =	.95 1
1 gram =	.035 ounces		1 ounce =	28.34 g
1 kilogram =	2.2 pounds		1 pound =	.453 kg
1 hectare =	2.47 acres		1 acre =	.405 ha

SCALE	LENGTH	VOLUME	WEIGHT	SURFACE
0.001	millimeter (mm)	milliliter (ml)	milligram (mg)	
0.01	centimeter (cm)			
0.1	decimeter (dm)			
1	meter (m)	liter (l)	gram (g)	are
10	dekameter (dkm)			
100	hectometer (hm)			hectare (ha)
1000	kilometer (km)		kilogram (kg)	

Figure Ap-1. Units of linear measure and some other common units of the metric system. Abbreviations are given in parentheses.

In countries using British units of measure, temperature is expressed on a scale devised by Gabriel Daniel Fahrenheit (1686-1736). (The British Weather Service has recently abandoned this scale.) In countries using the metric system, temperature is expressed on a scale devised by Anders Celsius (1701-1744). The Celsius scale is usually called centigrade. Figure Ap-2 compares the two scales.

There is only one system of units for measuring time, though in many parts of the world (and in the armed forces of the United States) hours are designated from midnight to midnight with one set of twenty-four numbers—thus making "A. M." and "P. M." unnecessary.

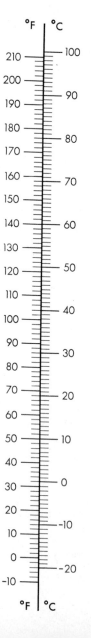

Figure Ap-2.
Comparison of Fahrenheit
and centigrade (Celsius)
temperature scales

Grateful acknowledgment is made to the following sources for photographs used in this manual:

Knipping, Paul, Figure 14.1–2; Larsen, Victor, Figure 2.2–1, Figure 6.1–1 (2); Manarchy, Frank, Figure 19.2–1 (3); Rogers, Charles, Figure 17.2–1; Thorne Films, Figure 14.3–1.